BASIC SCIENCE
for Christian Schools®

Bob Jones University Press, Greenville, South Carolina 29614
Textbook Division

BASIC SCIENCE

for Christian Schools®

John E. Jenkins
and George Mulfinger, Jr.

NOTE:

The fact that materials produced by other publishers may be referred to in this volume does not constitute an endorsement by Bob Jones University Press of the content or theological position of materials produced by such publishers. The position of the Bob Jones University Press, and the University itself, is well known. Any references and ancillary materials are listed as an aid to the student or the teacher and in an attempt to maintain the accepted academic standards of the publishing industry.

BASIC SCIENCE for Christian Schools®
Second Edition

John E. Jenkins, M.S.
George Mulfinger Jr., M.S.

for Christian Schools is a registered trademark of Bob Jones University Press.

Produced in cooperation with the Bob Jones University Division of Natural Science of the College of Arts and Science, the School of Religion, and Bob Jones Academy.

© 1983, 1999 Bob Jones University Press
Greenville, South Carolina 29614

Printed in the United States of America
All rights reserved

ISBN 0-89084-215-9

15   14   13   12   11   10   9   8

CONTENTS

INTRODUCTION

Do you know how television pictures are transmitted or why an atomic bomb can release enough energy to destroy an entire city? If you have questions like these about the world around you, then you are a curious person.

BASIC SCIENCE for Christian Schools® was written for you, the curious student. We have filled this textbook with answers to puzzling questions about why things happen and how things work. But this text should do more than simply answer your questions. It is intended to stimulate new questions that will cause you to expand your knowledge.

You will be introduced to realms that you have never before explored. This book will take you "inside" an atom; let you "see" what happens in solids, liquids, and gases; help you to discover the forces that make things move or keep things from moving; and show you forms of matter and energy that scientists are just beginning to understand.

BASIC SCIENCE was also written for you because you are a Christian student. Christians have a very special reason for being curious about the world around them: the physical universe reveals the power and majesty of our God. We can see the Creator clearly in His creation. Patterns in nature from the ordered movement of planets through space to the intricate movement of minute particles in matter give witness to His power. The entire universe, from atoms to galaxies, is governed and maintained by the infinite power of our God.

We have even deeper reasons for studying the physical universe. Not only did God create the universe for us, but He sent His Son to reconcile us to Himself when we rebelled in sin. Paul tells us in Colossians 1:12-17,

> Giving thanks unto the Father, which hath made us meet to be partakers of the inheritance of the saints in light: Who hath delivered us from the power of darkness, and hath translated us into the kingdom of his dear Son: In whom we have redemption through his blood, even the forgiveness

of sins: Who is the image of the invisible God, the firstborn of every creature: For by him were all things created, that are in heaven, and that are in earth, visible and invisible, whether they be thrones, or dominions, or principalities, or powers: all things were created by him, and for him: And he is before all things, and by him all things consist.

Here Paul reveals to us a very special truth: God used His Son, our Saviour, to frame the worlds (Heb. 1:2). In this course you will study the world that Christ created. As a Christian student you will have an opportunity to see Christ in His creation.

Paul continued his description of Christ to the church at Colosse by saying,

And he is the head of the body, the church: who is the beginning, the firstborn from the dead; that in all things he might have the preeminence. (Col. 1:18)

May your studies this year help you to honor Christ and to keep Him first in your life.

Format for *BASIC SCIENCE for Christian Schools*®

BASIC SCIENCE is divided into eight units with a single theme: matter, the "stuff" of the universe. The units are divided into chapters, and each chapter is divided into at least two sections.

Each chapter has several features that will help you study. Illustrations, captions, special notes, and tables will help you understand the material. Many important scientific terms are printed in boldface (a special dark type), each in the portion of text where it is defined. These terms are gathered after the text of each chapter in a list titled "Scientifically Speaking." Use this list as a tool for reviewing important concepts in the chapter. Also at the end of each chapter appears "Questions to Talk Over." You will not find answers for these questions in the text! They are designed to stimulate class discussion and to help you think of ways to apply what you have learned.

Some important terms appear in italic type. Many of these were boldfaced in earlier discussion and are important for you to note again. Other times, italic print is used to point out significant ideas, contrasts, or conditions. (If you cannot remember what a term means, look it up in the glossary at the back of the text.) After names and hard-to-pronounce words, you will find pronunciation guides in parentheses. The pronunciation key on page ix will tell you how to read them.

BASIC SCIENCE has two more special features: "Facets of Basic Science" and "Christian Men of Science." "Facets of Basic Science" are highlighted sections of information or application that add dimension to the topic. Be sure to read them; they are an important part of the text. The seven "Christian Men of Science" sections are biographies of scientists who served God. These men have been selected as examples of the balance that God expects in our Christian lives.

Pronunciation Key

The pronunciation key used in this text is designed to give the reader a self-evident, acceptable pronunciation for the word as he reads it from the page. For more nearly accurate pronunciations the reader should consult a good dictionary. This pronunciation key will help the student who has difficulty interpreting the diacritical marks used in most dictionaries.

Stress

Syllables with primary stress appear in LARGE CAPITAL letters. One-syllable words and syllables with secondary stress appear in SMALL CAPITAL letters. Unstressed syllables appear in lower-case letters. For example, the pronunciation of *kilogram* appears as (KILL uh GRAM).

Consonant Sounds

Most consonants and consonantal combinations in the key have only their one usual sound. There are a few exceptions:

Symbol	Example
c	voice = VOYCE
g	get = GET
j	gentle = JEN tul
th	thin = THIN
th	then = THEN
zh	vision = VIZH un

Vowel Sounds

Symbol	Example
a	cat = KAT
a-e	cape = KAPE
ay	paint = PAYNT
e	jet = JET
eh	special = SPEH shul
ee	fiend = FEEND
i	swim = SWIM
ih	pity = PIH tee
eye	ivory = EYE vuh ree
i-e	might = MITE
y	pint = PYNT
	mighty = MY tee
ye	Levi = LEE vye
ah	cot = KAHT
ar	car = KAR
aw	all = AWL
o	potion = PO shun
oa	don't = DOANT
o-e	groan = GRONE
oh	own = OHN
u	some = SUM
uh	abet = uh BET
oo	tune = TOON
oo	push = P*OO*SH
ou	loud = LOUD
oy	toil = TOYL

ONE

WHAT MATTERS TO THE CHRISTIAN

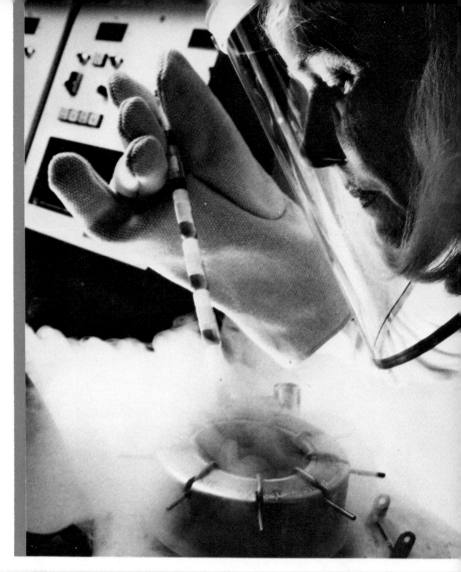

SCIENCE
AND THE BIBLE

CHAPTER
1

Science uses gleaming glassware and bubbling liquids. Science sends out space probes and space shuttles. Science takes place in the controlled environment of the laboratory and on the rolling decks of an oceanographic survey vessel. Science involves all these things and more. Yet all science has a common factor: activity. Someone is doing something or directing instruments to do something. What kind of activities make science special? And how do these activities affect you and me?

A Framework for Science

What do all the varied activities that we call science have in common? Whether he is on the deck of a survey vessel or in the laboratory of a university, every scientist uses his senses to record information about the physical universe that surrounds him. He might be looking at the microscopic structure of the wings on an insect, recording the sounds of a great gray whale, or examining the information and photographs sent back by a deep space probe, but in each case he is using his senses to collect scientific information called **data** (DAY tuh). Any collection of data through the senses (taste, touch, smell, sight, and hearing) is an **observation**. Scientists must carefully plan and control their observations. They also record them in minute detail so that other scientists can study the events that led up to a particular observation and confirm the results by duplicating it.

1-1 Scientists can use specially equipped buoys to collect data from the cold waters of the Arctic Ocean.

A Definition for Science

Basically, science is what scientists do. Since observations play a key role in the activities of scientists, we can define **science** as the systematic use of observations to study the physical universe. This definition implies both *purpose* and *persons*. Science does not just occur; it is carefully planned. Instruments are not science; they are simply the tools of the people who accomplish the activities we call science. Science cannot exist without purposeful observations by a human being. If something cannot be observed, it is outside the realm of science.

1-2 Scientists can observe things that are as small as an atom or as far away as another galaxy, but they can observe only the physical universe. Part of God's creation—the spiritual realm—lies beyond the scientists' power to observe.

Pure and Applied Science

Within the realm of science falls an alphabet of activities from astrophysics to zoology. Some of these activities attempt to discover new data just to satisfy man's basic curiosity about the **physical universe.** We call these activities **pure science.** Pure scientists study a myriad of interesting observations involving subjects ranging from the exploration of the basic nature of matter and energy to the mathematical analysis of the workings of the universe. Many times, however, scientific activities are directed toward solving a particular problem. We call these activities **applied science.** An applied scientist might be researching a cure for cancer, a new memory system for a computer, or new energy resources to replace our dwindling oil supplies.

Technology and Science

Technology is a practical use of the knowledge gained through pure and applied science. Science and technology are a research and development team: one discovers the information

FACETS
OF BASIC SCIENCE

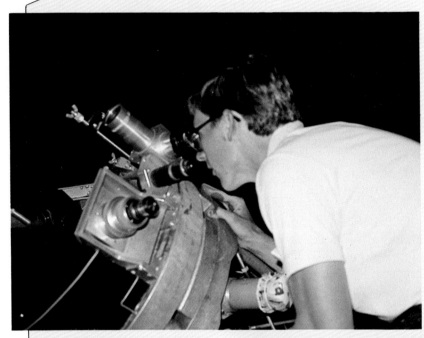

Observations

Some observations are direct: a scientist uses his senses to observe his surroundings directly. Often, however, he needs help to make a clear observation; he then uses instruments to increase his observational abilities.

Sometimes a scientist desires to make an observation in a place where he cannot go: he designs instruments to send back data for observation.

All of these involve a human observer (the scientist) recording what he has observed about an event in the physical universe. Can science deal with events, places, or things it cannot observe? Can a scientist make an observation about an event that neither he nor his instruments can witness?

Space probe

needed to solve a problem, and the other works out the everyday methods of applying the solutions. When the pure scientist Charles Townes developed the laser, for example, other scientists used his discovery in new methods of surgery and in transmitting messages across vast distances.

It is this important union between scientific information and its application that increasingly affects us. As we learn to apply scientific knowledge to more areas of our lives, we will be faced with increasingly difficult *choices.* We must examine the options that technology provides us in the light of their potential results. In the decades to come, we may have to make difficult choices about genetic engineering (manipulating a baby's physical and mental characteristics before it is born), food processing (as the world's population increases, we may turn to processed seaweeds for our staple diet!), and the energy needs of our country, to name just a few.

1-3 Engineers use a laser beam focused on a microcircuit to produce a very small, precise weld.

A Basis for Choosing

Most technological choices involve **value judgments** in which the benefits of an action must be weighed against its disadvantages. For instance, we may wish to preserve the natural beauty of wilderness areas for our children's children, but we also must recognize the pressing need for domestic sources of energy. If our Middle Eastern oil supplies were cut off, the free world would grind to a halt.

There is no clearly correct choice. The answer will probably be found in a balance of preserving and using our resources. But does technology or science offer guidelines for making such a choice? Technology offers applications, and science offers information, but neither can offer a basis for determining the worth of a choice. Choices must be based on a system of values. To make correct *choices,* you must have correct *values.*

Where can you find correct values? Many persons mistakenly look to science for values. These persons fool many people by presenting their personal system of beliefs (philosophy) as part of science without openly admitting or accepting what they have done. They focus on man and trust his ability to pass judgment on what is best for mankind. We call their philosophy **humanism** (HYOO muh NIZ um), for man is the center of their beliefs. The Christian looks to Christ. The Word of God is his authoritative source of values. For the born-again believer, the Bible is the *framework of truth* with which he can test any option.

FACETS
OF BASIC SCIENCE

A Technological Choice

The United States faces an oil shortage. American oil wells cannot supply enough fuel to meet the country's growing demands forever. Foreign sources grow more expensive all the time, and they sometimes fail to supply what they promise.

One way to solve the problem may be processing fuel from an oil-rich rock called oil shale. Shale was known as a source of oil in the early 1800s, even before the first oil well was drilled. Since other, more plentiful supplies of oil were found, shale was neglected in the search for energy.

Now scientists think that oil shale deposits in the United States may hold more than 4 trillion barrels of oil—many times as much as all the world's oil wells put together. The shale industry, using heat to free the oil from the rock, may be able to produce millions of barrels of oil per day by the year 2000. With this source, the United States could meet its energy needs without having to depend on other nations.

Should oil shale be developed as a major source of petroleum?

For many reasons, it seems to be an ideal solution to the problem. The supply is almost endless, and it comes from within the United States. Shale can be burned to produce power for its own processing plants. Processing shale should cause less air pollution than other synthetic fuel processes.

But in making a *choice* (choosing whether or not to use oil shale, or how much to use it), we must consider the possible consequences. Every option carries drawbacks that must be weighed against its benefits.

Consider the following positions and their consequences.

An Underground Method for Extracting Oil from Shale

1. Underground cavities are dug to begin the process.
2. The shale is removed from these cavities for above-ground processing.
3. Vertical holes for explosives are dug between cavities.
4. The shale is blasted into rubble, now filling large cavities called retorts.
5. Diesel fuel, air, and steam are piped into the retort and set on fire. The heat soars to over 900° C and drives the oil out of the shale in a process called retorting.
6. The retreating oil is collected at the bottom of the cavity and piped to the surface for processing.
7. The retort cavity takes 300 days to burn out completely. Each retort produces approximately 175,000 barrels of crude oil.

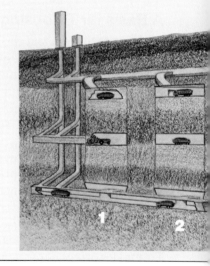

You will be faced with many technological choices in your lifetime. As a citizen you may face choices between the preservation of wilderness areas and the essential development of energy. You may be asked to decide questions about genetic engineering. You may even be offered the options of what characteristics you would like implanted in your unborn child. How will you decide these complex issues? You cannot look to science for answers; it can only provide you with options. You can look either to God or to man. Whom will you choose?

►Develop oil shale as a major source of energy.

1. Processing can create 100,000 tons of waste rock per day per plant. This processed shale may be dumped into canyons, compacted to prevent spread of dangerous chemicals, or covered with topsoil and seeded with native plants, which it may support. Some part of the environment must be permanently changed to dispose of the processed rock.

2. Removing oil from shale takes two to four barrels of water for each barrel of oil—as much as 1.5 million barrels per day for one major processing plant. Large communities for plant personnel would require still more water. Most oil shale deposits are located in areas without large water supplies; processing plants and communities would have to draw water from sources that already supply major western population centers.

►Develop oil shale on a limited basis.

1. Oil dependency would be reduced but not eliminated.

2. The environment would suffer, although not as much as it would if oil shale were used to the fullest.

►Stop developing oil shale resources.

1. The United States would continue to depend on foreign countries for oil unless other synthetic fuels were developed. Some of those fuels may have worse effects than oil shale.

2. Millions of dollars already spent on research, development, and planning would have been wasted. Which position would you choose? Why do you think you made the right choice? Are you sure?

An Outlook on Science

To a great extent your observation will be influenced by your *outlook.* John Godfrey Saxe illustrated this principle in his poem "The Blind Men and the Elephant." The poem tells the story of six blind wise men of India who observed an elephant.

It was six men of Indostan,
To learning much inclined,

Who went to see the Elephant
  (Though all of them were blind),
That each by observation
  Might satisfy his mind.

The *First* approached the Elephant,
  And happening to fall
Against his broad and sturdy side,
  At once began to bawl:
"God bless me! but the Elephant
  Is very like a wall!"

The *Second,* feeling of the tusk,
  Cried, "Ho! what have we here
So very round and smooth and sharp?
  To me 'tis mighty clear
This wonder of an Elephant
  Is very like a spear!"

The *Third* approached the animal,
  And happening to take
The squirming trunk within his hands,
  Thus boldly up and spake:
"I see," quoth he, "the Elephant
  Is very like a snake!"

The *Fourth* reached out an eager hand,
  And felt about the knee.
"What most this wondrous beast is like
  Is mighty plain," quoth he;
" 'Tis clear enough the Elephant
  Is very like a tree!"

The *Fifth,* who chanced to touch the ear,
  Said: "E'en the blindest man
Can tell what this resembles most;
  Deny the fact who can,
This marvel of an Elephant
  Is very like a fan!"

The *Sixth* no sooner had begun
  About the beast to grope,
Than seizing on the swinging tail
  That fell within his scope,
"I see," quoth he, "the Elephant
  Is very like a rope!"

Each of the blind men made accurate observations. Yet their limitations prevented them from perceiving the elephant as a whole. In the words of the poem:

> And so these men of Indostan
> Disputed loud and long,
> Each in his own opinion
> Exceeding stiff and strong,
> Though each was partly in the right,
> And all were in the wrong!

Two Basic Outlooks

Scientists, like the men of Indostan, interpret data in the light of their outlooks. They may misinterpret data if they do not have a correct perception of the whole. Some scientists interpret data to support their view that the physical universe somehow structured itself out of self-existing matter, and that its parts continue to organize themselves into more complex structures as time progresses. This outlook, called **evolution** (EV uh LOO shun), has been developed by men who have blinded themselves to the whole truth of God's Word. Those that hold this belief are called **evolutionists.**

The Christian looks to the Bible for a complete picture of the physical universe by the Person who created it. Scripture tells us that God spoke the universe into existence by the miraculous acts described in Genesis 1 and 2. Those whose outlook is based on their belief in a created universe are called **creationists** (kree AY shun ists).

An evolutionary view of the physical universe is built on assumed data which cannot be scientifically observed. It contradicts actual observations of the physical world and denies the biblical record of Creation. Rather than improvement and increased organization, we observe *decay, degeneration,* and *general disordering* processes in nature. Well-established scientific principles indicate that nature is running down, not building itself into more ordered and complex forms. Can a scientist who claims to base all his opinions on observation tolerate an outlook that is openly unscientific?

The creationist view of the physical universe, or **creationism,** is founded on the written record of the Creator. Although there was no human observer present at Creation, scientific observations of a world that is running down do not conflict with the biblical record of a world under God's curse.

1-4 Decay, disorder, and degeneration are easy to observe in our environment.

A Comparison of Evolution and Creationism

Evolution and creationism are complete opposites. The evolutionary outlook holds that natural processes can explain the origin of the physical universe, while the creationist view recognizes that supernatural (miraculous) acts were needed. Natural processes cannot explain origins. They cannot create new materials or new organization. They merely serve to maintain what God has created. Evolutionists must speak in terms of millions and billions of years as they try to explain the accidental formation of the physical universe. Creationists find no such vast periods of time recorded in Scripture. The clear meaning of the Bible is that in six literal days God made heaven and earth. The Bible records no time delay between the creative commands of God and the accomplishment of those commands.

For example, on the first day of Creation "God said, Let there be light: and there was light" (Gen. 1:3). There is no logical reason to believe that the light took millions of years to develop. The events of the other creative days are recorded in similar fashion. Concerning the Creation, Psalm 33:9 states, "He spake, and it was done." Evolutionists tell us that the world is still evolving. Creationists realize that Creation is finished. After the sixth day of Creation, the Bible declares, "The heavens and the earth were finished, and all the host of them" (Gen. 2:1).

These two outlooks are so directly opposed to each other that it seems impossible that a person could hold to both at the same time. Yet some Christians try to believe evolution. Their attempt to join together these two conflicting outlooks is called **theistic** (thee ISS tik) **evolution** (*theistic* means "pertaining to belief in a god"). It is based on the belief that God used evolutionary processes to create the universe.

Table 1-5

Viewpoints on Origins		
Evolution	**Creation**	**Theistic evolution**
Natural processes	Supernatural act	Supernatural direction
Billions of years	Six days	Billions of years
Evolving	Finished; degenerating	Evolving under direction

The act of creation — Natural processes | Supernatural act | Supernatural direction

The timetable of creation — Billions of years | Six days | Billions of years

The condition of creation — Evolving | Finished; degenerating | Evolving under direction

Theistic evolution might appear to be a way of satisfying the demands of both sides, enabling a person to hold on to his Christian beliefs with one hand and his evolutionary ideas with the other. However, those who hold firmly to the Bible know that it allows no room for evolution; and those who hold firmly to evolutionary theories tell us there is no room for God in the evolutionary outlook. Therefore, the person who attempts to "harmonize" the two does not have the blessing of either side. He must contradict the Scripture and deny God's very nature—His limitless power, His knowledge, and His purposefulness. The strong Christian cannot hold on to both sides, for the Bible states that "a double minded man is unstable in all his ways" (James 1:8).

Evolutionary Bias

Everyone has some form of **bias** (BY us) (mental leaning or inclination) in his thinking. Your bias on any subject will depend largely on what you have been taught about it. Bias is not necessarily bad. The right kind of bias often indicates knowledge or experience in a given subject. An electrician will be biased in favor of using copper wire, rather than tin or nickel wire, in motors. He has learned that copper has the best combination of important qualities such as good conductivity and low cost. A person cannot be completely unbiased about something unless he has either no knowledge of it or no interest in it.

There is another form of bias that is *not* desirable. This type is *prejudice*, or bias based on lack of knowledge. If a person closes his mind on a subject before he has learned enough about it to form a sensible opinion, he harms both himself and his fellow man. The Bible says, "He that answereth a matter before he heareth it, it is folly and shame unto him" (Prov. 18:13). In most scientific circles today there is an evolutionary prejudice. Yet such an attitude is anything but scientific. Scientists should be willing to study new facts as they appear, to see if their theories agree with the facts. Any theory that does not agree with the facts should be discarded.

In 1968 a human shoeprint was discovered in rock that evolutionists estimate to be between 500 and 600 million years old. (Remember, creationists do not accept these figures.) Something was clearly wrong here: evolutionists say that man has been on the earth only 3 or 4 million years. How could a man's shoeprint be found in rock that hardened 500 or 600

1-6 This shoeprint was found in rock that evolutionists claim was formed over 500 million years ago—long before man supposedly "appeared." Evolutionists have to reject evidence like this because it does not fit their theories. Is theirs a "scientific" reason for rejecting this human-shoeprint fossil?

11

million years ago? The shoeprint was taken to a large state university, where members of the geology department refused even to look at it. They had become so sure that the theory of evolution was correct that they automatically disregarded any evidence against it. This was not science; it was thoroughly unscientific and dishonest. This shoeprint is by no means the only recent evidence against evolution, but each new find is automatically rejected so that evolutionists never have to confront the evidence against their beliefs.

Imagine a courtroom trial in which an innocent man is about to be convicted on the basis of circumstantial evidence and incorrect testimony. At the last minute new facts that could prove his innocence are discovered, but the judge refuses to hear this information. So convinced is the judge of the defendant's guilt that he assumes the new evidence to be faulty. All would agree that the judge was unjust. Whether it be science or law, *all* the facts should be considered. Michael Faraday once said, "Though evidence may appear to preponderate extremely in favor of a certain decision, it is wise and proper to hear a counterstatement."

A Bias for Order

The bias of a creationist is based on his belief in **teleology** (TEL ee AH luh jee)— design or purpose in nature. An evolutionist must rely on accidental events to explain the ultimate origin and the supposed evolution of everything he observes. The creationist scientist seeks to uncover God's design in nature. He believes that God is actively controlling and purposefully directing His creation. When he studies an object or an event in nature, the Christian man of science will try, in the words of a famous German astronomer, "to think God's thoughts after Him."

Many avenues of scientific research point to God. The Christian researcher readily recognizes that the human body is "fearfully and wonderfully made" (Ps. 139:14). The unbeliever, because of his spiritual blindness, can study the same subject and miss completely the evidence of God's design. The Christian sees each part of the human body as a marvelously engineered device, perfect for performing its assigned function(s). In many cases the functions are obvious: the heart is designed for pumping blood, the eyes for seeing, the ears for hearing. In other cases our research has not shown us the specific function of an organ.

However, our knowledge is continually expanding, and science is determining the functions of organs formerly thought to be useless. At one time there were 180 organs classified as vestigial (veh STIJ ul) (useless). This number has now been reduced to a mere handful, and the list may eventually be eliminated altogether. In the meantime we should fully trust that God understood what He was doing when He created the human body, following the principle emphasized by evangelist Dr. Bob Jones, Sr.: "Give God and not the Devil the benefit of the doubt."

1-7 These organs were once thought to be useless "leftovers" from the evolutionary process. Modern medical science has discovered many of the purposes for these "vestigial" organs.

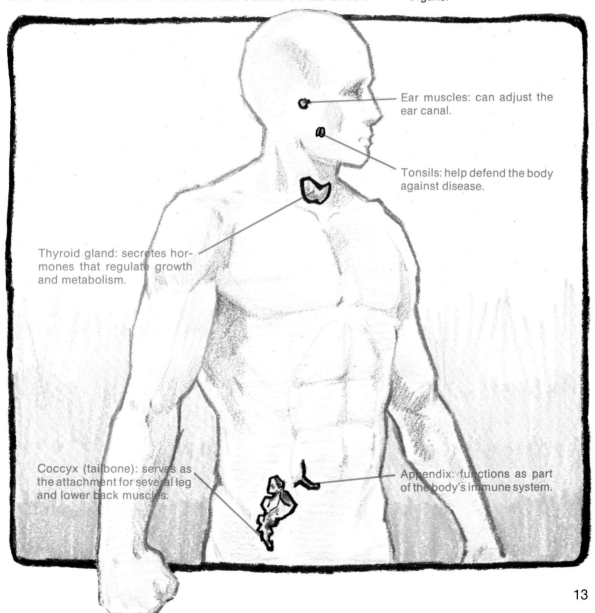

Ear muscles: can adjust the ear canal.

Tonsils: help defend the body against disease.

Thyroid gland: secretes hormones that regulate growth and metabolism.

Coccyx (tailbone): serves as the attachment for several leg and lower back muscles.

Appendix: functions as part of the body's immune system.

13

1-8 As far as scientists have been able to determine, only Earth is a suitable home for man.

We also see clear evidence of design when we look at the earth and its near surroundings. The earth is just the right distance from the sun. The sun provides a steady supply of exactly the right kinds of energy for living things on the earth. Our atmosphere contains the best possible mixture of oxygen and other gases. The earth's magnetic field protects us from cosmic rays. The ozone (OH zone) layer in the stratosphere (STRAT uh SFIHR) (upper layer of the earth's atmosphere) protects us from ultraviolet rays. The earth's rotational speed provides ideal periods of day and night. All these things, to the mind that is not blinded by sin, speak of God's creative design.

Sometimes God's design is not apparent to us. Some of our observations seem unexplainable. With further study, however, many of these begin to make sense. Even if we are not capable of understanding a certain fact of nature, every such fact exists and operates in accordance with some part of God's overall plan. Every fact in the universe is already known to God. The true order of the universe is visible to all those who ask. The psalmist tells us: "For thou wilt light my candle: the Lord my God will enlighten my darkness" (Ps. 18:28).

Science in the Bible

Although the Bible is not meant to be a textbook of science, it contains much valuable information that relates to science. In fact, Scripture answers questions about the universe that science cannot deal with: where did it come from? what will eventually happen to it? Scripture tells us that the universe came into being by the miraculous acts of an omnipotent Creator. This event, called the Creation, occurred at a definite time in the not-too-remote past. Scripture also states that the present universe will be dissolved, and a new heaven and a new earth will be established (Isa. 34:4; II Pet. 3:10; Rev. 21:1).

Remember that science is defined as *human observation.* Since scientists cannot now observe either past events or future events, science is totally unable to answer questions about how the universe began or how it will end. The Bible can speak with authority on these subjects because it is God's Word and He sees all eternity; science cannot speak about what it cannot observe.

Science is mainly concerned with *physical* observations; the Bible, with *spiritual* observations. But sometimes the two overlap. When they do, true science does not contradict the Bible. In fact, science has made observations that confirm the Bible's accurate descriptions of the physical universe. Some portions of Scripture show an understanding of natural processes that science has now been able to observe. When those portions were written, however, there was no way to perform the observations necessary to test those ideas about nature. By confirming the truth of these statements, scientific observations evidence the divine inspiration of Scripture. For example, Ecclesiastes 1:6 declares that the winds move in cycles: "The wind goeth toward the south, and turneth about unto the north; it whirleth about continually, and the wind returneth again according to his circuits." King Solomon wrote this statement approximately one thousand years before Christ, when no special equipment was available for observing wind currents aloft.

1-9 Galileo.

Jeremiah wrote, "the host of heaven cannot be numbered" (Jer. 33:22). Scripture compares the number of stars to the number of grains of sand on the seashore (Gen. 22:17). In contrast, many of the ancients thought there were only about a thousand stars, those that could be seen with the naked eye. Not until A.D. 1609, when Galileo (GAL uh LAY oh) turned his first telescope skyward, did men appreciate the truth of these verses. The stars are innumerable to man; there are so many stars in the Milky Way galaxy that many are hidden by others and cannot be seen to be counted. God not only sees all the stars and knows their total number, but He knows each one by name: "He telleth the number of the stars; he calleth them all by their names" (Ps. 147:4). Modern astronomers have estimated that there are at least *ten sextillion* (seks TIL yun) stars! Written out this number looks like this:

10,000,000,000,000,000,000,000

Other astronomers estimate that the number is as high as *one hundred octillion* (ahk TIL yun):

100,000,000,000,000,000,000,000,000,000

Of course, these estimates are mere guesses. The true number remains, as the Bible says it will, beyond man's reach.

1-10 There are over 100 billion stars in the Milky Way galaxy alone.

Astrology is another subject in which science supports the Bible. *Astrology* (uh STRAH luh jee) is the study of how the motions of the planets and stars supposedly influence human affairs. In ancient times almost all nations of the world believed and practiced some form of astrology. The Old Testament, however, clearly revealed that the practice was false—and forbade God's people to take part in it (Deut. 18:9-14; Isa. 47:13-14; Jer. 10:2). Over the centuries, as scientific knowledge has increased, science has demonstrated the truth of what the Bible has taught all along.

To the ancients nature must have seemed disorderly and mysterious. Planets wandered through the sky; comets and eclipses appeared suddenly and without warning, inspiring terror and predictions of doom. Such events would have seemed random—as if they had occurred by chance. But God's Word revealed even then that there are "ordinances of heaven" (Job 38:33): the celestial bodies move according to patterns. Not until perhaps thirty centuries later did Copernicus (ko PUR nih kus), Kepler, and Newton establish that these motions followed a definite pattern.

Science and the Christian

Some students are naturally attracted to science. They enjoy investigating nature or tinkering with machines. They may have a natural aptitude in mathematics. They pursue extra projects and reading just to satisfy their curiosity about the world around them. Many of these students will train for careers in science. They will become the nurses, doctors, dentists, research scientists, engineers, and technologists of the future. But you may not be one of those students. You may be thinking about a career as a businessman, housewife, teacher, or pastor. Will this science course be of any lasting benefit to you?

As you explore the physical universe and study the principles that govern its operations, you will learn to appreciate the complexity and order of God's creation. The psalmist held God's creation in such awe that he wrote, "When I consider thy heavens, the work of thy fingers, the moon and the stars, which thou hast ordained; What is man, that thou art mindful of him? and the son of man, that thou visitest him?" (Ps. 8:3-4). The psalmist's observations of the world around him helped him understand his smallness as compared to God's greatness. The study of science will help you gain a right perspective of God's power and majesty.

Though some scientists try to attack God's Word, science has played an important role in supporting the inerrancy of the Bible. Once liberal scholars and archaeologists scoffed at the passage in Deuteronomy 8:7-9: "For the Lord thy God bringeth thee into a good land . . . out of whose hills thou mayest dig brass

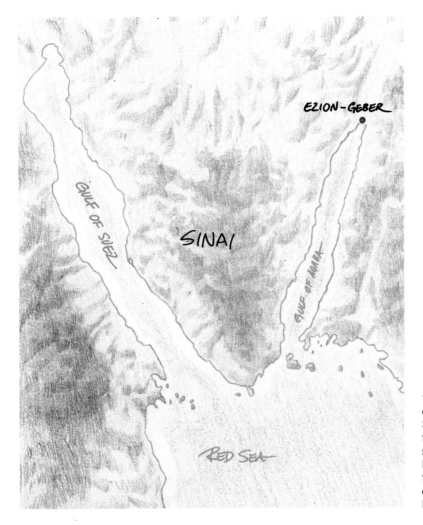

1-11 When Nelson Glueck discovered the location of Solomon's mines, many critics of the Bible's accuracy were silenced. The mines were located in an ideal location for trade—just at the tip of the Gulf of Aqaba in the city of Ezion-geber.

[copper]." The skeptics questioned the existence of copper deposits anywhere in Palestine.

Conservative scholars had long believed that Solomon mined and traded copper to the Persian kings in exchange for gold and spices. To confirm this, Dr. Nelson Glueck began the task of locating the lost mines. His team first uncovered the ancient city of Ezion-geber, the actual port from which eastbound copper had been shipped. Aerial surveys soon revealed water holes that had been used in ore smelting. Finally the abandoned mines were unearthed. In 1957 the unworked copper veins were put back into production and proved to be a profitable business. A literal reading of the Scriptures had borne fruit.

1-12 In the future you may be faced with questions about the use of the environment by industry. The knowledge you gain from this course will help you decide what is the correct position to take on many issues.

The study of science can also help you develop self-discipline. The activities of science require careful thought. You must follow precise instructions, make detailed observations, and develop a clear understanding of what you observe. This art—the art of critical thinking—will help you in every area of your life, whether in examining the news reports for the true story of an event or in applying Scripture in your daily life.

Science is also a vital topic in our world. Almost every day some aspect of science is the subject of debate, investigation, or legislation. The ability to speak intelligently on subjects such as atomic energy or genetic engineering might gain for you the respect of people who would not otherwise give credit to your views. Such knowledge will also be a tool to help you detect error and false reasoning and make wise decisions in today's technology-oriented society.

Finally, by studying science you can satisfy some of your curiosity about the world around you. You will develop a better understanding of what things are made of and how they work, and of the laws that govern their relationships and reactions to one another. As you satisfy your curiosity about matters of science, you may decide you want to pursue them further. If the Lord calls you into a science-related field of work, you will want to be ready—prepared by your early, foundational studies in science.

Scientifically Speaking

data	humanism
observation	evolution
science	evolutionists
physical universe	creationists
pure science	creationism
applied science	theistic evolution 17
technology	bias
value judgments	teleology

Questions to Talk Over

1. The fundamental activity of science is human observation. Discuss how each of these scientific activities has a human observer.
   a. an undersea probe sampling mineral nodules from the ocean floor
   b. a series of seismograph readings (measurements of the earth's vibrations) along the San Andreas Fault
   c. a Landsat satellite photographing land features from orbit
2. Science offers choices but cannot provide a basis for making a value judgment. Discuss what choices science offers in the field of genetic engineering and why science cannot determine what is the correct choice.
3. Some scientists who want to believe in both God and evolution try to reconcile their beliefs by saying that God used evolution to create the universe. What is wrong with this belief?
4. How does your point of view bias your judgment about handling a harmless garden spider?
5. List some of the orderly processes that you observe in creation that point to a Designer of the universe.
6. If you were called to be a preacher or a Bible teacher, how would the study of science help your future ministry?

THE
SCIENTIFIC
METHOD

CHAPTER
2

The physical universe is like an intricate tapestry woven by the hand of God. He spun it from asteroids, comets, planets, and blazing stars; dyed it with an infinite variety of colors; and designed it with patterns so minutely detailed that the casual observer seldom sees them.

Most of us are satisfied with the beauty that we see on the surface of God's creation, but the scientist seeks further. He desires to explore beyond the obvious.

How does he search out the delicate patterns of creation? How can he see beyond the surface and examine the underlying law and order of the physical universe? The answer lies in the method by which a scientist chooses answers. This method of inquiry has come to be known as the **scientific method**.

Perhaps the scientific method is misnamed, for it is not a formal procedure to be followed in careful detail. It is rather a pattern of thought that results in a certain approach to problem solving. It is a very effective approach to finding the solution to a problem; you have probably used it without noticing it. Yet it is the consistent use of this approach by scientists that makes science the discipline of discovery.

Before leaving for school in the morning, you decide what you should wear. You awake to find warm sunlight pouring through your windows. A quick check of the thermometer outside your window tells you that the temperature is a brisk 52° Fahrenheit. As you dress, you hear the branches of a tree beating against the side of the house. On the basis of these three observations, you put on a windbreaker and start out for school. Whether or not you realize it, you have used the scientific method to solve a problem.

The decision you made about what you should wear to school was based on *observations*, and making observations is a key step in the scientific approach to problem solving. First you became aware of a problem. In this case it could be stated: "What shall I wear to go outside?" Then you collected observations that were relevant to the problem. You observed the sunshine, noted the temperature, and heard the moving branches of the trees. Next you mentally organized the data. From your information you chose a workable solution from the variety of possibilities in your closet—you decided to wear a jacket. The final step in the process was verifying your choice. Your windbreaker protected you from the chilly breezes outside, confirming that you had made a wise decision.

2-1 If the thermometer read 11° C, would you still wear a jacket?

Table 2-2

The Steps of the Scientific Method
1. Recognize a problem.
2. Make observations.
3. Organize your data.
4. Choose a solution.
5. Verify your solution.

Choices

All our lives we are faced with problems to solve. Often a problem will have several seemingly good answers. Sometimes a particular problem will have no apparent answer at all. How do we select the best answer for a particular problem?

The surest solutions to many of the problems that we face are found in God's Word. There we have a direct revelation of God's answers to man's problems. However, God has chosen not to reveal to mankind everything about His creation. Some knowledge He has commissioned us to discover.

We are then faced with a *choice*: what is the most reliable way to find answers that are not revealed in Scripture? There are only a few possibilities: guesswork, intuition (IN too ISH un), a prediction from a known trend, and the scientific method. Of these choices, only the scientific method offers us a reliable way to collect and confirm information about the physical universe.

What makes the scientific method such a good choice? Basically, the *scientific method* is a systematic way of finding possible solutions to problems by making observations. It sometimes involves intelligent guesswork, intuition, and prediction, but subjects them all to the rigorous test of observation. All proposed solutions must be tested and retested by making carefully controlled observations.

We have discussed the use of the scientific method to solve the everyday problem of how to dress to go outside. What if you had used some other method to choose what to wear? You could have based your selection on a trend in weather conditions. If the temperature had been low for several days before, you would have selected warm clothes for the next day. Yet if a sudden change in the weather had occurred, your choice might have made you very uncomfortable.

The scientific method allows you to check a prediction with observations. By using the scientific method, you could be sure that you were dressing wisely for that day's weather conditions. This commonplace example illustrates an important point: the strength of the scientific method lies in its ability to test its solutions. Guesswork, intuition, or prediction alone cannot do this, but combined with the scientific method they can play an important role in discovery.

Intelligent guesswork teamed with the scientific method to help Charles Goodyear develop a way to make rubber products practical. In the early 1800s, companies making india-rubber

2-3 Charles Goodyear at work in his home laboratory.

caps, shoes, coats, and wagon covers sprang up at a phenomenal rate. However, within two years after rubber was introduced into the American marketplace, the india-rubber boom was over. The heat of summer reduced the rubber products to molten masses that gave off such an offensive odor that they had to be buried.

Goodyear had just sold his interest in a hardware store so that he could devote his life to a career of invention. He decided to take on the challenge of making rubber useful. He felt that he could solve the problem with this gum elastic (rubber) in just a few months, but later wrote that he was "blessed" with ignorance of the obstacles he would meet. Several winters and summers

FACETS
OF BASIC SCIENCE

Observing the Lord

The value of observation is not limited to the field of science. Observations are significant in the Scriptures as well. Beginning in Genesis with the mark of Cain and the first rainbow, God called on man to observe many things. One of the most important calls was to observe His Son.

"Behold the Lamb of God, which taketh away the sin of the world." (John 1:29)

John the Baptist first called men to look upon Jesus Christ. The Lord was about to begin His public ministry when John asked men to *observe* Him—to use their physical senses to perceive the precious Gift of God. Later, when John sent two of his disciples to ask Jesus if He were indeed the Promised One, "Jesus answered and said unto them, Go and shew John again those things which ye do hear and see" (Matt. 11:4). They were to testify to others the things they had observed of Christ.

"Behold the man!" (John 19:5)

This time it was Pontius Pilate who called men to behold the Lamb of God. The Saviour was on His way to the cross that would thrust Him high above the stark hill of Calvary, into the view of men for all the ages to come. The jeering crowd at the foot of the cross saw Him hanging there; they demanded, mocking, "Let Christ the King of Israel descend now from the cross, that we may see and believe" (Mark 15:32).

He did not come down from the cross; they would not have believed if He had. But the mockers heard for themselves His last words and His last breath, and saw for themselves the darkness, and felt the earthquake that declared this to be the death of the Son of God.

His disciples, too, saw Him there. They "stood afar off, beholding these things" (Luke 23:49). Then, because they were trusting in their physical vision alone, they went their way in grief and not in hope.

"Behold my hands and my feet, that it is I myself: handle me, and see; for a spirit hath not flesh and bones, as ye see me have." (Luke 24:39)

The risen Saviour spoke to calm His troubled disciples. Already He had given them proof of His resurrection: the angel at the empty tomb had told the two women that He lived again; then Mary Magdalene had seen Him and had spoken with Him in the garden. But the apostles would not believe these reports; "their words seemed to them as idle tales" (Luke 24:11).

That same day, the Lord had appeared to two of the apostles as they traveled to Emmaus. He kept them from knowing who He was; they told Him all that had happened, and of their disappointment and sadness. The Lord responded, "O fools, and slow of heart to believe all that the prophets have spoken" (Luke 24:25). To these who had believed neither His promise nor the witness of others, He explained the Scriptures that testified of Him. Only then did He open their eyes so that they could see and know Him, and

return to Jerusalem to testify, "The Lord is risen indeed" (Luke 24:34).

Now He stood before them as He had promised and as Scripture had prophesied—and they were afraid. He invited them to observe for themselves His resurrected body, to see and to touch, and to be "not faithless, but believing" (John 20:27). Christ was truly the Lord; He lived again as He had promised.

"Ye men of Galilee, why stand ye gazing up into heaven? this same Jesus, which is taken up from you into heaven, shall so

come in like manner as ye have seen him go into heaven." (Acts 1:11)

The disciples stood staring at the sky as the heavenly messengers spoke to them. A moment before, the Lord had been with them, talking with them and instructing them as He had so many times before. Then, as they watched, "he was taken up; and a cloud received him out of their sight" (Acts 1:9). He had left them again—not alone or hopeless, but with the promise of the Holy Spirit, and of power, and of His coming to earth again as they had seen Him go. He had also left with them a mission: to bear witness of Him throughout the earth.

They did go to the ends of the earth, preaching, teaching, and writing, to share with the lost world what they had observed of the Saviour: "That which was from the beginning, which we have heard, which we have seen with our eyes, which we have looked upon, and our hands have handled, of the Word of life . . . declare we unto you, that ye also may have fellowship with us: and truly our fellowship is with the Father, and with his Son Jesus Christ" (I John 1:1, 3).

Men on earth will behold the Lord again when He returns as He promised. For those who have heard and believed the witness of Christ, seeing Him will bring great joy and reunion with their Redeemer. For those, however, who have not believed the report, seeing Him will not bring joy, but judgment:

"Behold, he cometh with clouds; and every eye shall see him, and they also which pierced him: and all kindreds of the earth shall wail because of him. Even so, Amen" (Rev. 1:7).

would pass before he could successfully test his products with observations.

His road to discovery was not an easy one. He tried mixing witch hazel, black ink, and even cream cheese into the rubber to make it stable, but his efforts failed dismally. His lack of training in chemistry handicapped him. Nevertheless, his persistent use of trial and error, tested by observations, kept him on the road to discovery. It was not until he treated the crude rubber with sulfur and subjected it to heat that he found success. This process, now called vulcanization (VUL kuh nuh ZAY shun), resulted in a stable compound that had both strength and elasticity (ih LAS TIS uh tee). Soon factories were producing Goodyear's rubber all across Europe and America. The results of careful observations finally paid off.

Whether they are searching for specific applications or new information, most scientists use some form of the scientific method to find solutions. There is no single, simple list of the exact steps that all scientists follow, but they share some important activities that we should consider. The steps that we shall discuss are only a broad outline of the procedures used in most scientific problem solving. Not every point can be applied to every research project, and some projects might require additional steps. Our discussion will simply help us to understand the way a scientist approaches a problem.

Observations

Scientists are *curious* people. That is not to say that they are odd, but that they are interested in anything that seems strange or new or different. Curiosity is important to science. It involves an alert mind that constantly compares facts. It requires a willingness to examine established ideas in the light of new observations. Sometimes these observations will agree with established ideas and strengthen them. In other cases observations may disagree with opinions and cause the curious mind to carefully reexamine a particular fact or idea.

Curiosity has propelled many important advances in science and technology. Someone wonders how or why a particular phenomenon (fih NAHM uh NAHN) (any event apparent to the senses) takes place; then he takes the time and the initiative to propose and test an answer. When he recognizes a problem that he can investigate, the scientist starts on that road to discovery that we call the scientific method.

Recognizing a problem

One scientist whose curiosity led her to an important discovery was Marie Curie (KYOO ree). In 1896 Henry Becquerel (beh KREL) had discovered that uranium sends out spontaneous rays, which he could detect by using photographic plates. He believed that the element was breaking apart, shooting particles of itself into space. His ideas fascinated Madame Curie. Wondering if there might be other "self-destructive" elements in nature, she began to investigate all the known elements. She found her answer in the element thorium: it sent out rays as uranium did. With her discovery she added a new term to the scientific vocabulary: she named the phenomenon *radioactivity* (RAY dee oh AK TIV uh tee).

In her experiments Madame Curie measured some mysteriously high levels of radiation in pitchblende, a uranium ore. These measurements puzzled her. She knew that the ore contained both uranium and thorium, but these elements alone could not produce as much radiation as she had found. Her curiosity was aroused. She suspected that there was another element in the ore, one even more radioactive than uranium and thorium.

Marie Curie had recognized a problem and guessed at the most probable solution. Such a "scientific" or "educated" guess (proposed answer) is called a **hypothesis** (hye PAH thuh sis). A scientist uses a hypothesis to guide his investigations. Madame Curie investigated carefully for many long months, seeking to prove her hypothesis that pitchblende contained unknown radioactive elements. Her hard work paid off, and in 1898 she announced that she had discovered two new radioactive elements: radium and polonium.

2-4 Pierre and Marie Curie, whose use of the scientific method led to the discovery of radioactivity and many radioactive elements.

Making observations

Scientists gather data by making observations. Even when a scientist collects a portion of his data from a book, an article in a magazine, or another scientist's report, he uses a written record of someone else's observations. Without observers, the scientific method could not exist.

Making observations and recording them is called *data gathering*. This activity is a crucial part of the scientific method. Good researchers learn to write down observations immediately, before any of the details are forgotten. They will not trust memory, even for a short period of time. They repeat each observation several times to insure that their data are accurate. Good researchers record details carefully, so that their observations can be reproduced or compared with similar observations. In most research, if an observation cannot be duplicated, it should not be accepted.

In 1962 a group of scientists announced the discovery of polywater (PAHL ih WAH tur), a new substance thought to be water molecules linked together to form long chains. Many wondered if the world's water supplies might be in danger, for polywater would not support life. Many researchers attempted to reproduce the original observations, but no one could arrive at exactly the same results. Soon the discoverers themselves realized that their observations were faulty. If they were extremely careful to keep their glassware clean, they could not produce polywater. They found that polywater was not a new substance, but a highly concentrated form of something that has been around for a long time—dirty water!

Some data gathered by observations are **qualitative** (KWAHL uh TAY tiv) **data.** They do not involve the use of numbers or measurements; rather, they describe an event or condition. Some examples of such data are descriptions of the color of a liquid before, during, and after a chemical reaction; the physical characteristics of a certain biological species; and the quality of a certain sound.

Measurable or numerical data are **quantitative** (KWAHN tuh TAY tiv) **data.** Scientists gather many quantitative measurements. Doctors order tests that count blood cells and measure chemicals in the blood. Nurses take blood pressure and temperature readings. Scientists in the laboratory use complex instruments to detect light, measure volumes and masses, and calculate exact times. Today's researcher is faced with so many numbers that he often depends on the computer as a tool to organize his data.

Scientists prefer numerical data because they are less affected by the observer's *bias*. But quantitative measurements are limited in their accuracy: they cannot be more precise than the instruments used to make them. You would not try to measure microseconds (one-millionth of a second) with your wristwatch. A good observer will use an instrument to its fullest potential, but he will never push it beyond its built-in limitations.

Both qualitative and quantitative data can be gathered in two distinctly different ways. Scientists use the **survey** (SUR vay) to gather data about an existing situation or object. Each year, to

2-5 These medical technicians are testing solutions with blocks of a special substance that changes color in the presence of a certain chemical.

help set hunting limits, naturalists survey the populations of game animals. Environmental chemists survey the quality of water by taking samples from lakes and streams. Another way to collect data is by **experiment**. An experiment is a carefully controlled arrangement for testing a specific problem. Scientists observe the reactions of materials in this special setup. These setups are valuable because they allow researchers to control experimental conditions.

Table 2-6
Gathering Quantitative Data

Scientists collect quantitative, or numerical, data through many different techniques. A few of them are pictured here.

a This scientist is measuring a group of animals to survey their growth rate.

b This scientist is using a bomb calorimeter. She can measure the thermal energy present in a substance by exploding it in a special chamber in the instrument.

d These scientists are receiving quantitative data about the ocean from sensitive monitoring equipment supported by a buoy near their ship.

e This scientist is checking a detailed readout from an x-ray diffraction machine, which explores the structures of crystals.

c This scientist is doing cryogenic (KRY oh JEN ik) research, measuring the properties of materials at temperatures far below normal.

Chapter 2

Organizing the data

When the scientist has completed his observations, his next step is to decide what the collected information means. Organizing scientific data involves classifying the data (separating data into groups) and then analyzing those groups. Classifying the data allows the scientist to see and investigate relationships. Did the data suggest a trend? Did they indicate a steady condition? Did they reveal a cause-and-effect relationship in which one factor caused a change in another? Charting or graphing groups of data is often the best way to analyze them. **Charts** and **graphs** both make visible the relationships in the data and help the scientist to answer his questions.

FACETS
OF BASIC SCIENCE

Developing Data

When Mr. Behn assigned science projects, Julia decided that she wanted to experiment with photography. After talking with her teacher and with her father's friend Mr. Wilt, Julia decided to test the effect of temperature on the development of color prints. Mr. Wilt was a professional photographer, and he told Julia that he would help her in any way he could. She studied his photography manuals until she understood the developing process. Then she bought the necessary chemicals and asked the photographer to help her print some photos on color paper.

For each print, Julia carefully adjusted the temperature of the developing solution and timed the period needed for processing. She timed the process at five different temperatures and then repeated the experiment to insure the accuracy of her results. She carefully recorded all her data in a notebook.

The next day Julia showed the data to her teacher, Mr. Behn.

"What do my results mean?"

"Well, Julia, it's hard to find a relationship when you simply *list* your data. You were trying to show the effect of temperature on the development time, right? I think the best way to show that type of relationship is to graph your results."

"How do I do that, Mr. Behn?"

This is how Mr. Behn set up Julia's graph:

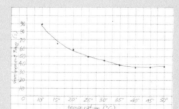

temperature (°C)

Then Julia plotted her data. "Now what does your graph show?"

"That's great! The graph shows me that increasing the temperature speeds up the developing process. The bottom of the graph begins to level out. That probably means that after the solution reaches a certain temperature, heating it anymore doesn't help."

"I think you've done an excellent science project, Julia!"

"Thanks, Mr. Behn!"

Solutions

After a scientist organizes the observed data, he sifts through the numbers, measurements, and descriptions for an answer to the problem he is investigating. He must use the data and his own judgment to choose the answer that seems to work best.

Choosing an answer

It may come as a surprise to you that the conclusions of science are not discovered, but are chosen from an array of alternatives. This makes the scientist's ability to make correct choices very important. A scientist is looking for the most workable answer to the problem. His hypothesis may prove to be correct. He may have to change it to make it better fit the data. In some cases he may need to reject his hypothesis altogether.

> **Good solutions should . . .**
> 1. describe the observation.
> 2. account for the data.
> 3. predict new data.
> 4. stay as simple as possible!

The scientist's choice should have certain characteristics. It should describe what happened. It must agree with the observed data. The chosen solution should also predict what would happen in similar circumstances, and it may direct the scientist to applications or further research. Finally, a good solution should be kept as simple as possible. Not all problems will have simple solutions. In the seventeenth century the English physician William Harvey investigated the circulation of the blood. He concluded that a single mechanism controlled blood pressure. Since then, scientists have gathered much more data about human anatomy. We now believe that at least twenty-four different mechanisms help control blood pressure. Sometimes God's designs are complex, and only a complex answer will account for the observed data.

The selection of a solution by a scientist is a subjective process. His choice will be influenced by his bias. Therefore not even careful scientific conclusions are considered absolute or final. Any solution is subject to possible challenges and may eventually be rejected. This process of testing solutions is called **verification** (VEHR uh fuh KAY shun).

2-7 In the seventeenth century, William Harvey made observations about the circulation of blood. Although some of his theories were incorrect, he gave medicine its first clear idea of the function of the heart.

31

2-8 Verifying the results of an experiment can uncover a large problem.

Verifying the solution

To verify (VEHR uh FY) a piece of research means to check its correctness. A solution may be verified by several different methods. One is to simply repeat the entire experiment. Another is to perform a different experiment that should lead to similar results. A third method is to make a prediction based on the solution and to test whether the prediction is accurate. Even verification, however, does not make a solution absolute fact; it simply makes it more likely to be true.

Sometimes a researcher's work does not "check out." His equipment may have malfunctioned when he did the experiment, or he may have made an error in judgment when he chose the solution to his problem. However, the scientist who later disproves his own solution still makes progress. If the scientist is convinced that his equipment caused the problem, he will modify or replace the equipment and perform the experiment again. He may realize that he must completely rethink and restructure his research. He may have to try several times, but with perseverance he should eventually produce verifiable results. Verifying the solution serves both to confirm correct work and to uncover incorrect work.

Using the solution

A research project may have a variety of outcomes. It may provide only a specific answer to the original problem. It could lead to a broader conclusion, such as a theory or a law. A **theory** is a partially verified idea that ties together a number of different observations. Theories should not be confused with hypotheses. A theory is an idea that has been tested by many observations. A hypothesis is an "educated guess" that guides scientists as they plan their observations. A hypothesis is unconfirmed. A theory has been verified to some extent.

Theories play a double role in research. While showing patterns in data, they also introduce new lines of research. The famous research of Lord Rayleigh (RAY lee) at Cambridge University's Cavendish Laboratory illustrates these roles. In 1882 Rayleigh noticed that the liquid nitrogen he had condensed from the air differed slightly from the nitrogen he had produced from other sources. First he guessed that nitrogen might have several different chemical forms. When he could not support that idea, he attributed the difference to impurities. Some other gas or gases must have condensed with the nitrogen. With the help of William Ramsay, Rayleigh soon isolated the impurity.

The newly detected gas was very stable and highly unreactive. They named it *argon,* from the Greek word for "lazy."

Their work caught the eye of a French scientist, Lecoq de Boisbaudran (leh KAWK duh ʙwaʜ boh DRAHN). Lecoq projected a theory from the data. Argon must belong to a family of unreactive gases that were present in very small quantities in the air. Ramsay took this new theory as a challenge and began to experiment. He eventually located four more gases that fit Lecoq's theory: helium (found earlier in the sun), krypton (Greek for "hidden"), neon (Greek for "new"), and xenon (Greek for "stranger"). This family of elements is now known as the *noble gases.*

Scientific **laws** are chosen to describe consistent patterns of phenomena in nature. When a scientist observes a sequence of events that occurs nearly the same way every time, he can frame a scientific law. Some scientific laws are expressed by mathematical relationships. Coulomb's (koo LAWNZ) law is a mathematical equation that lets us calculate the strength of the force between electrical charges. This is an example of a quantitative physical law. Other physical laws are qualitative; they describe relationships that are not expressed in numbers. For instance, the law of electrical charges says that like charges repel and opposite charges attract. It does not state how strongly they attract or repel.

Some laws describe relationships very accurately. Others are only approximate. Some work well under ordinary conditions but break down under unusual ones. Scientific laws, like scientific solutions, are chosen rather than discovered. How well they work depends on how well they are chosen. Can nature "violate" a scientific law? Yes it can, if the law is not well chosen or not well stated. If a "violation" of the law is observed, the law should be rewritten so that it more accurately describes what actually happens.

Limitations

Some people have exaggerated ideas of what science is and what it can do. Although science does occupy an important role in modern life, it cannot solve all man's problems. Science is only a means of gathering information, and that information poses questions: Is the information correct? How should it be used? To properly answer these questions, we must understand the limitations of the scientific method.

Evolution as a Hypothesis

In almost every textbook, the ideas of evolutionists are labeled *theories.* But is it correct to call them theories? Do scientists have any clear-cut evidence of evolution that cannot be challenged? Since it has not been verified to any degree, the "theory" of evolution should be labeled an evolutionary *hypothesis.*

Limitations in collecting data

A scientist collects information by observing physical phenomena. Only information that a scientist can gather with his senses, either with or without the aid of instruments, can be scientific data. Information can be collected only from the physical universe. But some phenomena are too small, occur too quickly, or happen too far away to be observed with man's unaided senses. Can scientists collect information about these? Much of our scientific information has come through instruments that allow man to extend his senses so that he can collect data about events he cannot readily observe. When a scientist investigates the impact of a bullet, the event occurs too quickly for him to see it. Using stroboscopes (STRO buh SKOAPS) and high-speed photography, he can "slow down" the event to a rate that he can observe. If a phenomenon cannot be observed, then it is beyond the limits of science. Science cannot deal with the spiritual realm, because it can use only the physical senses to collect data. Science cannot deal with the origins of the universe because no human observer was present to collect information about them.

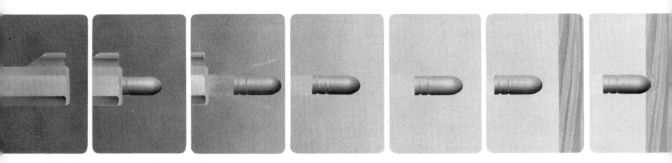

2-9 Stroboscopic photography can "slow down" motion to show the effect of a bullet as it penetrates a wooden barrier and strikes a steel barrier.

Scientific data can describe phenomena in qualitative and quantitative terms. This information helps scientists understand how, where, and when a phenomenon will occur. Yet scientific data cannot explain *why* something happens. When a chemist observes a reaction, he collects data about the temperature, rate, color changes, and amount of products. He uses this information to determine the conditions (when and where) and the process (how) needed for the reaction. This information can tell him how to control the reaction, but not why the reaction occurred. He cannot assign a motive or sense of purpose to the chemicals.

Scientists should observe these limitations, but unfortunately some scientists imagine that at one time motives and purposes did guide chemical reactions. They suggest that billions of years ago, in the prebiotic (PREE bye AHT ik) (before-life) soup that supposedly developed into the oceans, some force led molecules to combine and recombine until they became a living unit. This imagined process was driven by an evolutionary motive to create life. These scientists have failed to recognize the limitations of their research.

Science cannot establish truth. Scientific conclusions are always subject to change as new information is collected. There is only one Truth. Christ said, "I am the way, the truth, and the life: no man cometh unto the Father, but by me" (John 14:6). This truth does not change. With God there "is no variableness, neither shadow of turning" (James 1:17b). His Word reveals to us His truth: "Sanctify them through thy truth: thy word is truth" (John 17:17).

Scientists are subject to all the limitations of human nature. They can miscalculate, misunderstand, and misapply information. Therefore science is limited by the persons who practice it. History records many scientific blunders that happened because man misinterpreted natural phenomena. One such error was the caloric theory of heat. At one time scientists thought that heat

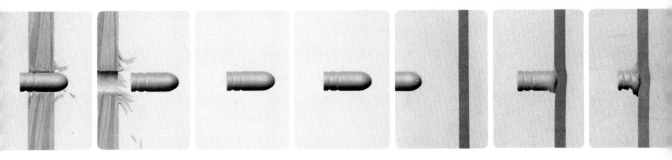

was a substance that flowed from hot objects to cooler ones. Scientists now realize that heat is energy, not matter. This is just one illustration of the fact that all human activity is subject to error.

Remember, scientific information is changeable. If you were to compare the "facts" held by science fifty years ago with what science holds today, you would be surprised at the number of "proven facts" that have changed. Mars was once thought to have canals; the atom was once believed to be unsplittable; and several creatures thought to be extinct have turned up alive and well! People who put their faith in science are bound to be disappointed.

2-10 *"Who* doesn't exist?"

Limitations in using information

Scientists use information to develop laws and theories that describe the way things work. With this information they have found cures for diseases, reached into the heavens, and delved into the minute structure of matter. But there are things that science cannot do.

Science cannot prove a **universal negative.** A universal negative is an absolute statement of denial. Suppose someone states, "There is no such thing as a sea monster." How would you go about proving or disproving this claim? You would probably investigate reports of large, unclassified marine creatures—carcasses that have been washed ashore, footprints on beaches, and similar observations. Suppose that you can discredit the data you are given. In each instance you can prove that the "sea monster" is either some common creature or an outright hoax. You still have not proved that sea monsters do not exist. To prove that, you would have to gather information about every ocean, at all depths, over the entire earth, and on every other planet that has oceans. Not only that, you would have to observe every region at the same time: while you were looking in one place, the slippery sea monster could have gone somewhere else. Science *cannot establish* the universal nonexistence of anything. Only a very limited, local nonexistence can be proved, and that only in certain situations. For instance, a limited statement such as, "There are no sea monsters within 1000 feet of Jamaica," could be investigated and proved, with enough equipment and manpower.

Table 2-11

The Limitations of Science
1. Science must deal with observable physical phenomena.
2. Science can describe how, when, and where, but it cannot explain why.
3. Science cannot establish truth.
4. Science is limited by the persons who practice it.
5. Science cannot prove a universal negative.
6. Science cannot make value judgments.
7. Science cannot make moral judgments.

The existence of miracles is one of the things science cannot disprove. Many people choose not to believe in anything they do not personally experience. That is their privilege. But to say that science has disproved the existence of miracles is completely untrue. Since science cannot establish the universal nonexistence of anything, it can never be used to prove statements like "There is no God" or "There are no miracles." A person who makes such statements is telling you his *beliefs,* not his scientific conclusions.

Scientific information cannot form the basis of **moral judgments**. We make these decisions based on the rightness or wrongness of a particular choice. Consider the following "scientific" view of a bank robbery. Every Friday, the First National Bank receives a one-million-dollar cash shipment to cover the cashing of payroll checks. The security system at the bank is outdated, and no cameras cover the delivery entrance. Security is lax; there is only one guard. The data show that you *could* rob this bank. *Should* you rob it?

2-12 A computer can provide information but it cannot make a moral choice.

37

There is no scientific way to collect information on the morality of robbing a bank. Science cannot tell right from wrong. It can tell you only if something might work. Through science we have obtained atomic energy, but no guidelines for its use. Science may find ways to improve the human race genetically, but it cannot choose who will decide which families should have children. Could a computer pass judgment on moral issues for us? A computer is nothing more than a complex piece of machinery. It cannot produce answers of any kind until it is programmed with specific guidelines. Even then, the computer itself cannot make a decision. It can only reflect the decision already made by the person who programmed it. If a thief programs a computer to choose which banks could be robbed, the computer will produce the information without any judgment. The moral judgment was made by the thief who programmed it. Science can provide only information, not the guidelines for making moral judgments.

Science, by its very nature, can never answer all our questions. Scientific inquiry is limited, and the work of scientific research is never finished. We will never know everything about the physical universe. It has been estimated that for each question science is able to answer, ten new questions are raised. This is precisely what God has ordained. If we could understand everything God did, we would be thinking on His level. But we know that His thoughts are infinitely higher than our thoughts. "Great things doeth he, which we cannot comprehend" (Job 37:5).

Reverence and humility are appropriate attitudes for anyone connected with science. All scientific endeavor, properly pursued, will glorify God the Creator rather than man the creature. The best scientific researcher is the one who can utter from his heart the words of David in Chronicles, "Thine, O Lord, is the greatness, and the power, and the glory, and the victory, and the majesty: for all that is in the heaven and in the earth is thine; thine is the kingdom, O Lord, and thou art exalted as head above all" (I Chron. 29:11).

2-13 One of the most important scientists of the nineteenth century, James Clerk Maxwell, believed that science was a God-ordained means of subduing the earth. This prayer was found among his notes:

"Almighty God, Who has created man in Thine own image, and made him a living soul that he might seek after Thee, and have dominion over Thy creatures, teach us to study the works of Thy hands, that we may subdue the earth to our use, and strengthen the reason for Thy service; so to receive Thy blessed Word, that we may believe on Him Whom Thou hast sent, to give us the knowledge of salvation and the remission of our sins. All of which we ask in the name of the same Jesus Christ, Our Lord."

Scientifically Speaking

scientific method	qualitative data
phenomenon	quantitative data
hypothesis	survey

experiment   theory
charts   laws
graphs   universal negative
verification   moral judgments

Questions to Talk Over

1. Jason is learning how to pitch a baseball for his school's team. He spends several hours every afternoon pitching to Keith, the team's catcher. How is Jason using the scientific method to develop his pitches?

2. Susan wonders if food drops into her stomach because of gravity or if the muscles in her throat carry the food downward. After thinking about this question, Susan chooses the muscle idea as the better hypothesis. How can Susan make observations to test this hypothesis?

3. The Nobel-Prize-winning geneticist Thomas Morgan discovered that the acidity of seawater increases the fertility of sea creatures. When he struck upon the idea, he was at home with no scientific apparatus or laboratory chemicals to test it, so he went to a nearby grocery store and purchased a lemon. He squeezed the citric acid (lemon juice) into his aquarium and carefully recorded the results. Later laboratory experiments confirmed his hypothesis: the acidity of seawater does affect the fertility of sea creatures. By what methods could you confirm his theory in your home or at your school?

4. After investigating the deep trenches on the bottom of the ocean, some scientists were quick to assert that no life could exist under conditions of high pressure and total darkness. What is wrong with their assertion? Can you research any new evidence that might prove their statement wrong?

5. Can science prove the existence of God? Why or why not?

TWO

A DESCRIPTION OF MATTER

THE MEASUREMENT OF MATTER

CHAPTER 3

What is matter? Every object in the physical universe contains matter. The air you breathe, the food you eat, the clothes you wear, and a multitude of other things that you encounter every day illustrate the numberless forms that matter takes. No one could describe all the different objects that God has created. Faced with the infinite variety of matter, scientists have chosen to define matter by the properties it has in every form. All physical objects have two characteristics in common. All objects have a certain quantity of matter (mass), and all occupy space. Therefore, **matter** is defined by its measurable properties of mass and volume.

Why do scientists choose *measurable* properties to define matter? Scientific information is useless unless it can be communicated. Such information can be communicated in either numerical measurements or word descriptions. Why have scientists chosen numerical data?

Suppose you observe a ball swinging at the end of a string. The name of this apparatus is a pendulum. Observations of the setup could include many things: How long is the string? How big is the ball? How much time does one swing take? How high does the ball swing? If you reported that a light ball on the end of a short string took a surprisingly long time for one swing and rose quite high, would this word description be worth anything to a scientist? How long is "long"? What is "quite high"? What seems "light" to one observer might be "heavy" to someone else.

What if you reported that the length of the string was 25, the ball had a mass of 30, the time of one swing was 1, and the height of the swing was 5. Would these numbers be any better than the first data? Numbers alone are not very useful. Is the length of the string 25 inches, 25 meters, or 25 feet? No one could tell from this information! Numbers must go with units to have meaning. For the observations of the pendulum to be useful, all of the data should be recorded in numbers with corresponding units. A correct form for the data from the observation would be, "A 30-gram ball on the end of a 25-centimeter string took 1 second to make a complete swing and rose to a height of 5 centimeters."

The most precise information is communicated with *numerical* (noo MEHR ih kul) data. Lord Kelvin knew how important precise measurements are in science. He said, "When you can measure what you are speaking about, and express it in numbers, you know something about it; but when you cannot express it in numbers, . . . it may be the beginning of knowledge, but you have scarcely, in your thoughts, advanced to the stage of science."

"HEY TOM! I THOUGHT YOU SAID YOU CAUGHT A **BIG FISH**!?"
(3-1)

The Metric System

Man has used many different systems of units. In Bible times length was measured in cubits and spans. (The giant Goliath was 6 cubits and 1 span tall.) Since then ells, fathoms, leagues, miles, yards, feet, and inches have been used to designate lengths. The names of some of these units are fascinating. Using them is not! Why are these units difficult to use?

First, they are based on *changeable* standards. The inch was originally defined as the length of three barley seeds placed end to end. In ancient times inches varied with the quality of the barley crop. King Henry I of England established the yard as a

FACETS
OF BASIC SCIENCE

When Is An Ell Not An Ell?

How would you react if you went to the store this evening, bought a "2-liter" bottle of cola, took it home, and discovered that it was only three-fourths as large as the "2-liter" bottle you bought yesterday in a nearby town? If we did not have a common system of units that were the same size everywhere, you would encounter situations like this every day. You would never know how much of anything you were actually buying.

That was the state of affairs in England until the thirteenth century. The people constantly battled fraud and confusion because they had not agreed on any consistent units for their country. Because each baron was free to establish his own units for his domain, trade was almost impossible. It is no wonder that when the English barons demanded basic political rights in the Magna Carta (MAG nuh KAHR tuh), they also forced King John to establish standard units of measure. One clause of the charter says,

> "Throughout the kingdom there shall be standard measures of wine, ale, and corn. Also there shall be a standard width of dyed cloth; namely two ells within the selvedges [edges]. Weights are to be standardized similarly."

Even though men in the Middle Ages did not have a "technologically advanced" society like

ours, they knew how important consistent units were. Today SI provides a system of measurements that is consistent world-wide, eliminating many problems of trade, aiding the scientific community, and generally simplifying communication.

unit of measurement. He defined it as the distance from the tip of his nose to the end of his outstretched hand. Unfortunately, when he died a new standard had to be found. Barley seeds and arms are not the best standards for units of scientific measure, but they did become the basis of the English system of measurement.

Second, there are *too many* different units. In the English system alone, length is measured in miles, furlongs, rods, yards, spans, feet, hands, and inches. This list does not include units of nautical length and surveyors' lengths. There are literally hundreds of different units in the English system. You can imagine what confusion they can create!

Finally, the *conversion* from one unit to another can be very difficult. Try this English system conversion quiz.

1. How many feet tall is a racehorse that measures 15 hands in height?
2. What is the weight in ounces of a pickup truck weighing one ton?
3. How many pints of gasoline are there in a full 18-gallon tank?

Give up yet? To answer these questions you would need to know how to relate one English unit to another. There are 3 hands in a foot, 16 ounces in a pound, and 2000 pounds in a ton. A liquid gallon contains 8 pints. Converting one English unit into another is not easy. (See Appendix A for help.) In the metric system, however, conversion from one unit into another is simple.

Metric units

The entire **metric system** is based on a unit of length called the **meter** (MEE tur). This unit of measure did not spring from variable human anatomy. It was based on a more permanent standard. The meter was originally defined as one ten-millionth of the distance from the North Pole to the equator. Today scientists define the length of a meter with incredible precision; it is 1,650,763.73 wavelengths of the light given off by krypton-86. The meter can now be measured within one wavelength in one billion. This allows scientists to have an extremely precise standard for the meter.

The metric system is a *decimal* system. Since all the units are related to each other by multiples of ten, you can make smaller or larger units by simply moving the decimal place. From the basic unit of length, a unit of volume called the **liter** (LEE tur)

3-2 The standard kilogram is kept by the International Bureau of Weights and Measures. It is stored under three vacuum domes to assure that it remains accurate.

was derived. A liter is the volume of a cube with sides one-tenth of a meter (.1 meter, called a decimeter) long. This unit of volume was then used to produce the basic unit of mass. The mass of one liter of water is one **kilogram** (KIL uh GRAM), or 1000 grams.

Table 3-3

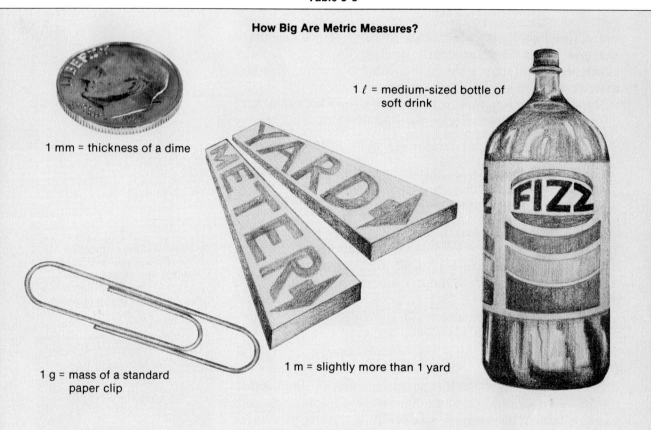

How Big Are Metric Measures?

1 mm = thickness of a dime

1 ℓ = medium-sized bottle of soft drink

1 g = mass of a standard paper clip

1 m = slightly more than 1 yard

Scientists can easily check the accuracy of these units in the laboratory. To confirm the weight of a pound, the volume of a quart, or the length of a foot, however, would require a trip to the National Bureau of Standards near Washington, D.C. Over the decades, the metric system has been expanded into what is now known as **SI,** or *Système International.* SI units include a basic unit of time (the second), a unit of temperature (the degree Kelvin), and a unit of electrical current (the ampere). This unified system simplifies and standardizes all scientific work.

Metric prefixes

Many times the basic SI units are too small or too large to use for a specific measurement. The meter is too small to measure the distances between cities and far too large to measure the thickness of aluminum foil. The volume of a hypodermic syringe is too small to be measured in liters. Likewise, it would be

FACETS
OF BASIC SCIENCE

How Far Is Around The World?

Measuring a planet with a meter stick sounds like a long, hard job—especially if the planet is Jupiter! Yet an encyclopedia will list for you the circumference of each planet in our solar system, and give you the same information about the sun!

How do scientists measure things they cannot reach or handle even with the help of instruments? Some amounts are not *measured* in the usual sense. They are *calculated*. Centuries ago scientists and mathematicians found that they could find new information by using mathematical formulas with information they already had.

Eratosthenes (EHR uh TAHS thuh NEEZ), a Greek astronomer who lived more than 2000 years ago, was the first to accurately calculate the size of the earth. He knew that at noon on the first day of summer, the sun's rays cast no shadows and reached the bottom of a deep well in Syene, Egypt. This information told him that the sun was directly overhead. At the same time in

Alexandria, a city 800 km to the north, the sun *did* cast shadows. He could tell by measuring these shadows that the sun was about 7° "lower" in the sky at the second city.

Eratosthenes already knew that the earth was round (360°) and that all the sun's rays striking the earth were parallel. Using geometry, he figured out that an angle at the earth's center formed by imaginary lines from

the two cities would also be 7°— or approximately $1/50$ of the circle of the earth. Therefore he could multiply by fifty the distance between Syene and Alexandria and find the distance around the earth.

Eratosthenes' method worked so well that his results came within 1 percent of the correct circumference: 50 x 800 km, or 40,000 kilometers.

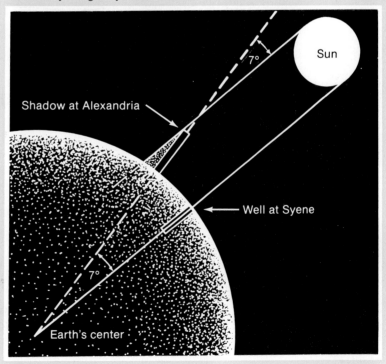

Shadow at Alexandria

Sun

7°

Well at Syene

7°

Earth's center

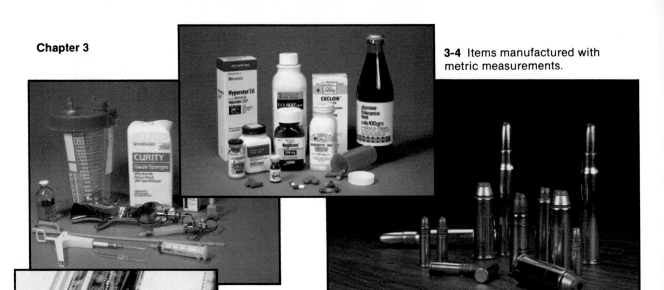

3-4 Items manufactured with metric measurements.

Table 3-5

Metric System Prefixes				
Abbrev-iation	Prefix	Pronun-ciation	Meaning	Decimal Relationship
M	mega	MEG uh	1,000,000 times the basic unit	1,000,000x
k	kilo	KIL oh	1,000 times the basic unit	1,000x
h	hecto	HEK to	100 times the basic unit	100x
da	deka	DEK uh	10 times the basic unit	10x
	(no prefix)		the basic unit	1x
d	deci	DESS uh	1/10 of the basic unit	0.1x
c	centi	SEN tuh	1/100 of the basic unit	0.01x
m	milli	MIL uh	1/1,000 of the basic unit	0.001x
μ	micro	MY kroh	1/1,000,000 of the basic unit	0.000001x

difficult to express a dosage of medicine in kilograms. A prefix system was developed to allow us to modify the basic unit into units that can apply to other situations. The prefix tells how many of the basic units are to be used. For example, the prefix *kilo* means "1000"; therefore a *kilo*meter (KIL uh MEE tur) is *1000* meters, and a meter is $1/1000$ of a kilometer. *Milli* means "$1/1000$." A *milli*liter is $1/1000$ of a liter. Adding one of the standard prefixes changes the basic unit by a multiple of ten.

We can adapt the basic metric units for almost any measurement. Distances between cities are measured in kilometers. The thickness of aluminum foil is measured in millimeters. Hypodermic syringes are calibrated (KAL uh BRATE id) in milliliters, and the dosages of many medications are calculated in milligrams.

Table 3-6

Metric Measures of Length		
Unit	**Abbreviation**	**Size Compared to Meter**
megameter	Mm	1,000,000 times as large
kilometer	km	1,000 times as large
hectometer	hm	100 times as large
dekameter	dam	10 times as large
meter	m	the basic unit
decimeter	dm	1/10 as large
centimeter	cm	1/100 as large
millimeter	mm	1/1,000 as large

Unit conversions

Unit analysis is a way to convert among units. It is a mathematical tool for expressing the way we think about these conversions. If someone asks you how many dozen eggs is 6 eggs, you might stop and think and then answer that 6 eggs is $1/2$ dozen. How did you perform the conversion from single-egg units into dozen-egg units? The conversion was based on two facts: there are 12 eggs in 1 dozen, and 6 is one-half of twelve.

If you summarized your thoughts in a mathematical equation, they could be stated this way:

$$12 \text{ eggs} = 1 \text{ dozen eggs}$$

$$\text{Therefore } \frac{1 \text{ dozen eggs}}{12 \text{ eggs}} = 1$$

because a number divided by itself or its equivalent is always equal to one.

$$6 \text{ eggs} \times \frac{1 \text{ dozen eggs}}{12 \text{ eggs}} = 6/12 \text{ dozen eggs or } \frac{1}{2} \text{ dozen eggs}$$

Remember that multiplying by one does not change the value of the measurement. It changes only the units.

You may not have realized that you used all these steps as you thought, but this type of analysis is the key to the conversion of units.

Three groups of students were given the assignment of measuring a table in their classroom. Each group was supplied with a different measuring device. One device was calibrated in meters, one in centimeters, and the third in millimeters. The teacher recorded the results on the blackboard:

Group A	2000 millimeters
Group B	200 centimeters
Group C	2 meters

3-7 The class records their results.

3-8 Thinking through the
cancelling of units.

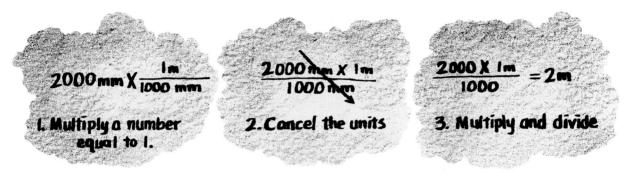

1. Multiply a number equal to 1.
    2. Cancel the units
    3. Multiply and divide

Do their measurements agree? We can check their results by converting all of the measurements into the same units. The first measurement, 2000 millimeters (mm), can be converted into meter (m) units by applying the fact that there are 1000 millimeters in a meter. (See Table 3-6.) If 1000 millimeters are the same as one meter, then 2000 millimeters must be equal to 2 meters. The following equation summarizes this process:

$$2000 \text{ mm} \times \frac{1 \text{ m}}{1000 \text{ mm}} = 2 \text{ m}$$

The millimeter units cancel, and the answer is expressed in meters. We have simply multiplied the number and the unit that we wish to convert by the relationship between the two units. This relationship is stated as a ratio that is equal to 1. A meter and 1000 millimeters are exactly the same length. If you divide a length by itself the answer is 1! Multiplying by 1 does not change the size of the measurement. It changes only the units of the measurement. The same process can be used to convert other metric units.

Check the measurement made by the second group. Are 200 centimeters the same as 2 meters? We can solve for the answer by using this relationship: 1 meter = 100 centimeters.

$$200 \text{ centimeters} \times \frac{1 \text{ meter}}{100 \text{ centimeters}} = 2 \text{ meters}$$

The unit that you are converting *into* is always on the *top* of the fraction. Can we use this method to confirm that 2 meters are the same as 2000 millimeters? What is the relationship between the two units? 1 meter = 1000 millimeters. How would we set up the *unit analysis*? We start with meters and convert into millimeters.

$$2 \text{ meters} \times \frac{1000 \text{ millimeters}}{1 \text{ meter}} = 2000 \text{ millimeters}$$

Why did we use the relationship 1000 millimeters = 1 meter? Why did we place the millimeters on the top of that relationship?

In checking our work, we have confirmed that the groups made identical measurements. They simply expressed them in different units. You will often need to convert several different units into the same units for comparison. Be sure to learn the metric prefixes so that you can convert units easily.

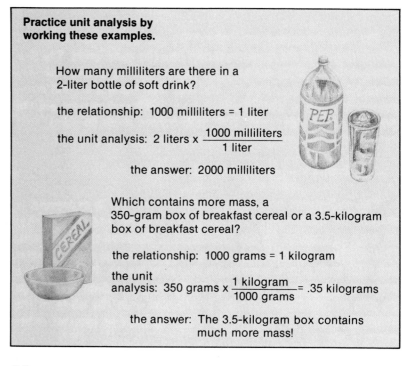

Practice unit analysis by working these examples.

How many milliliters are there in a 2-liter bottle of soft drink?

the relationship: 1000 milliliters = 1 liter

the unit analysis: $2 \text{ liters} \times \dfrac{1000 \text{ milliliters}}{1 \text{ liter}}$

the answer: 2000 milliliters

Which contains more mass, a 350-gram box of breakfast cereal or a 3.5-kilogram box of breakfast cereal?

the relationship: 1000 grams = 1 kilogram

the unit analysis: $350 \text{ grams} \times \dfrac{1 \text{ kilogram}}{1000 \text{ grams}} = .35 \text{ kilograms}$

the answer: The 3.5-kilogram box contains much more mass!

Mass

In making a snowball, you pack a certain amount of snow into a sphere. As it is packed, the snow decreases in size, but does it lose matter? Is size a dependable measure of the amount of matter in an object? What about the astronauts as they travel through space? In the ready room of the launchpad, an astronaut weighs 160 pounds. Far out in space, the astronaut is "weightless." Is part of the astronaut lost as he travels into space? Could

3-9 Is this astronaut "weightless" because he has no mass?

weight be a dependable measurement of the amount of matter in an object?

The measurement of matter

Mass is defined as the quantity of matter in an object. Mass does not change when an object is compressed. It will not change with the pull of gravity. An object that has a mass of 4 kilograms on earth will have that same mass in space. Mass is a constant. It does not change unless matter is added or removed.

The mass of an object can be determined on a **balance.** Balances are measuring devices that compare the amount of matter in an object to a known amount of matter. The simplest type of balance is the double-pan balance. The object to be measured is placed on the left pan, causing the balance to shift to that side. Separate *masses* with known values are placed on the other pan until the center scale shows that the pans are *balanced.*

Table 3-10
Types of Balances

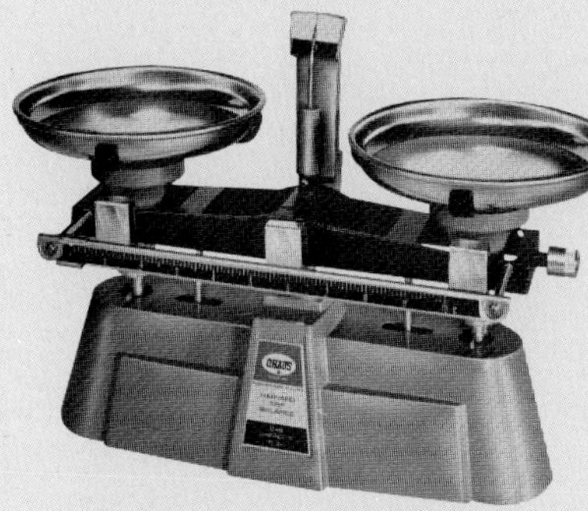

Double-pan balance

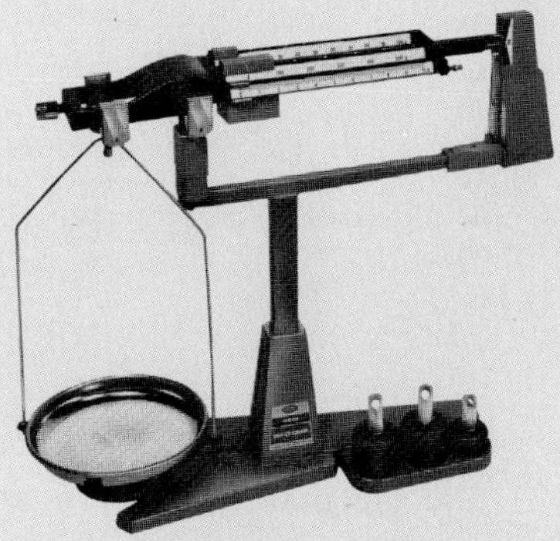

Triple-beam balance

Precision electronic balance

Since each pan now holds an equal amount of mass, the sum of the known masses equals the mass of the object being measured.

Multiple-beam balances are very practical devices for determining the mass of an object. They are simpler to use because they require no separate known masses. These balances usually have two to four specially calibrated beams. The calibrations might stand for hundreds of grams, tens of grams, grams, and tenths of grams. The object to be measured is placed on the pan, and the riders (known masses that slide on the beams) are moved until the scale balances. Measurements can be made to the nearest centigram. When more accurate measurements are needed, analytical balances are used. These precision instruments give readings to the nearest $1/10$ of a milligram (.0001 gram).

The conservation of mass

Matter undergoes many changes. It can be crushed, powdered, or subjected to chemical reactions. It can be frozen, melted, or boiled. But under ordinary circumstances it cannot

3-11 God established the water cycle to conserve this vital substance in His creation.

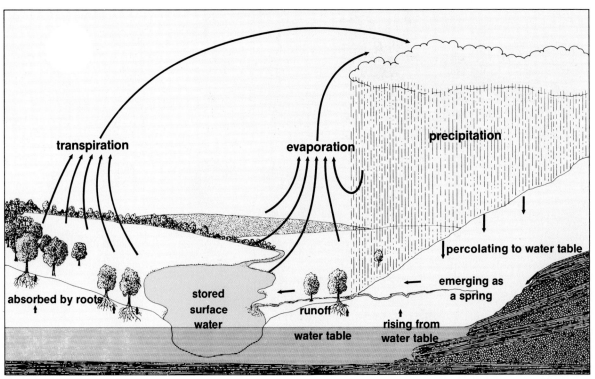

be destroyed. When an object is crushed or powdered, it retains its original mass. When objects undergo chemical reactions, the products of those reactions will have the same mass as the original objects. Water does not gain or lose mass as it is frozen or boiled. In all physical and chemical changes, matter is neither created nor destroyed. It is *conserved* (kun SURVD).

In the eighteenth century the French chemist Antoine Lavoisier (lah vwah ZYAY) stated this important principle:

> We must lay it down as an incontestable axiom [rule], that in all operations of art and nature, nothing is created; an equal quantity of matter exists before and after the experiment . . . .

Scientists call this principle the **law of mass conservation** (KAHN sur VAY shun). It describes one way that God sustains the physical universe. Water evaporates from the oceans, falls as rain, and returns to the oceans in streams and rivers. Trees feed on the nutrients in the soil, grow, die, and decompose to fertilize other plants. In all chemical and physical changes matter is conserved. The matter that God created is continually recycled. He sustains His creation without creating new matter.

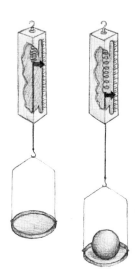

3-12 An object in the pan of a spring scale stretches the spring, moving a weight indicator down the scale.

A comparison of mass and weight

Weight is the measure of the force of gravity on an object. We measure this force in SI units called **newtons** (NOOT nz). This textbook weighs about 10 newtons (2.25 lb.). The average ninth grader weighs 500 newtons (112 lb.). Since gravitational forces vary, the weight of an object can change as conditions change. An astronaut who weighs 710 newtons (160 lb.) on earth seems to be "weightless" in space. But his mass has not changed; only the effect of the gravitational pull has. On the moon's surface the astronaut weighs only one-sixth of his weight on earth. The gravitational pull of the moon is one-sixth that of the earth. Your weight will change when you ride in an airplane. At an altitude of 8000 meters, the average ninth grader weighs 13.5 newtons less than he does at sea level.

Mass and weight are often confused. Weight is not a measure of matter. It is the measure of the attraction of one object (such as the earth) for another (such as you). We weigh objects on **spring scales.** The more the object weighs, the more the spring in the scale stretches.

3-13 One cubic centimeter (cc) is equal to 1 milliliter.

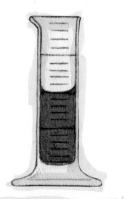

3-14 In a graduated cylinder, the volume is measured at the lowest point of the meniscus.

Volume

All matter takes up space. To occupy space, matter must have three dimensions: length, width, and height. The space described by these dimensions is called **volume** (VAHL yum).

Calculating volume

As long as an object has a standard geometric shape (such as a cube, cylinder, or sphere), we can calculate its volume by simple arithmetic. These mathematical formulas were worked out by ancient Greek mathematicians. Familiarize yourself with the common shapes and their volume formulas. (See Table 3-16.)

What is the volume of a rectangular solid 6 cm long, 3 cm wide, and 2 cm high? The formula for the volume of a rectangular solid is

length x width x height = volume.

Placing the data in the formula, we have

$$6 \text{ cm x } 3 \text{ cm x } 2 \text{ cm} = 36 \text{ cm}^3$$

The unit of volume is the cubic centimeter (cm^3). Sometimes it is abbreviated "cc." It is the same volume as a milliliter.

When scientists measure the volume of large solids or large amounts of fluids (liquids or gases), they use liters. A chamber that is 100 cm on each side will have a volume of 1,000,000 cm^3, or 1,000,000 ml.

$$100 \text{ cm x } 100 \text{ cm x } 100 \text{ cm} = 1,000,000 \text{ cm}^3$$

For even larger volumes, scientists use cubic meters. An empty room that measures 5 m x 6 m x 4 m contains 120 m^3 of air.

Measuring volume

You can easily find the volume of a *regular solid* by measuring with a ruler or meter stick and using arithmetic. But how can you measure liquids and irregular solids? Scientists use many types of specialized glassware to measure liquids. Some types measure volumes as small as $1/100$ of a milliliter.

Graduated cylinders are used to measure liquids in most laboratories. The volume of the liquid is indicated by precise markings on the side of the cylinder. Study Figure 3-14. You will notice that the surface of the liquid in the cylinder is not flat. This curve is called a *meniscus* (muh NIS kus). When using a graduated cylinder, be sure to read the marking at the lowest point of the meniscus if the liquid is water or behaves like water.

Table 3-15
Volumetric Glassware

Scientists use these three types of glassware to measure volumes of liquids: **(left to right)** graduated cylinders, calibrated beakers, and volumetric flasks. Of these three types, the volumetric flask is the most precise. Each flask is hand blown and individually calibrated to measure an exact volume.

Table 3-16

Shape	Relationship	Formula
cube	side • side • side = volume	$V = s^3$
solid rectangle	length • width • height = volume	$V = l \bullet w \bullet h$
sphere	(4π • radius • radius • radius) ÷ 3 = volume	$V = \dfrac{4\pi r^3}{3}$
cylinder	π • radius • radius • height = volume	$V = \pi r^2 h$
cone	(π • radius • radius • height) ÷ 3 = volume	$V = \dfrac{\pi r^2 h}{3}$

Note: π = 3.14

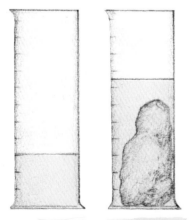

3-17 The difference between the two readings on the graduated cylinder is equal to the volume of the object.

Irregularly shaped solids can be measured by the water displacement method. A graduated cylinder is filled with enough water to cover the object being measured. A reading is taken at the bottom of the meniscus. The object is then carefully placed in the water and the water level is read, again using the bottom of the curve. The volume of the object is the difference between the first reading and the second reading. If the first reading were 33 ml and the second reading were 78 ml, the volume of the object would be 78 ml - 33 ml, or 45 ml.

Imagine trying to calculate the volume of an object such as a stone without using this simple method. The process would require an extremely complex mathematical formula, and even then the answer would be only approximate.

Overflow cans are used to measure irregular objects too large to fit into graduated cylinders. The overflow can is filled until the water begins to flow out the spout. An empty beaker is then placed below the spout, and the object is carefully placed in the overflow can. The water that runs out is measured in a graduated cylinder. This volume is the same as the volume of the object.

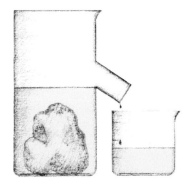

3-18 The volume of the water in the beaker is equal to the volume of the irregular solid.

Density

Which has more mass, a kilogram of paper or a kilogram of lead? You might have been tempted to answer, "A kilogram of lead!" If so, you were probably thinking that a certain *volume* of lead has considerably more mass than an equal *volume* of paper. A kilogram of paper does occupy more space than a kilogram of lead. But one kilogram of paper has the same amount of matter as one kilogram of lead; the lead is simply more *dense*. The term **density** (DEN suh tee) relates mass and volume. Density is defined as the mass in each unit of volume.

$$\text{Density} = \frac{\text{Mass}}{\text{Volume}}$$

Table 3-19

Densities of Some Elements and Common Substances (in g/cm³)			
osmium	22.48	opal	2.2
iridium	22.42	rock salt	2.18
platinum	21.45	bone	1.85
gold	19.3	magnesium	1.74
uranium	18.7	brick	1.7
mercury	13.6	sugar	1.59
lead	11.3	gelatin	1.27
copper	8.92	rubber, hard	1.19
iron	7.86	seawater	1.03
diamond	3.26	pure water	1.00
cement, set	2.8	ice	0.92
aluminum	2.7	butter	0.86
glass	2.6	ethyl alcohol	0.79
chalk	2.4	seasoned oak	0.75
clay	2.2	cardboard	0.69

Density is measured in units like kilograms per liter (kg/l) or grams per milliliter (g/ml) for liquids, and grams per cubic

3-20 Mercury has a density of 13.6 g/cm³, which means that every metal with a density less than 13.6 g/cm³ (even lead) will float in mercury. Brass (density between 8 and 9 g/cm³) floats easily in mercury. Why would brass not float in water?

centimeter (g/cm^3) for most solids. The density of lead is 11.3 g/cm^3. The density of most paper is less than one-tenth of that. Lead is not the most dense substance known to man. That substance is osmium (22.48 g/cm^3). A brick-sized chunk of osmium would weigh more than half as much as an average ninth grader!

You can find the density of any material by dividing its mass by its volume. If a chunk of lead displaced 36 cm^3 (ml) of water and had a mass of 407 g, its density would be

$$D = \frac{M}{V} = \frac{407 \text{ g}}{36 \text{ cm}^3} \text{ or } 11.3 \text{ g/cm}^3$$

Note the way the units are handled. Grams divided by cubic centimeters gives grams per cubic centimeters in the answer.

The Bob Jones University science department was once asked to determine the composition of the ancient Roman coins in a special collection. The museum curator who sent them specified that the coins could not be tested chemically or defaced in any way. He assured the science department that the coins were mostly copper or gold or some mixture of the two metals. Fortunately, copper and gold have widely differing densities. Each coin was weighed and its volume determined by the water displacement method. The mass of each coin was then divided by its volume. For instance, one coin had a volume of 1.2 cm^3 and a mass of 10.5 grams. Its density was therefore

$$D = \frac{M}{V} = \frac{10.5 \text{ g}}{1.2 \text{ cm}^3} = 8.7 \text{ g/cm}^3$$

The densities of the ten coins tested ranged from 7 to 10 g/cm^3.

FACETS OF BASIC SCIENCE

Adding Significance to the Second

The fundamental unit of time in both the metric system and the English system is the **second** (abbreviated *s*). The first attempts to accurately measure seconds were made with mechanical clocks. A second was measured by the clicks of a pendulum-powered gear. Pendulum clocks were eventually replaced by a more efficient system. These new clocks used a wound spring and flywheel for power, but the second was still measured by the clicks of the clock's gear.

Science demanded a still more accurate timing device. More advanced research needed a highly accurate device that could be based on a natural phenomenon that any laboratory could reproduce. Scientists discovered that a quartz crystal would vibrate when voltage was applied to it. This phenomenon is called the piezoelectric (pee AY zo uh LEK trik) effect. Using that effect, scientists were able to develop a timing device that measured the second by the vibrations of the quartz crystal— approximately 30,000 of them. This new clock was accurate to within one second per year. But

Since copper has a density of 8.92 g/cm^3 and gold is more than twice as dense (19.3 g/cm^3), the scientists concluded that all the coins were predominantly copper. The composition of the coins varied, but if they had contained very much gold, their densities would have been much higher.

Uncertainty in Measurements

Three students were told to determine the volume of a small cube. The first used a meter stick calibrated in centimeters. He found that each side of the cube was between 3 and 4 cm long. Since the smallest division on the meter stick was the centimeter, he estimated the length to be 3$^1/_3$ cm and calculated that the volume was 37 cm^3. The second student used a ruler marked in millimeters and measured the length to be 33 mm. He converted this measurement to 3.3 cm and found the volume to be 36 cm^3. The third student measured the cube with a precise measuring

Student	One	Two	Three
Measuring device	meter stick	ruler	caliper
Calibration	centimeters	millimeters	1/100 mm
Length	3 1/3 cm	33 mm	32.27 mm
Volume	37 cm^3	36 cm^3	34.97 cm^3

device called a *caliper* (KAL uh pur), and found that a side was 32.70 mm or 3.270 cm long. He calculated that the volume was 34.97 cm^3. Who was correct?

even this level of accuracy was not sufficient for some of the demands of science.

Further research led to the development of the atomic clock. This highly accurate clock uses the vibrations of a cesium-133 atom to measure a second. Today we can define a second as 9,192,631,770 vibrations of a cesium atom.

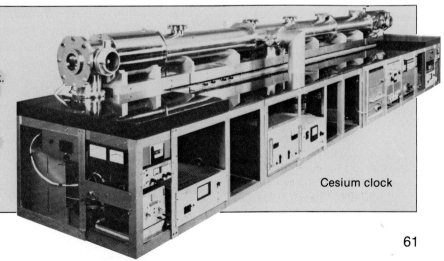

Cesium clock

Each student's measurement was limited by his judgment and the precision of the instrument. Yet each student made the best measurement possible within these limitations. Scientists have long recognized that all measurements are limited by the instruments used to make them. They also recognize that many measurements must be estimated. Many times a scientist states a measurement with a range of possible error. If a geologist determines the mass of a rock by using a balance that is accurate within one centigram, he states the mass of the rock as 45.45 ± .01 g. When other scientists examine his work, they see that the measurement he took has specific limitations. If the geologist uses a more precise balance, he might be able to state the mass to the nearest milligram. Every measurement he makes, even with the most precise balance he can find, will be limited to some degree.

Scientists have developed a code to tell each other how accurately a measurement has been made. They use the concept of **significant** (sig NIF ih kunt) **figures.** In any measurement, all of the digits that are known to be certain are used, plus one that is doubtful. If a measurement is 8 cm, for example, it has one significant figure. Since the last significant figure in any measurement is doubtful, writing "8 cm" tells scientists that this measurement may have been rounded. The actual measurement could have been any number between 7.5 and 8.5 cm. If the measurement had two significant figures, it would be more precise. The figure 8.0 cm tells scientists that the actual measurement fell between 7.95 cm and 8.05 cm.

The number of significant figures indicates the accuracy being claimed for that measurement. A measurement of 8.000 cm would indicate that the actual measurement fell within ± .0005 cm of that value. Precise instruments can produce measurements with many significant figures. As the last digit becomes a smaller part of the total measurement, the doubtfulness becomes less important.

Remember that there can be no more significant figures in an answer than appear in the *least* accurate measurement that enters into the computation. How would you calculate the area of a room? The length of the room is measured very accurately to four significant figures: 5.824 m. The width is measured with less accuracy to three figures: 4.20 m. Substituting these numbers into the area formula, A = LW, gives the equation

$$A = (5.824 \text{ m}) \cdot (4.20 \text{ m})$$
$$= 24.4608 \text{ m}^2$$
$$\text{or, rounded off, } 24.5 \text{ m}^2$$

Only three figures should be given in the answer, the same as the less accurate of the two original measurements. The last digits should not be used.

48,600
.0008727

FACETS
OF BASIC SCIENCE

Scientific Notation

Scientific research often involves numbers that are very large or very small. Astronomers have calculated the mass of the earth to be 5,980,000,000,000, 000,000,000,000 kg. Atomic physicists have determined that the mass of a hydrogen atom is 0.000000000000000000000000000167 kg! Such large and small numbers are difficult to write and even more difficult to use in a mathematical operation like multiplication or division.

These numbers can be much more conveniently expressed in **scientific notation**. Large or small numbers can be converted into the product of a power of 10 and a number between 1 and 10. Move the decimal place to make the number fall between 1 and 10. Then count each space that the decimal was moved, and make that number the exponent for the power of ten. Consider the following illustration:

Convert 5,600,000,000.0 into scientific notation.

The number between 1 and 10 is 5.6.

The decimal place was moved 9 places to the left.

Therefore the scientific notation is 5.6×10^9.

If the number is very small, the decimal place will be moved to the right. The exponent on the power of ten will be negative. Consider this example:

Convert 0.000000045 into scientific notation.

The number between 1 and 10 is 4.5.

The decimal place was moved 8 places to the right.

Therefore the scientific notation is 4.5×10^{-8}.

Scientifically Speaking

matter

metric system

meter

liter

kilogram

SI

unit analysis

mass

balance

law of mass conservation

weight

newtons

spring scales

volume

density

significant figures

second

Questions to Talk Over

1. What measurable properties do these forms of matter have in common?
   a. natural gas
   b. gasoline
   c. coal
2. Using the metric prefix chart on page 48, choose the best unit(s) of length for measuring your height. Defend your choice(s).
3. What would happen to your measured weight and mass as you voyaged from the earth to a space station in the asteroid belt?
4. The volume of the cylinders in the engines of many cars is measured in liters. Why is this the most appropriate unit for these measurements? (Hint: How would the volume be measured?)
5. Most notebook paper is 10.5 inches by 8 inches. Why is it unlikely that a paper manufacturer would ever state that his product was 10.5000 x 8.0000 inches?

THE PROPERTIES OF MATTER

CHAPTER 4

We know that something *is* matter if it has mass and occupies space, but how do we *identify* the different kinds of matter? Think of all the materials that surround you. Various metals, plastics, fibers, foods, woods, and other solids, liquids, and gases—you probably will not be able to list them all. How do you know that each material is a different kind of matter?

We can identify many of the different kinds of matter by their physical properties. A **physical property** is one that can be observed and measured without a change in the kind of matter being studied. Some of the physical properties of matter are color, density, shape, electrical conductivity, hardness, and texture. These physical properties help determine the uses of materials. A diamond-tipped drill can pierce through bedrock, but if the diamonds were replaced with quartz crystals, the drill would grind to a halt.

Why do the diamonds work better than the quartz? They share several of the same physical properties. Both are transparent minerals. Both can be cut into beautiful faceted shapes. Yet the industrial diamonds used in drill bits are 400 times harder than quartz. This physical property—hardness—makes diamonds ideal for drilling through layers of rock.

Matter can also be identified by its chemical properties. A **chemical property** describes how matter will react and change in the presence of other kinds of matter. The tendency of iron to rust is a chemical property; another is the resistance of chrome to rust. We will study the chemical properties of matter in more detail in a later chapter.

When we observe the world about us, we see that matter is continually changing. Some of the changes we observe are in the shape or state of the material. A change that does not alter the identity of the material is called a **physical change.**

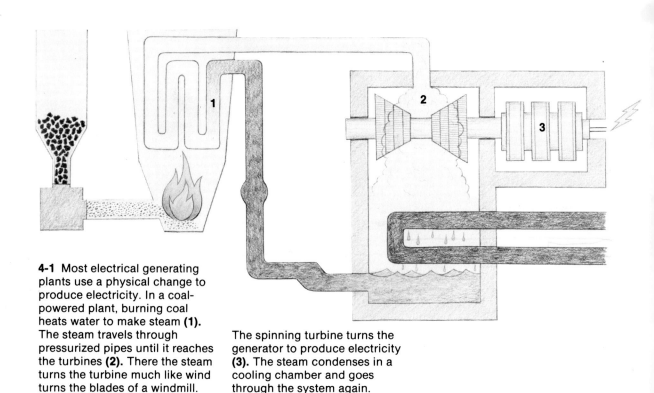

4-1 Most electrical generating plants use a physical change to produce electricity. In a coal-powered plant, burning coal heats water to make steam **(1).** The steam travels through pressurized pipes until it reaches the turbines **(2).** There the steam turns the turbine much like wind turns the blades of a windmill. The spinning turbine turns the generator to produce electricity **(3).** The steam condenses in a cooling chamber and goes through the system again.

Most kinds of matter occur in the solid, the liquid, or the gaseous state. Matter can change its *state* and still remain the same *kind* of matter. Water freezes, but it is still water. Alcohol may evaporate, but it is still alcohol. Matter may also change its *physical form* and still remain the same *kind* of matter. Sugar can be dissolved in water, but it is still sugar. Wood can be ground into sawdust, but it is still wood.

Many physical changes have been harnessed for practical purposes. For example, much of our electrical energy is produced by huge steam turbines. These are powered by a physical change. Water is heated by coal, oil, or nuclear fuel to produce steam under high pressure. This steam turns the turbines, which turn the generators. As another example, many of our tools are made by die casting, a process that relies on physical changes. Metals are heated until they become liquid and then are poured into a mold. As the metal cools, a physical change occurs: the metal returns to the solid state. When the mold is broken away, the solid metal tool is left.

4-2 This die caster is using long tongs to protect himself from the extreme heat of molten metal. Many useful metal items (such as tools, engine parts, and kitchen utensils) are formed by the die-casting process.

A change that alters the identity of the material is called a **chemical change**. When a chemical change occurs, new kinds of matter are formed. Water can be chemically split into hydrogen and oxygen. Sugar will decompose when heated, and wood will burn. Each of these changes produces new substances. We will study chemical changes in Chapter 9. In this chapter you will explore the models that scientists have developed to describe the physical properties and physical changes. These models will help you to understand and predict the behavior of matter.

The Particle Model of Matter

About four hundred years before Christ, the Greek philosophers began a great debate about the nature of matter. Several philosophers proposed that all matter was *continuous*. They argued that any material could be subdivided an infinite number of times and still be the same kind of matter. If a water droplet were subdivided again and again, it would always be water. Other philosophers were convinced that matter could *not* be infinitely subdivided. They felt that if a material were broken into smaller and smaller pieces, it would eventually reach a point where it could not be subdivided any further and remain the same kind of matter. If a water droplet were subdivided again and again, at some point the smallest particle of water would be found. If this particle were subdivided further, it would no longer be water.

This debate lasted for more than two thousand years, until scientists were able to collect enough evidence to support one model over the other. Eventually the **particle model** was accepted, but only in recent times have scientists realized how small a particle of matter is, or how many particles a visible piece of matter contains. The diameters of these particles are measured in hundred-millionths of a centimeter (10^{-8} cm) called angstroms (ANG strumz; abbreviated Å). If you could lay one million particles of water side by side, they would match the thickness of a piece of construction paper!

Can we observe anything so small? Even with the most powerful microscopes, scientists have not been able to actually *see* the basic particles of a material. Then how do we know that the particle model is the best description of matter? How do we know that the right side won the debate?

FACETS OF BASIC SCIENCE

Using Models

What *really* takes place when something freezes, boils, or condenses? Scientists have long sought to describe what actually occurs in a physical change. They are not satisfied with simply labeling what they observe: they want to understand *how* it is happening.

When scientists cannot directly observe what is taking place, they rely on their instruments to extend their observing ability. But the best instruments available have not been able to *see* what actually occurs in a physical change. They have only been able to give us clues as to what might be occurring. Scientists have pieced together these clues to develop working representations, or models, of what might be happening.

To be good models, these representations must have certain characteristics:

1. They should help us organize ideas.
2. They should faithfully describe what is observed.
3. They should help us visualize things that happen at a level that is too small, too large, or too complex for us to observe.
4. They should help us predict what will happen under certain circumstances.

One of the most famous scientific models is the Copernican model of planetary motion. Since the solar system is too large and too complex to be observed all at once, Copernicus had to piece together many observations about the motion of the planets to make a model. He based his model on the *heliocentric* (HEE lee oh SEN trik) theory since his observations indicated that the sun *(helio-)* was the center *(-centric)* of the solar system. In his model the planets followed certain orbits around the sun. His model worked. It described the motion of the planets and allowed scientists to predict the approx-imate time when a planet should appear in the sky. Although it has been modified by later astronomers, we still use the Copernican model of the solar system to plan our space flights and planetary probes.

No model is absolutely perfect and often we must choose among several different ones. Sometimes we will reject one model in favor of a better one. The best model is the one that describes the most observations and makes the most accurate predictions, or simply the one that works the best. But even the best model will change as more information is collected.

Evidence for the particle model

A good model should faithfully describe what we observe about matter. If the particle model is correct, then it should be able to describe everyday observations.

4-3 Sugar in any form is still sugar.

4-4 A mortar (bowl) and pestle (clublike instrument) are used to grind substances into fine powder.

Why does a sweetened drink taste sweet? The answer must lie in the sugar particles. If you crush a lump of sugar into many small pieces and then grind those pieces into a fine powder with a mortar and pestle, you can still observe sugar. But when you dissolve that powder in a glass of tea, the sugar disappears. It has become subdivided until it *cannot* be seen with even the most powerful microscopes. We *can* observe that every part of the drink tastes sweet. Therefore, sugar must exist as tiny particles that can spread equally throughout the solution. These particles are so small that they cannot be seen, but each of them must have all the properties of sugar if every part of the drink tastes sweet.

Is your favorite instant drink mix made up of particles? We can observe some color changes to find out. When a packet of instant cherry drink mix is dissolved in a pitcher of water, it makes a bright red solution. What would happen if that same packet were poured into a bathtub of water? Or a swimming pool? In each case the color of the resulting solution would be considerably lighter, but a faint color would still be present. For any color to appear in such a weak solution, the drink mix must consist of a very large number of particles.

Scientists have used observations like these to reach an important conclusion about matter:

All matter is made up of extremely small particles. But the particle model of matter is not yet complete. Other evidence that scientists have collected indicates that the particles that make up matter are in *constant motion*. Consider the following evidence.

Solid potassium permanganate occurs as purple crystals. If you place a crystal of potassium permanganate in a glass of water and stir, the water will turn purple. The particles of the chemical have been distributed throughout the solution. But what happens when you carefully drop a crystal into the water without stirring it? Patient observation will show that the crystal gradually breaks apart and slowly spreads throughout the liquid. How can we account for this mixing without stirring?

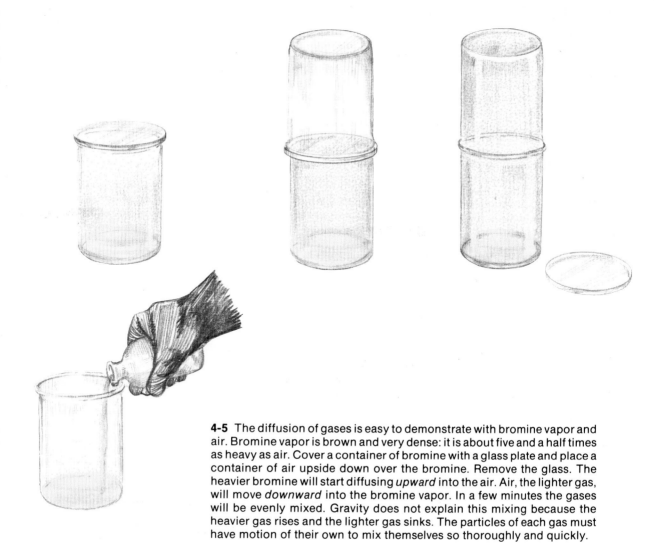

4-5 The diffusion of gases is easy to demonstrate with bromine vapor and air. Bromine vapor is brown and very dense: it is about five and a half times as heavy as air. Cover a container of bromine with a glass plate and place a container of air upside down over the bromine. Remove the glass. The heavier bromine will start diffusing *upward* into the air. Air, the lighter gas, will move *downward* into the bromine vapor. In a few minutes the gases will be evenly mixed. Gravity does not explain this mixing because the heavier gas rises and the lighter gas sinks. The particles of each gas must have motion of their own to mix themselves so thoroughly and quickly.

71

Scientists believe that the particles that make up water are in constant motion. These moving particles spread the purple potassium permanganate particles through the solution. The process of mixing by particle motion is called **diffusion** (dih FYOO zhun). Diffusion can occur in all the states of matter, but it happens by far the most rapidly in gases. This leads us to believe that the particles of a gas move much more rapidly than the particles in a solid or a liquid. You have probably noticed that a few drops of perfume spilled from a bottle on one side of a room can soon be smelled on the far side of the room. As the perfume evaporates, the particles of the perfume change from the liquid state to the gaseous state. These particles are quickly scattered by the rapidly moving particles of the air until perfume particles have diffused to all parts of the room.

The motion of particles in matter was first observed in 1827. Robert Brown, an English botanist, was examining with a microscope tiny plant spores floating on water. Much to his amazement, he saw the spores jostling back and forth as if they were being struck repeatedly from different sides. Yet nothing was touching them except the water in which they were floating. He realized that the particles of water must be causing the motion of the spores. Since there was no pattern to this movement, he proposed that all of the particles of a liquid are in constant random motion. Today, we call this effect **Brownian movement** in honor of its discoverer.

These are only a few of the many evidences that have led scientists to conclude that all matter is made up of tiny particles in constant motion.

4-6 Particles in Brownian movement act very much like the marbles in this photograph. Every second the rapidly moving particles in air collide and scatter in an ever-changing random pattern.

The Physical States of Matter

All matter exists in one of four states: solid, liquid, gas, or plasma. Because many materials can exist in more than one physical state, scientists often refer to these as the phases of matter. In what phases have you observed water? Water occurs in nature as ice (solid), liquid, and vapor or steam (gas). Some kinds of matter are commonly observed in only one of their phases. Oxygen occurs most often as a gas, yet liquid oxygen is used to power rockets. How can one material occur in different physical states?

Our model of matter is based on the idea of constantly moving, extremely tiny particles. Scientists believe that the physical state of a material is determined by the positions and

4-7 A melting ice cube shows the three states of matter: gas, liquid, and solid.

the energy of its particles. This special description of the various phases of matter is called the **kinetic** (kih NET ik) **theory**. How does it work?

The kinetic theory identifies two basic forces in matter that determine the physical state. One force acts to hold the particles together, and one force acts to move the particles apart. It is the relationship between these two forces that determines the state of matter.

The first force is the *attraction* between particles. Since different particles have different levels of attraction for each other, the strength of this force is determined by the kinds of particles involved. If the attractive forces are strong, then the particles will be tightly bound together.

The opposing force causes motion. It is related to **kinetic energy**—the energy of motion. This force tends to be *disruptive*: if it is stronger than the attractive forces, then the particles separate. The kinetic energy will increase as the temperature of the material is increased. This is why the positions of the particles, and therefore the physical state of the particles, change as temperature changes. We will consider this relationship in the next section of this chapter. For now, we will concentrate on the relationship between the disruptive and attractive forces in each of the four physical states.

Table 4-8

Comparison of Three Physical States of Matter		
Solid at room temperature: iron, sugar, salt, diamond, sand, gold	**Liquid** at room temperature: water, alcohol, mercury, gasoline, benzene, ether	**Gas** at room temperature: oxygen, hydrogen, carbon dioxide, helium, ammonia

ice 273K (0° C) or below	**water** 294K (21° C) to 372 K (99° C)	**steam** 373K (100° C) or above
Definite volume Low compressibility Definite shape	Definite volume Low compressibility Indefinite shape (assumes shape of container)	Indefinite volume High compressibility Indefinite shape (assumes both shape and volume of container)
Attractive forces overcome weak disruptive forces to hold vibrating particles in fixed positions.	Attractive forces and disruptive forces are balanced, allowing particles to move randomly (Brownian movement).	Attractive forces are completely overcome by very strong disruptive forces, causing particles to have rapid, random movement.

Solids

The particles in a **solid** have very low kinetic energy. Therefore, the disruptive forces are smaller than the attractive forces. How does this relationship of forces affect the matter? If the forces that hold the particles together are stronger than the forces that cause movement, then the particles will be held in place. They are not completely motionless; since they have *some* kinetic energy, they have *some* motion. However, this motion is limited to vibrating in a fixed position.

If this is a good model of solid matter, then it should explain the characteristics of solids. All solid materials have definite shape and a high density and are very hard to compress. Can the kinetic model of solids explain these characteristics?

Definite shape	Because of strong attractive forces, the particles are held in fixed positions. The shape cannot change, because the particles cannot move.
High density	The particles are held close together by the attractive forces.
Low compressibility	Since the particles are already close together, pressure cannot move them much closer together.

The kinetic model of solids also helps us to understand why solids occur in two basic forms, crystalline (KRIH stuh lin) and amorphous (uh MOR fus). In a **crystalline solid** the individual particles are held in a fixed, repeating pattern. In an **amorphous solid** the particles are held in a random placement with no apparent pattern. Both of these are solid. Both have definite shape, high density, and low compressibility, yet they have very different physical appearances. How do crystalline and amorphous solids form?

4-9 Three forms of sulfur are illustrated here. One is sulfur's pure crystalline form. Another is hard-packed sulfur powder. The third is the amorphous form of sulfur. Can you tell which is which?

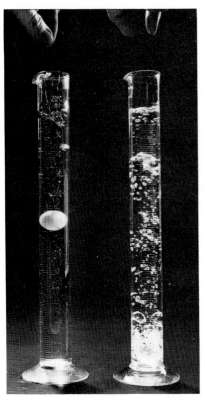

4-10 Some liquids are "thicker" than others. The difference is caused by the strength of the attraction between the liquid's particles. Liquids with very strong attraction between their particles do not flow easily; scientists call them *viscous*. Therefore *viscosity* is the measure of the attractive forces in liquids. In this picture, two marbles were dropped into two different liquids at exactly the same time. Which liquid has the greater viscosity?

As a liquid cools, its particles lose energy until the attractive forces can completely overcome the disruptive force of kinetic energy. If the energy is lost slowly, the particles can position themselves in well ordered, equally spaced patterns, but if the process occurs very rapidly, the particles are "frozen" in place in a random, unordered pattern.

Liquids

Every **liquid** takes the shape of its container. Liquids have relatively high density and low compressibility. According to the kinetic theory, particles in the liquid state are still held very close together, but they are in constant random motion. The disruptive forces (caused by kinetic energy) are strong enough to partially overcome the attractive forces between the particles and permit limited motion. Does this model explain the observed characteristics of liquids?

Indefinite shape	The particles of a liquid are not completely independent, but their limited motion allows the liquid to assume the shape of the container.
High density	Because of the balance between the attractive forces and the disruptive forces, the particles are held relatively close together.
Low compressibility	Since the particles are already close together, pressure cannot move them much closer.

Gases

A **gas** has neither a definite shape nor a set volume. Unlike a solid or a liquid, a gas can be compressed into a small container and will expand to distribute itself evenly throughout a larger container. In either case, the gas assumes both the volume and the shape of its container. In the gaseous state, particles are relatively far apart and move at very high speeds. A typical particle in the gaseous state moves 490 meters per second, or 1.5 times the speed of sound. If a gas molecule could travel straight forward without any collisions, it could cover the distance across the United States in less than three hours! But particles in the gaseous state experience more than 10 million collisions per second (without slowing down), and thus cannot travel in a straight line.

In order to move at such great speeds, particles in the gaseous state must have a large amount of kinetic energy. Therefore, the disruptive forces must be considerably stronger than the attractive forces. In fact, they are so much stronger that we do not consider the effect of the attractive forces in our gas model. Will this model explain the observed properties of gases?

Indefinite shape	Since the disruptive forces are far stronger than the attractive forces, the particles are free to travel in all directions. Their movement is limited only by the volume and the shape of their container.
Low density	Because the molecules are widely separated, there are very few of them in a given volume.
High compressibility	Because the particles are far apart, pressure can easily push them closer together.

4-11 What is happening to the particles on the surface of the liquid that allows them to escape and form steam?

The kinetic theory also helps us understand a phenomenon related to gases—**gas pressure**. Particles of a gas enclosed in a container collide not only with one another but also with the walls of the container. Imagine how the particles of the gas bombard the walls of the container; billions of them hit each square centimeter every second! The impact of a single particle would never be noticed, but the impact of billions of those particles can exert a great deal of pressure.

Table 4-12

Characteristics Shown by the Kinetic Model of Gas

Large distances between particles
High kinetic energy displayed in:
  —high speed particles
  —attractive forces completely overcome by disruptive forces

FACETS
OF BASIC SCIENCE

Two Important Gas Laws

Boyle's Law

Examine this photograph of a high-altitude weather balloon. Why is it not fully inflated? Did the scientists who launched it run out of helium, or was the amount of gas carefully planned?

As the balloon ascends, the gas inside it will expand greatly. Scientists carefully calculated the initial volume of the gas so that it could not expand enough to burst the balloon. What causes the gas to expand as the balloon rises?

At higher altitudes, fewer air particles collide with the external surface of the balloon. Since these collisions cause the pressure on the balloon, the external pressure decreases. Since the number of particles on the inside stays the same, the balloon will expand until the number of particles colliding against the outside of the balloon is the same as the number of particles colliding against the inside. On its way up, this weather balloon

will expand to many times its original volume.

In 1660 Robert Boyle (BOYL) developed a way to calculate this relationship between pressure and the volume of a gas. To test this relationship he set up a large J-shaped tube, closed at the short end and open at the long end. By pouring varying amounts of mercury into the open end, he was able to regulate the pressure on the gas trapped in the short end.

Boyle found that when he doubled the pressure on a gas, its volume was reduced to one-half its original size. When he tripled the pressure, the volume was reduced to one-third its original size. If he was careful to keep the temperature the same, the results were always similar.

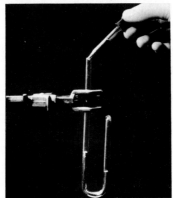

No matter how the pressure was varied, the product of the changed pressure and the changed volume was always the same.

Pressure	Volume	Pressure x Volume
1 atm	1 liter	1 x 1 = 1
2 atm	½ liter	2 x ½ = 1
3 atm	⅓ liter	3 x ⅓ = 1
4 atm	¼ liter	4 x ¼ = 1

This relationship can be stated as a mathematical equation:

$$P_1 V_1 = P_2 V_2$$

The small numbers after each letter are called *sub*scripts because they are written *below* the line. They help us to identify the symbols in the equation. P_1 is the pressure of the gas before the change. V_1 is the original volume of the gas. P_2 is the pressure of the gas after the change, and V_2 is its final volume.

This mathematical relationship is called **Boyle's law**. It is called an **inverse proportion** because one value will increase only as the other value decreases. Boyle stated his law this way: "The volume of a dry gas is inversely proportional to the pressure, provided the temperature remains constant."

Here are some examples of how you can apply Boyle's law. Example 1:

Atmospheric pressure is measured by a barometer in millimeters of mercury. Normal

atmospheric pressure (for which we have used the term *one atmosphere*) is measured at $\overline{760}$ mm of mercury on a barometer.

(The line over the zero indicates that the digit is significant.) If the pressure on 2.00ℓ of a gas at normal atmospheric pressure (76$\bar{0}$ mm) were increased to 1520 mm, what would be the final volume of the gas?

Solution:

First identify the values of the symbols in the Boyle's law equation:

P_1 = 76$\bar{0}$ mm
V_1 = 2.00ℓ
P_2 = 1520 mm
V_2 = ? (The problem directs you to solve for the final volume.)

Now, substitute these values into the equation:

$$P_1 \cdot V_1 = P_2 \cdot V_2$$
$$76\bar{0} \text{ mm} \cdot 2.00\ell = 1520 \text{ mm} \cdot V_2$$

Divide both sides by P_2 and cancel the units:

$$\frac{76\bar{0} \text{ mm} \cdot 2.00\ell}{1520 \text{ mm}} = \frac{1520 \text{ mm} \cdot V_2}{1520 \text{ mm}}$$
units cancel   cancels to 1

Solve for V_2:

$$\frac{76\bar{0} \cdot 2.00\ell}{1520} = 1 \cdot V_2$$
$$1.00\ell = V_2$$

Special note: All of the data given in the problem have at least three significant digits. Therefore, the answer *must* have three significant digits.

Example 2:

A cylinder was expanded from an original volume of 400.0 ml to a final volume of 100$\bar{0}$ ml. If the original pressure of the gas inside the cylinder was 304$\bar{0}$ mm, what is the final pressure?

Solution:
First identify the values:

P_1 = 304$\bar{0}$ mm P_2 = ?
V_1 = 400.0 ml V_2 = 100$\bar{0}$ ml

Substitute these into the equation:

$$P_1 \cdot V_1 = P_2 \cdot V_2$$
$$304\bar{0} \text{ mm} \cdot 400.0 \text{ ml} = P_2 \cdot 100\bar{0} \text{ ml}$$

Divide by V_2 and cancel units:

$$\frac{304\bar{0} \text{ mm} \cdot 400.0 \text{ ml}}{100\bar{0} \text{ ml}} = \frac{P_2 \cdot 100\bar{0} \text{ ml}}{100\bar{0} \text{ ml}}$$
units cancel   cancels to 1

Solve for P_2:

$$\frac{304\bar{0} \text{ mm} \cdot 400.0}{100\bar{0}} = P_2 \cdot 1$$
$$1216 \text{ mm} = P_2$$

Note: This time four significant figures were maintained.

Charles's Law

Why do bicycle tires seem to go flat in the winter? On a cold day, you can pump up a soccer ball indoors until it is firm, but it seems to go soft when you take it outside. What happened? These common occurrences tell us that there is a relationship between temperature and gas pressure. This relationship was first studied by Jacques Charles (1746-1823). **Charles's law** states that if the pressure on a dry gas is kept constant, its volume will be in **direct proportion** to its Kelvin temperature. That is to say, the hotter the gas becomes, the greater its volume will be.

Expressed as an equation, Charles's law is:

$$\frac{V_1}{T_1} = \frac{V_2}{T_2}$$

V_1 is the original volume of the gas, and T_1 is its original temperature in kelvins (abbreviated K). V_2 is its final volume, and T_2 is its final Kelvin temperature. If you are given the temperatures in Celsius degrees, you must first convert them to kelvins by adding 273.

Example:

At 27° C, an amount of gas has a volume of 2.0ℓ. What volume will it occupy if it is heated to 87° C? (Assume that the pressure on the gas is constant.)

Solution:
Identify the values:

V_1 = 2.0ℓ
T_1 = 27° C + 273 = 3$\bar{0}$0 K
V_2 = ?
T_2 = 87° C + 273 = 360 K

Substitute the values into the Charles's law equation:

$$\frac{V_1}{T_1} = \frac{V_2}{T_2}$$
$$\frac{2.0\ell}{3\bar{0}0 \text{ K}} = \frac{V_2}{360 \text{ K}}$$

Cross multiply and cancel:

$$2.0 \, \ell \cdot 360 \text{ K} = 3\bar{0}0 \text{ K} \cdot V_2$$

$$\frac{2.0\ell \cdot 360 \text{ K}}{3\bar{0}0 \text{ K}} = \frac{3\bar{0}0 \text{ K} \cdot V_2}{3\bar{0}0 \text{ K}}$$
units cancel   cancels to 1

Solve for V_2:

$$\frac{2.0\ell \cdot 360}{3\bar{0}0} = 1 \cdot V_2$$
$$2.4\ell = V_2$$

As with Boyle's law, the final units will always be the same as the original units. The answer that we found "makes sense." The gas was heated 20 percent hotter (on the Kelvin scale) and its volume increased by 20 percent.

The pressure caused by gases is sometimes measured in units called **atmospheres** (AT muh sFIRZ). Normal atmospheric pressure at sea level is measured as one atmosphere (atm). At room temperature, it takes approximately *300,000,000,000,000,000, 000,000 collisions per square centimeter per second* to exert *one atmosphere of pressure!* The pressure inside a pumped-up football or basketball is greater than normal atmospheric pressure because the particles of air have been packed together by the pump. Because the number of particles bouncing off each unit of area is much greater on the inside than on the outside, the surface of the ball is tightly pushed out in all directions.

Because we live at the bottom of a great ocean of air, we are continually bombarded by air particles. We experience air pressure, but we are not aware of it. Why? Because the amount of pressure inside our bodies is equal to the pressure exerted by the atmosphere on the outside of our bodies. What would happen if the pressure inside your body were less than the pressure of the atmosphere?

4-13 What happens when you pump up a basketball? The pump forces more particles of air into the ball. As the number of particles increases, the pressure increases; more particles are colliding with the inside surface of the ball than are colliding with the outside surface. What would happen if the number of collisions on the inside surface became too great?

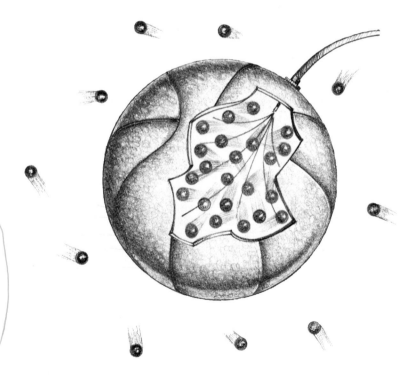

Plasma

We have studied the states of matter in order of increasing kinetic energy. The particles in the solid state vibrate. The particles in the liquid state have limited random motion. The particles in the gaseous state have independent rapid motion. The last state of matter that we will study is called **plasma** (PLAZ muh). How do scientists picture the kinetic energy of particles in the plasma state?

Particles in the plasma state travel at fantastic speeds. They must have tremendous kinetic energy. Like gas particles, they collide many times each second. But unlike gas particles, plasma particles collide with such force that the very nature of the particles is changed. Part of each particle is knocked away, and it receives an electrical charge. Where can particles with such high levels of kinetic energy be found?

Fluorescent lights

Surface of the sun

Exhaust from a rocket

Oxyacetylene torch

4-14 Matter in the plasma state.

Think of the energy that must be present on the surface of the sun, where temperatures exceed 5000° C. Particles can exist only in the plasma state under such conditions. Plasma exists not only on the surface of stars; trace amounts of plasma have been found throughout outer space and in the magnetic belts (the Van Allen belts) that surround our planet. Right here on earth we can find plasma as close as the nearest fluorescent light. Neon tubes and the halogen lights that illuminate our streets also contain plasma. A glance at the number of stars in the night sky will tell you that plasma is the most common state of matter in most of the physical universe.

The Phase Changes in Matter

If you drop several ice cubes into a hot frying pan, the spitting, popping cubes will dance about the pan as they melt into a liquid and then sizzle into steam. The matter changed physical states but still remained the same kind of matter. Ice, liquid water, and steam are all composed of water particles. If the particles themselves were not altered, what changed as the ice melted into liquid and the liquid boiled into steam?

The kinetic theory states that the position and movement of the particles in a material determine its physical state. Therefore, as phase changes occur, *something* is happening to the position and movement of the particles. The position and movement of particles are governed by two kinds of forces: the forces of attraction (caused by the particles themselves), and the forces of disruption (caused by the kinetic energy of the particles). The forces of attraction remain the same in every phase of a material, because the particles themselves do not change. However, the disruptive forces can be changed. These forces are caused by the kinetic energy of the particles, and the kinetic energy of a particle is directly related to its temperature. The higher the temperature, the greater the kinetic energy of the particle. Adding or removing kinetic energy by raising or lowering the temperature of a material is the cause of **phase changes.**

This model helps us to visualize the phase changes that we observe every day. If a solid is heated enough, it will melt. If a liquid is heated enough, it will boil. If a liquid is cooled enough, it will freeze. Each of the phase changes occurs because the change in temperature alters the kinetic energy of the particles of that material.

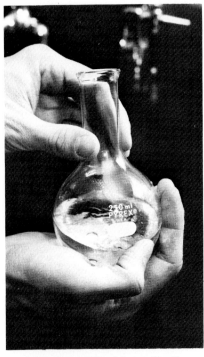

4-15 Not all liquids are "hot" when they boil. Some organic liquids will boil from the heat present in your hands.

Adding energy in a phase change

Melting occurs when the temperature of a solid is increased to the point where the kinetic energy of the particles equals the attractive forces between the particles. In the solid state the attractive forces between the particles predominate. The particles have only enough kinetic energy to allow them to vibrate in place. But when the temperature of a solid is increased, these particles gain kinetic energy. At some temperature they gain enough kinetic energy to balance the attractive forces and allow the particles to flow over each other. This temperature is called the **melting point** of the solid.

4-16 Lead is a very soft, easily melted metal. It will melt at only 327° C. A burner on a gas range can reach 500° C. Would you trust cookware made of lead?

Some solids have extremely low melting points. In these materials the attractive forces between the particles are very weak. The addition of a very small amount of energy will allow the particles to flow over each other. Mercury, a liquid at room temperature, melts at -39° C. Phenol, a common disinfectant, melts at room temperature, while some metals and minerals will melt only at extremely high temperatures. The melting point of a material is determined by the strength of the attractive forces between its particles.

In the liquid state, particles constantly interact with one another. They roll, slide, and collide with one another in a constant balance of kinetic energy and attractive forces. Because the movement in a liquid is random, not all the particles move at the same speed. Some might have a series of collisions that increase their speeds, while others might have head-on collisions that bring them to a "halt," only to be set in motion again by random collisions.

When we talk about the *speed* of liquid particles, we are talking about their *kinetic energy*. Since a change in temperature produces a change in the speed of particles, temperature is a measure of the kinetic energy of a material. This measurement is an average of the kinetic energies of all the particles present in a liquid. Most of the particles are moving at a moderate speed, but a few are moving very fast or very slowly.

When one of these very fast particles reaches the surface of a liquid, it sometimes has enough energy to overcome both the attraction of its neighboring particles and the pressure of the gas particles striking the surface of the liquid. When this occurs, the particle escapes from the liquid and changes phase to a gas. This process is known as **evaporation.** The energy for evaporation can come from the uneven distribution of speeds in a liquid, but

FACETS
OF BASIC SCIENCE

SUBLIMATION—The Phase Change that Skips a Step

By increasing their temperature, solids can be melted to form liquids, and liquids can be boiled to form gases. But can solids be changed directly into gases without going through a liquid phase? Here are some examples of materials that do!

Have you ever noticed that the mothballs in your closets seem to disappear? You do not see them melt into a liquid and then evaporate; yet you can smell a distinct "mothball gas." What happens to mothballs?

Mothballs are made from a white crystalline chemical called naphthalene. The strong odor of

mothballs indicates that particles of the solid naphthalene are gaining enough energy from the temperature of the closet to change directly to a gas without passing through the liquid phase. This process is called **sublimation** (SUB luh MAY shun).

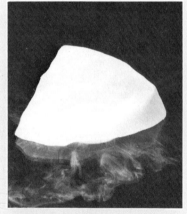

Dry ice (frozen carbon dioxide) is another material that sublimates. Have you seen dry ice in an ice cream parlor? Did you notice that the dry ice seems to "melt" without leaving a puddle? This indicates that the solid carbon dioxide particles are gaining from their surroundings the necessary energy to sublimate.

it can also come from heat provided by warmer surroundings or by sunlight striking the surface of the liquid.

God designed our bodies to use the process of evaporation for cooling. When you perspire, your sweat glands produce a liquid on the surface of your skin. The particles in that liquid absorb the heat energy of your body and use it to overcome both the attractive forces and the pressure forces that are holding it in the liquid state. When this occurs, heat energy is removed and your body is cooled. Does this explain why you sometimes shiver when you are wet, even on a hot, sunny day?

If heat is added to a liquid in large quantities, the particles *inside* the liquid gain enough energy to overcome completely the attractive forces. They form bubbles inside the liquid as they change from the liquid state to the gaseous state. These bubbles rise to the surface in the action that we call **boiling**. The temperature at which this action occurs is called the **boiling point** of the liquid.

Ice particles can also make the leap from the solid to the gaseous phase. Have you ever noticed that ice cubes left in a freezer tend to "shrink?" Even wet clothes will dry at temperatures below freezing. If wet clothes are put on a line in sub-freezing temperatures, the ice that forms on the clothing will sublimate, leaving them dry!

Iodine will sublimate in pure crystals on a cool surface like the watchglass pictured here.

The weight of ice sublimating on airplane wings could easily cause the plane to crash.

The boiling point of a liquid is affected by two forces. The first cannot be changed. It is the attraction between the particles. This must be completely overcome by the kinetic energy of the individual particles before they can change phase. The other force is pressure on the surface of the liquid. If this pressure is increased, then the boiling point will be higher. As the pressure increases, more kinetic energy will be needed to overcome that pressure.

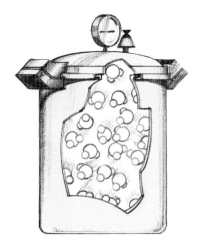

4-17 Pressure cookers are sealed pots that use pressure to cook more efficiently. As water in the pan heats, steam forms, increasing the pressure on the surface of the liquid and therefore raising its boiling temperature. The steam produced is hotter than it would be under normal conditions. The increased temperature allows pressure cookers to cook food in a fraction of the time it would take in an open pan.

Removing energy in a phase change

Phase changes also occur when kinetic energy is removed from particles by lowering the temperature. **Condensation** is the phase change from gas to liquid. It occurs when the particles of a gas lose enough energy for the attractive forces to pull the particles together. At that temperature, called the **condensation point**, the gas changes phase to liquid.

Dew is a good example of condensation in action. In the cool of the evening, water vapor particles lose kinetic energy because of the drop in temperature. Soon the attractive forces between the scattered particles can pull them together. They condense on fallen leaves, blades of grass, cars, bicycles, spider webs, and other objects on or near the ground. Why does the dew form there? When water changes from its gaseous phase to its liquid phase, its density greatly increases. The water-laden air is "heavy" and "sinks" to ground level, where the liquid particles join to form droplets on any surface that is cooler than the surrounding air. The temperature at which this occurs is called the dew point.

Freezing is the phase change from liquid to solid. It occurs when the temperature lowers until the liquid no longer has enough kinetic energy to balance the attractive forces between its particles. The particles are then "frozen" into place in the solid state. The temperature at which this occurs is called the freezing point. The term *freezing* should not always be associated with what we consider "cold" temperatures. Molten iron freezes at more than 1500° C!

Measuring energy in a phase change

We have stated that the kinetic energy of a particle is directly related to its **temperature**. For that reason, the temperature of a material acts as a *molecular speedometer*. The temperature determines whether the particles are in a solid state (low kinetic energy limits them to vibrating in place) or a liquid state (medium kinetic energy allows them to move) or a gaseous state (high kinetic energy makes them speed!).

We measure the relative kinetic energy of particles with *thermometers*. These tell us the range of temperatures in which a certain material will exist as a solid, a liquid, or a gas. For example, water is a gas above 100° C, a liquid between 0° C and 100° C, and a solid below 0° C.

The thermometer scale commonly used by many scientists is the Celsius (SEL see us) scale. In 1742 Anders Celsius invented a temperature scale with one hundred degrees between the boiling point and the freezing point of water. His scale has been very useful, but it has led to a popular misconception about temperature. Many people think that there is no kinetic energy below 0° C. This is not true; some materials have enough energy to exist as gases far below 0° on the Celsius scale. Very little kinetic energy is needed for their particles to completely overcome their attractive forces. Oxygen is one of these materials. What would happen to life on earth if the atmosphere condensed from the gaseous phase to the liquid phase at 0° C?

To combat this misconception about temperature, Lord Kelvin (KEL vin) developed a new temperature scale. He based

4-18 Small droplets of water have formed on the cool leaves of this plant. We call these droplets dew.

4-19 Particles at low temperatures have relatively slow speed compared to those at high temperatures. Which cube contains the particles at higher temperature?

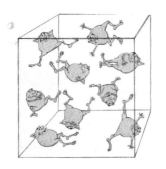 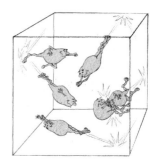

it on degrees the same "size" as those Celsius used, but his scale had an important difference. On his scale, he defined 0° K as *absolute zero*. Absolute zero is the point at which there is the least possible kinetic energy. Absolute zero has been calculated to be approximately -273° C. Kelvin used this calculation to define zero on his scale. The chart below will help you see the relationship between the *Celsius* and *Kelvin* scales.

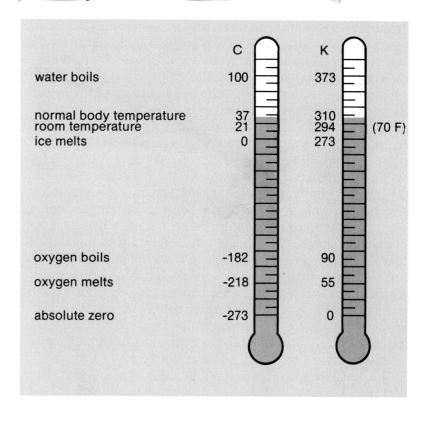

	C	K	
water boils	100	373	
normal body temperature	37	310	
room temperature	21	294	(70 F)
ice melts	0	273	
oxygen boils	-182	90	
oxygen melts	-218	55	
absolute zero	-273	0	

You can convert temperatures in Celsius degrees to **kelvins**, or degrees on the Kelvin scale, by adding 273. You can convert temperatures in kelvins to Celsius degrees by subtracting 273.

Scientifically Speaking

physical property	boiling point	amorphous solid
chemical property	sublimation	liquid
physical change	condensation	gas
chemical change	condensation point	gas pressure
particle model	freezing	atmospheres
angstroms	temperature	plasma
diffusion	kelvins	phase changes
Brownian movement	Boyle's law	melting
kinetic theory	inverse proportion	melting point
kinetic energy	Charles's law	evaporation
solid	direct proportion	boiling
crystalline solid		

Questions to Talk Over

1. In colonial days, blacksmiths beat metals into usable items such as horseshoes, wheel rims, and household utensils. Would it be more important for a blacksmith to understand the chemical properties or the physical properties of the metal he worked with? Why?
2. What are the similarities and differences between a checkerboard that has been set up for a game and the structure of a solid?
3. Sometimes ice forms on the wings of planes as they fly at high altitudes. The added weight of the ice could cause the plane to plummet to the ground. Why does this ice form? What phase change is occurring? From your knowledge of phase changes, what would be the best way to prevent ice buildup on airplane wings?
4. When an inflated balloon is immersed in a container of liquid nitrogen (about -200° C), it collapses completely; when it is removed, it inflates again. Using the kinetic theory, explain what happens to matter *inside* the balloon in each stage of this process.
5. Charles's law and Boyle's law deal with the effects of temperature and pressure on volume. As a hot-air balloon rises through the atmosphere, the pressure on the outside of the balloon decreases. The temperature of the air outside the balloon also decreases. How will these changing conditions affect the volume of the balloon?

LORD KELVIN
IRISH PHYSICIST (1824-1907)

Lord Kelvin (William Thomson) is probably best known for the absolute scale of temperature that bears his name. He was also the mastermind behind the building of the first transatlantic telegraph cable and the first scientist to adopt the term *energy* to describe the most important of all quantities dealt with in physics. Kelvin was equally learned in both the theoretical and the practical branches of science. He contributed much to our knowledge of thermodynamics and pure mathematics. He also patented seventy inventions.

This giant of science was born in Belfast, Ireland, in 1824. He was the fourth of the seven children of James Thomson, a Scottish mathematics professor. The Thomson children were brought up in the Established (Presbyterian) Church of Scotland. The preaching they heard was fundamental and practical.

William responded favorably to the gospel message and was saved at an early age. During his years at Cambridge University, he was a brilliant scholar and maintained a good Christian testimony before his professors and fellow students. Upon graduation he was awarded, among other academic honors, a special citation "in consideration of his great mind and exemplary conduct."

After receiving his bachelor of arts degree in 1845, young Thomson chose to broaden his horizons by working for a year at the Regnault (reh NYO) Laboratories in Paris, France. He earned his master of arts degree, also from Cambridge University, in 1848. At the age of 22, Thomson accepted an appointment as professor of natural philosophy at the University of Glasgow, a post he filled until his retirement fifty-three years later.

Thomson and four of his contemporaries are generally credited with formulating the second law of thermodynamics. Thomson's definitive paper on

the subject appeared in 1852. Although many people have never heard of this law, its meaning is extremely important to all of us. It indicates that the entire universe is degenerating (running down). The universe, therefore, cannot be eternal (infinitely old), or it would have run down completely long ago. Thus, by the mid-1800s, scientists had established the fact that there must have been a definite time of creation. Skeptics could still deny that there was ever a creation by God, but they would now do so in opposition to the clear findings of science.

The second law of thermodynamics also clearly contradicts any theory of evolution that has ever been proposed. If, indeed, degeneration is the trend of nature, we could hardly expect increasing order and complexity to arise from less organized forms of matter. It was no secret that William Thomson strongly opposed the evolutionary teachings of Charles Darwin.

Moreover, the Irish physicist stoutly rejected the idea that life on the earth could have arisen spontaneously. "Mathematics and dynamics fail us," he wrote, "when we contemplate the earth, fitted for life but lifeless, and try to imagine the commencement of life upon it. This certainly did not take place by any action of chemistry, or electricity, or crystalline grouping of molecules under the influence of force, or by any possible kind of fortuitous concourse [lucky combination] of atoms. We must pause, face to face with the mystery and miracle of the Creation of living creatures." We can readily see

the sharp contrast between Thomson's clear insight, derived from the biblical account of Creation, and modern philosophy, which regards life as a mere collection of chemicals.

In 1856 Thomson was elected a director of the Atlantic Telegraph Company, which was formed for the purpose of installing a transatlantic telegraph cable from Ireland to North America. By this time the use of Samuel Morse's telegraph had spread through much of the world. Wires were humming with messages on both the North American and European continents. Short lengths of submarine cables, such as the cable connecting England with the Netherlands, had been successfully laid. But the feat of spanning the 4000 km between the British Isles and America still posed many problems. The ocean was known to be almost 5 km deep in places, and no ship in existence could carry the tremendous amount of cable needed to open the Atlantic.

The Atlantic Telegraph Company decided to use two ships, the British battleship *Agamemnon* and the United States frigate *Niagara*. When the company's electrician fell ill and was unable to accompany the expedition, Thomson volunteered his services and supervised the operations from aboard the *Agamemnon*. After several discouraging failures, the cable was finally completed on August 5, 1858. It connected Valencia

Bay, Ireland, to Heart's Content, Newfoundland, Canada. Wild celebrations erupted on both sides of the Atlantic Ocean as Queen Victoria and President Buchanan exchanged congratulatory messages. Many newspaper headlines hailed the completed cable as the feat of the century.

For this and other accomplishments Thomson was knighted. In 1892, he was again honored by the Queen of England, who conferred on him the official title Baron Kelvin of Largs. Although he had been born a commoner, William Thomson was now considered a nobleman and known as Lord Kelvin. Kelvin's total list of distinctions grew to an imposing length and included honorary doctorates from twenty-one universities throughout Europe and America.

Kelvin's was an unusually full life. He derived a wonderful sense of fulfillment from his life's work, counting the privilege of scientific investigation one of the Creator's greatest gifts to mankind. He lived to the age of 83, enjoying the blessings of good health and a keen mind until a month or two before his death. Lord Kelvin is buried in Westminster Abbey in London, where he has been honored with a magnificent Gothic stained glass window bearing this inscription: *In memory of Baron Kelvin of Largs, Engineer, Natural Philosopher, B: 1824 D: 1907.*

THE CLASSIFICATION OF MATTER
CHAPTER
5

Imagine that a friend has offered to show you his stamp collection. He pulls out a tattered shoe box filled with stamps of every kind imaginable. He picks them up one by one.

"This one with the tiger on it is from Hong Kong. And this 1964 five-cent stamp commemorates amateur radio. My dad saved that one because he's a ham operator."

"That stamp is older than we are!"

"I know—and I have some even older than that. Oh—here's one you'll like. It's a block of stamps that commemorates the first space shuttle flight."

"I didn't even know they came in sets like that. There was a picture of a space stamp in our science book. The teacher said it was issued in 1969. It commemorated *Apollo 8,* the first manned flight to orbit the moon. Do you have that one?"

"I sure do! It's right here—uh—no, that's not it. Well, I know it's here *somewhere.*"

Your friend shuffles and searches through the box, but it may take hours to find the "Earthrise" stamp: he has thousands of stamps and has never bothered to put them in any kind of order. If he had classified them by the date of issue, he could have found the *Apollo 8* commemorative in only a few seconds!

Can you imagine how many different kinds of matter there are in the universe? If scientists could not classify this incredible jumble of items, there would be no way to study them successfully. Part of the physical scientist's job is to find ways to sort all the kinds of matter into different categories. By doing that, he makes the study of matter possible.

In Chapter 4 we studied one way that scientists classify matter: by physical states (solids, liquids, gases, and plasmas). But this classification system presents some problems. One kind of matter or substance can exist in more than one state. Water exists as a solid, a liquid, and a gas. Also, substances that are very different can be grouped in the same phase. Should silver, salt, steel, iron, and ice be grouped together simply because they are all solids? Oxygen and carbon dioxide are both clear gases present in our atmosphere, but their properties are different in many ways. Should they be grouped together?

To study matter in better detail, scientists have developed a system for classifying matter according to its makeup. They study what materials are composed of by the process of **analysis** (uh NAL uh sis). Analysis is the study of materials by breaking them down. In using analysis, scientists determine the kinds of matter or substances in a material. This process has allowed scientists to classify all the materials in the universe into three classes—elements, compounds, and mixtures.

Elements

The physical universe is like a complex puzzle made from a countless number of individual pieces. For all its complexity, the puzzle is made from only about one hundred different types of pieces. They are joined in innumerable combinations to make the varied forms of matter that surround us. These pieces have a name. They are called **elements** (EL uh munts).

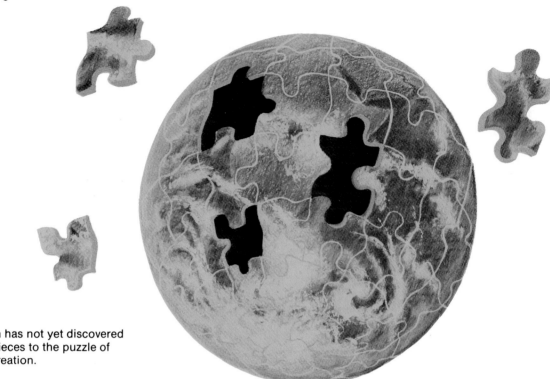

5-1 Man has not yet discovered all the pieces to the puzzle of God's creation.

A definition of elements

Man has long probed for the basic pieces in God's design of the physical universe. At first he thought the puzzle was not complex, just as you would if you examined a puzzle from a distance. The individual outline or identity of each piece would not be clear. The early Greek philosophers thought that all matter was made from one element and that the different kinds of materials were simply different forms of that element. Some believed that this element was water, which by evaporating or condensing could produce all the other elements. Some identified this element as air. They believed that the atmosphere condensed into water, solidified into earth, and rarefied into fire. Other philosophers declared that fire was the central piece of the puzzle.

After much debate, the Greek philosophers settled on a theory of four elements. About 440 years before Christ, a Greek philosopher named Empedocles (em PED uh kleez) proposed that all matter was made from particles of earth, air, fire, and water. This theory held sway over science for centuries.

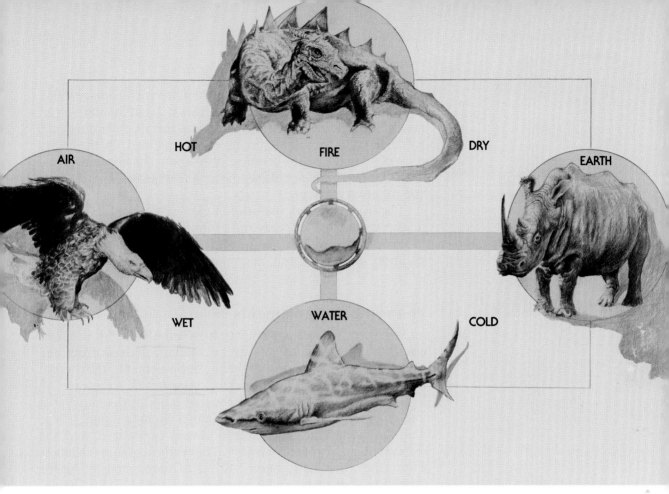

HOT

AIR

FIRE

DRY

EARTH

WET

WATER

COLD

Today we realize that neither earth, nor water, nor air, nor fire is a single element. Earth is the most complex of all these, for soil can contain many different elements, depending upon its type and condition. Scientists have isolated many gases from the atmosphere, including nitrogen, oxygen, and argon. Water can be chemically broken down into hydrogen and oxygen, and fire is nothing more than the glowing gases produced when a substance burns.

Soon men began to realize that God's creation was far more complex than they had imagined. In 1661 Robert Boyle published a book called *The Sceptical Chymist*. It was a very appropriate title indeed, for Boyle had just cause to be "skeptical" about the ancient definition of elements. In his book Boyle defined an element as any substance that could not be broken down into simpler substances by ordinary chemical means. He opened the door to the chemical exploration of matter. Scientists began to analyze substances to find their simplest parts—the pieces called elements.

5-2 The ancient Greeks believed that all matter was composed of only four elements. Aristotle added to the system the four basic properties that describe the elements. This illustration shows the relationships among the Greek elements and their properties.

In Boyle's day only a few of the elements we recognize today had been discovered. The early chemists knew of carbon, sulfur, arsenic, antimony, bismuth, and several metals, including zinc, gold, silver, copper, iron, tin, mercury, and lead. By the beginning of the eighteenth century, only about 30 substances had been classified as elements. Today scientists have identified over 106 different elements!

The overwhelming majority of elements are solids at room temperature. Two, mercury and bromine, are liquids. Eleven are gases—hydrogen, helium, nitrogen, oxygen, fluorine, neon, chlorine, argon, krypton, xenon, and radon.

The symbols of elements

Scientists represent elements by **symbols**—a "shorthand" notation consisting of one or two letters derived from the element's name. For many of the common elements, the symbol is simply the first letter of its name: oxygen = O, nitrogen = N, hydrogen = H. For others it is the first letter of the name plus one other letter from the name: silicon = Si, magnesium = Mg, platinum = Pt. The first letter is always capitalized, and the second letter is always lowercased. The symbols of some elements come from their Latin names. Silver is represented by Ag for *argentum*, sodium by Na for *natrium*, and iron by Fe for *ferrum*.

Table 5-3

Some Common Elements and Their Symbols							
Aluminum	Al	Copper	Cu	Mercury	Hg	Silicon	Si
Argon	Ar	Fluorine	F	Neon	Ne	Silver	Ag
Arsenic	As	Gold	Au	Nickel	Ni	Sodium	Na
Barium	Ba	Helium	He	Nitrogen	N	Sulfur	S
Bromine	Br	Hydrogen	H	Oxygen	O	Tin	Sn
Calcium	Ca	Iodine	I	Phosphorus	P	Uranium	U
Carbon	C	Iron	Fe	Platinum	Pt	Zinc	Zn
Chlorine	Cl	Lead	Pb	Potassium	K		
Chromium	Cr	Magnesium	Mg	Radium	Ra		

These common elements and their symbols will be used throughout this text. A complete listing of the elements and their symbols is found in Appendix B.

Table 5-4

The Names of Elements

The name of an element is sometimes a clue to its properties. The names of many metals end in *-um* or *-ium* (alumin*um,* chrom*ium*). The names of nonmetals often end in *-n* or *-ine* (nitrog*en,* chlor*ine*). Many elements were named by their discoverer for a person, place, or thing.

For persons (real or imaginary)—

einsteinium	for *Einstein*
curium	for *Curie*
mendelevium	for *Mendeleev*
rutherfordium	for *Rutherford*
fermium	for *Fermi*
thorium and	for the mythological
promethium	characters *Thor* and *Prometheus*

For places—

americium	for *America*
californium	for *California*
germanium	for *Germany*
polonium	for *Poland*
francium	for *France*

For things—

plutonium and	for the planets *Pluto*
neptunium	and *Neptune*

5-5 What type of tradesman gets his name from the element with which he works? Here is a hint: he works with lead pipes. The symbol for lead, Pb, comes from the Latin word *plumbum.* What is this tradesman called?

The atoms of elements

When is a substance classified as an element? A substance is identified as an element when it cannot be broken down into simpler substances by ordinary chemical means. A metallurgist (MET ul UR jist) refines silver ore to separate the elemental silver from the dross. Whether the ore comes from Mexico, Colorado, Australia, or any other location, the silver will be exactly the same element. No matter where the element comes from, particles of the same element are similar to one another and different from particles of any other element. These small, unique particles of an element are called **atoms**.

5-6 Only about 90 of the more than 106 known elements occur in nature. Several elements have been manufactured in laboratories such as the famous Lawrence Laboratories at Berkeley, California. Scientists there discovered such elements as neptunium, berkelium, californium, einsteinium, mendelevium, nobelium, and lawrencium.

FACETS OF BASIC SCIENCE

Elements in the Bible

Seven of the 106 elements now known to science are mentioned in the Old Testament. Several of those are used to illustrate spiritual truths, and a few give significant evidence for the reliability of the Old Testament.

Copper   The element copper is mentioned by name only once in the Bible. Ezra 8:27 speaks of "two vessels of fine copper." However, the word *brass* appears many times. It is often used figuratively to represent strength or hardness (Job 40:18) and judgment (Lev. 26:19). Today, *brass* means an alloy of copper and zinc, but zinc was unknown in biblical times. Biblical scholars believe that the brass mentioned in the Bible is the simple metal copper, or an alloy of copper and tin.

Deuteronomy 8:7-9 makes an important reference to copper: "For the Lord thy God bringeth thee into a good land . . . out of whose hills thou mayest dig brass." For a long time no one could find any copper deposits in Israel, and many liberal scholars tried to use these verses to deny the inspiration of the Bible. However, Dr. Nelson Glueck of the Hebrew Union College believed that the Bible was right and began to search the region for copper mines. He found not only the copper mines he was looking for, but also copper smelters and refineries used in the time of Solomon!

Gold   Part of Job 23:10 says, "When he hath tried me, I shall come forth as gold." Gold is a remarkable element. Because it is so beautiful and so easily worked, and because it does not easily tarnish or corrode, gold has been a symbol of value and riches since the beginning of history. The Scriptures often use gold to represent the believer, who has a precious soul, which should be beautiful and remain unaffected by the world.

Compounds

In nature, elements rarely occur as single atoms. Atoms are usually joined chemically to other atoms. These "multi-atom" particles are called **molecules** (MAHL uh KYOOLZ). When 2 atoms of the same element join together, we call the resulting particle a *diatomic* (DY uh TAHM ik) *molecule* (2-atom molecule). The common elements oxygen and nitrogen form diatomic gas molecules in the air you breathe.

The molecules of compounds

Most of the substances in nature are **compounds.** The molecules of a compound are formed when two or more atoms from *different* elements join chemically. Water is one of the most

Iron   The statue in King Nebuchadnezzar's dream had "legs of iron, his feet part of iron and part of clay" (Dan. 2:33). The iron part is generally thought to represent power and dictatorship.

Lead   Jeremiah 6:29 illustrates the character of lead when it says, "The lead is consumed of the fire." Lead is not an attractive metal. Because it absorbs impurities quickly, its silvery surface becomes dull gray as soon as it is exposed to air. Because it lacks strength, it has only limited uses in building. Lead symbolizes the corruptible and temporal.

Silver   Silver is mentioned often in the Bible. It has been used as money since Old Testament times. Abraham paid 400 shekels (about 6 kg) of silver for the cave of Machpelah and the land around it (Gen. 23:16-17). This metal was also used to make trumpets, platters, and bowls. In Solomon's time it was used to make tables and candlesticks for the Temple.

In Proverbs 25:4-5 silver illustrates a principle of government: "Take away the dross from the silver, and there shall come forth a vessel for the [re]finer. Take away the wicked from before the king, and his throne shall be established in righteousness." The dross is the layer of impurities that rises to the top of molten metal. The metal is pure when the dross is removed; in the same way, a government will be strong and righteous if wicked men are removed from it. Does this principle still apply today?

Sulfur   Known in Scripture as "brimstone" (Gen. 19:24), sulfur is a symbol of God's judgment. He used it to destroy the cities of Sodom and Gomorrah, and He will use it for judgment in the future. Brimstone is mentioned no fewer than six times in the book of the Revelation (Rev. 9:17, 18; 14:10; 19:20; 20:10; and 21:8).

Tin   The element tin is mentioned several times in Scripture (Num. 31:22; Isa. 1:25; Ezek. 22:18, 20; 27:12). During biblical times the Phoenicians mined it in the British Isles; some suggest that the name *Britain* comes from the Phoenician *barat-anac,* "land of tin." Tin was often alloyed with copper to make bronze.

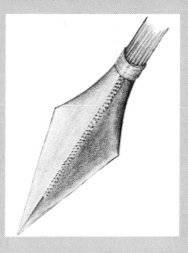

familiar and abundant compounds on the earth's surface. If there were no water on the earth, we would not be here either! (Astronomers have not been able to find significant amounts of water in any other place in the universe. This is a very clear indication of God's design in His creation. He designed the earth as a perfect home for His creatures.) Molecules of water consist of 2 hydrogen atoms chemically joined to a central oxygen atom. Another compound that might be *too* familiar to you is sugar. A molecule of sugar consists of 45 atoms: 12 atoms of carbon, 22 atoms of hydrogen, and 11 atoms of oxygen. But even this is not an example of the largest molecule in nature. A single molecule of protein may consist of thousands of atoms chemically joined together in one long chain!

There are twenty-six letters in our alphabet. These twenty-six individual letters can be joined together to form *thousands* of words. More than 106 elements are known; they can join to produce *millions* of compounds. In fact, scientists have been able to identify more than 3 million different chemical compounds.

5-7 A special note about the molecular representations in this book: The colors and the shapes of the molecules and atoms in these drawings were chosen to help you visualize concepts and processes. No scientist has ever seen an atom or a molecule, so these illustrations are not drawings of the actual particle. They are simply to help you learn.

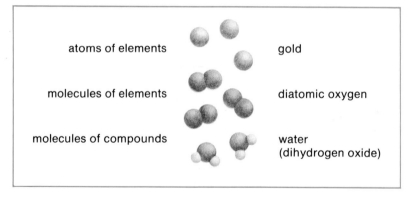

atoms of elements — gold

molecules of elements — diatomic oxygen

molecules of compounds — water (dihydrogen oxide)

The composition of compounds

The number of possible combinations of the 106 known elements is unimaginable! Yet only about 3 million different compounds exist. Why do only certain combinations of elements occur?

The behavior of elements is controlled by their chemical properties. Some elements are very *reactive.* Others are very *stable.* Each element will combine with only a select few other elements that have the necessary chemical properties. Iron will react with oxygen in the air to form rust. Silver tarnishes because it reacts with sulfur in the air. Gold neither rusts nor tarnishes.

The chemical properties of gold make it one of the most stable and least reactive metals.

Once elements combine to form a compound, they lose their individual properties. In general, the properties of a compound are very different from those of the individual elements that formed it. In some cases, man benefits greatly by the change. Salt, for instance, is a very common compound that we use to season our food. It is made by a chemical union of sodium and chlorine. Sodium is a silvery metal that reacts violently with water. Chlorine is a greenish gas that is extremely poisonous. Individually these elements are dangerous, but in chemical combination they form a substance that is essential for our bodies.

Just as all atoms of a certain element are alike, all molecules of a certain compound are alike. Each has the same **chemical composition.** Each molecule of water is made up of 2 hydrogen atoms and 1 oxygen atom. Each molecule of carbon dioxide is made up of 1 carbon atom and 2 oxygen atoms. Every compound has its own unique molecule with its own unique combination of elements. We call this very important principle the **law of definite composition.**

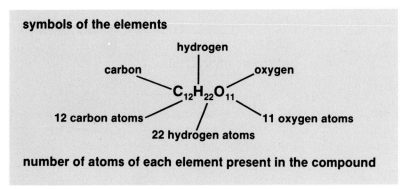

5-8 The molecules of a compound are made up of two or more different atoms from different elements. What elements combine to form this ammonia molecule?

The formulas of compounds

Scientists use the symbols for the elements to write **chemical formulas** (FOR myuh luhz), a "shorthand" way to describe the makeup of compounds. Instead of saying that sulfuric acid is 2 hydrogen atoms, 1 sulfur atom, and 4 oxygen atoms chemically combined, we simply write the formula H_2SO_4. The number of atoms of each element in a molecule of the compound is indicated by a *subscript*. When there is only one atom of a certain element in a compound, no subscript is used.

symbols of the elements

carbon   hydrogen   oxygen

$$C_{12}H_{22}O_{11}$$

12 carbon atoms   22 hydrogen atoms   11 oxygen atoms

number of atoms of each element present in the compound

5-9 The formula for sucrose (table sugar).

Table 5-10

Some Common Compounds			
Name	**Formula**	**Molecular Representation**	**Uses**
Ammonia	NH_3		manufacturing fertilizer, explosives, textiles, insecticides, and detergents
Baking soda (sodium bicarbonate)	$NaHCO_3$		producing carbon dioxide in beverages, fire extinguishers, and baked goods; antacid
Carbon dioxide	CO_2		frozen to form dry ice for refrigeration; fire prevention
Chalk (calcium carbonate)	$CaCO_3$		antacid; manufacture of paint, ceramics, polishes, inks, and cosmetics
Natural gas (mainly methane)	CH_4		fuel
Sand (silicon dioxide)	SiO_2		manufacturing glass, abrasives, ceramics, and enamels
Sodium fluoride	NaF		insecticide; fluoridating drinking water and toothpaste; frosting glass
Sulfuric acid	H_2SO_4		cleaning steel; manufacturing electric batteries, explosives, dyes, glue, and parchment paper
Table salt (sodium chloride)	$NaCl$		seasoning; preserving; glazing pottery; tanning; manufacturing dyes
Water	H_2O		most nearly universal solvent known; essential for life

Mixtures

Elements and compounds are each made up of a single kind of matter. A pure element consists of similar particles which are either atoms or molecules composed of identical atoms. A compound consists of similar molecules. Because both elements and compounds are the same throughout, they are both classified as **pure substances**. Yet most substances in the physical universe cannot be classified simply as elements or compounds. The overwhelming majority of substances are **mixtures**.

The nature of mixtures

Mixtures have three basic characteristics. First, all mixtures consist of two or more pure substances. Salt water is a common example of a mixture. It consists of two compounds, sodium chloride (salt) and water. Second, the parts of a mixture keep their own properties. Sodium and chlorine lose their properties when they chemically combine to form sodium chloride. But salt is still salt, and water is still water in a saltwater mixture. The two compounds are only physically associated and can be separated by ordinary physical means. If you boil away the water, the salt will remain. However, you cannot "boil" the sodium out of sodium chloride. Third, the parts of a mixture may be associated in any proportion. The first grain of salt added to the water makes it a saltwater mixture. It remains a saltwater mixture, no matter how much salt is added.

Elements use symbols, and compounds use formulas, but solutions are most commonly described by *percentage composition.* Percentage composition is a way of comparing the amount of one substance with another by comparing their masses. A salt solution that is made up of 10 g of salt dissolved in 90 g of water would be labeled a 10-percent salt solution.

Some common mixtures are air (nitrogen, oxygen, argon, carbon dioxide, and very small amounts of other gases), milk, (water, lactose, butterfat, proteins, etc.), seawater (water, sodium chloride, and small amounts of dissolved minerals), stainless steel (iron, carbon, and chromium), and 14-karat gold (gold and copper).

The categories of mixtures

Mixtures are divided into two categories—homogeneous (HO muh JEE nee us) and heterogeneous (HET ur oh JEE nee us). If a mixture is so well mixed that it appears the same throughout,

Table 5-11
Some Common Mixtures

Brass

Chocolate

Concrete

Gasoline

14-karat gold

Ink

Milk

Orange juice

Seawater

Stainless steel

5-12 Types of mixtures.

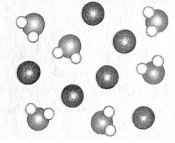

**Homogeneous
(solutions)**

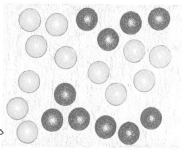

Heterogeneous

it is called a **homogeneous mixture.** Air is a prime example of a homogeneous mixture, as are stainless steel and 14-karat gold. In fact, any alloy (AL oy) (a mixture of two or more metals) is a homogeneous mixture.

Another name for a homogeneous mixture is a solution. You might think that all solutions must contain water, but alloys are solid-solid solutions, just as salt water is a solid-liquid (salt-water) solution. Solutions are a very important part of the

Table 5-13

Three Classes of Matter		
Elements	**Compounds**	**Mixtures**
lead, gold, carbon, zinc, neon, oxygen, copper, calcium	water, sugar, salt, ammonia, carbon dioxide	air, paint, rock, sweetened iced tea, brass
Represented by symbols Example: C = carbon	Represented by formulas Example: CO_2 = carbon dioxide	Represented by percentage composition Example: 10% salt solution
106 known; few found pure in nature	more than 3 million known	almost everything
Monatomic Diatomic	Molecular compound	
All atoms identical	Atoms of two or more elements joined chemically	Two or more substances combined physically
Definite composition	Definite composition	Indefinite composition
Properties of all samples similar	Components lose their individual properties	Parts keep their properties and identity
	Properties of compounds unlike those of components	
Cannot be broken down into simpler substances by ordinary chemical means	Can be separated into components only by chemical means	Can be separated into parts by physical or chemical means

mixtures in the physical universe. We will study more about solutions in Chapter 10. If a mixture has different appearances in its different parts, it is called a heterogeneous mixture. One example of this is granite. If you closely examine a piece of granite, you can see the black grains of mica, white grains of quartz, and pink or brown grains of feldspar.

Scientifically Speaking

analysis	law of definite composition
elements	chemical formulas
symbols	pure substances
atoms	mixtures
molecules	homogeneous mixture
compounds	heterogeneous mixture
chemical composition	

Questions to Talk Over

1. A chess game is made up of pieces that represent the roles people played in medieval society. If you were given a chess set, how many different ways could you classify the pieces?
2. The symbol for aluminum is Al; the symbol for arsenic is As; the symbol for argon is Ar. What symbol might be used for astatine? Why did you choose those letters?
3. Both compounds and mixtures contain more than one kind of atom. Hydrogen and oxygen are present in the compound water, but they also can be present in a mixture. What relationships between these atoms make their compound different from their mixture?
4. Look at the list of mixtures in Table 5-11. Why are these substances classified as mixtures?
5. A scientist received a sample to analyze. It appeared to be made entirely of small, white crystals. When he heated the sample, he observed that the solid changed into a green gas and a brownish liquid. Was the sample an element, a compound, or a mixture? Explain your choice.

THREE

THE STRUCTURE OF MATTER

MODELS OF ATOMS

CHAPTER 6

Think back to one of your birthdays. Did you ever receive a mysterious package that you were told not to open before your party? It probably sparked your curiosity and made waiting very difficult. Since you could not open the package, you tried to collect some indirect evidence about its contents. First, you noted the size of the box. Then you lifted it to find out how heavy it was. Finally, you shook it and listened for any tell-tale rattles. As a result of your investigations, you probably developed a mental image of your present. A scientist is often faced with similar mysteries. Sometimes he cannot directly observe the situation he is studying. Just as you did, he collects indirect evidence and uses it to form a mental or mathematical model.

As we saw in Chapter 4, scientists frequently use models to

represent the things they study. Like the birthday present, some situations cannot be directly observed. The scientist is forced to deduce "what it is really like inside." Using bits and pieces of *indirect* evidence, he constructs different models and checks them to see how each fits the observed data. After careful study he selects the model that best describes his data, then discards the others. If the thing being investigated is too complicated to analyze completely, the scientist might use a simplified model to make his task more manageable. Calculations based on such a model may not be exact, but they are useful. If scientists did not use models, they could not make any calculations at all!

When scientists "shook" the mysterious package called matter, they discovered that it was made up of many smaller mysteries. It was just like a gift that is opened only to reveal even more wrapped packages inside. These smaller mysteries were atoms, the fundamental units of matter. Since scientists have not been able to observe the atom directly, and since their indirect evidence indicates that atoms are extremely complicated, scientists have developed atomic models. Even now our model of the atom is changing. Recent evidence suggests that the atom may be far more complicated than we ever imagined.

Different models of the atom are used for different applications. We will use *structural models* because we want to study how the atom works. A nuclear physicist might develop a *mathematical model* to study the amount of energy in the various parts of the atom. Although both models are useful for different purposes, neither model is exact. Remember, models are simply useful tools. Their worth is determined by how well they predict the way atoms behave. When you see these models illustrated, always remember that the colors, the size of the parts, and the shapes are representations chosen to help us understand the mysterious package called the atom.

The Development of the Atomic Model

The first ideas about atoms can be traced to the ancient Greek philosophers. The concept of atoms was originated by Leucippus (lyoo SIP us) and developed by his student Democritus (dih MAHK ruh tus) over four hundred years before the birth of Christ. Democritus coined the word *atom,* meaning "indivisible." He stated that these atoms are the only things that exist, that they have always existed, and that they will always continue to exist.

6-1 In Democritus' model, matter was held together by means of little hooks covering the particles.

The Greek philosophers believed that reasoning, not experimentation, was the way to gain knowledge. Therefore, Democritus did not try to collect evidence to test his ideas. Today we realize that many of his ideas were wrong. For example, we know from Scripture that atoms have not always existed. God created them at a definite point in time (John 1:3). We know from observations that some things that exist are not made of atoms. Light waves, magnetic fields, and other forms of energy consist of waves, not particles. Not all of Democritus' ideas were exactly right, but he was the first to develop the idea that matter was made of many very tiny particles, which he called atoms.

It was not until the beginning of the eighteenth century that the first models of atoms were proposed by an English schoolteacher named John Dalton. He was the first to blend theory and experimentation to develop a workable atomic model.

Dalton and the atomic theory

Dalton used his knowledge of the way chemicals react to guide the development of his atomic model. One of the most important experimental evidences to influence his thinking was the **law of definite proportions.** Chemists had wondered for some time why every compound had a definite composition by mass. For example, they noticed that when 18 g of water was broken down, it always yielded 2 g of hydrogen and 16 g of oxygen. When 9 g of water was broken down, the results would be 1 g of hydrogen and 8 g of oxygen. The ratio of hydrogen to oxygen was always 1:8 by mass. Dalton saw that each compound is always made of the same combination of elements.

6-2 Dalton pictured atoms as hard spheres.

To Dalton the atom was indivisible, a solid core surrounded by an envelope of heat. The heat envelopes helped to explain the varying sizes of atoms: the larger the heat envelope, the larger the atom. He believed that every element was composed of atoms and that each element had its own unique kind of atom. All matter, he asserted, must be made from combinations of these atoms. His ideas about the relationships among atoms, elements, and compounds were surprisingly accurate, but his *"core-envelope" model* of the atom was later disproved. Shortly after Dalton proposed his model, heat was shown to be energy, not matter. Nevertheless, Dalton had laid the foundation for modern atomic theory and had shown the correct relationship between atoms and elements.

J. J. Thomson and the electron

A significant discovery by J. J. Thomson in 1897 dealt the deathblow to Dalton's "core-envelope" theory. Dalton had based his model on the belief that atoms were indivisible; J. J. Thomson discovered some astounding new evidence that led him to conclude that atoms consisted of charged particles. Scientists of that time knew that energized metals gave off streams of negatively charged energy. Was this stream a group of waves or a mass of tiny particles? Thomson proved that the metals were giving off negatively charged particles called **electrons** (ih LEK TRONZ). This introduced a revolutionary new concept: the atom could be divided!

Thomson knew that negative charges should repel each other. If atoms were made of smaller negative electrons, something must be holding them together. To solve this problem, he included positive charges in his atomic model to hold the electrons in the atom. He pictured the atom as a mass of positively charged material. The negatively charged electrons were imbedded in the positive material like plums in a plum pudding. We frequently call Thomson's model the *plum-pudding model* for that reason.

For his day, Thomson's model was quite remarkable. If atoms were not electrically neutral, you would get a shock every time you touched anything. His model ingeniously accounted for this fact. The positive charge on the material ("pudding") balanced the negative charges on the electrons ("plums"). The electrons were held in place by the attractive forces between these opposite charges.

6-3 The Thomson model had negatively charged electrons embedded in a positive "pudding."

Rutherford and the nucleus

In 1903 Philipp Lenard (LAY NAHRT), a German physicist, succeeded in passing electrons through sheets of metal. This came as a complete surprise to many people. Scientists realized that if rays of electrons could pass through the atoms of a metal, there must be empty space within the atoms and between them. Then in 1908 Ernest Rutherford (RUTH ur furd) penetrated a

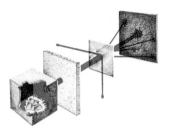

6-4 Rutherford's experimental setup.

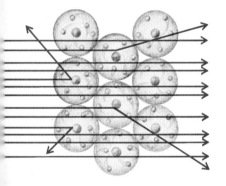

6-5 The deflection of particles.

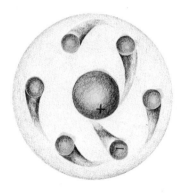

6-6 Rutherford's model.

thin sheet of gold with positively charged particles. These positively charged particles are over 7000 times as massive as an electron. This was like switching from BBs to cannonballs! This experiment showed that the spaces in matter must be very large.

Figure 6-4 shows the experimental setup Rutherford used in this classic experiment. When the positively charged particles were shot at the gold foil, most of them went straight through it as if nothing were in the way, but some particles were deflected. The most astonishing thing was that some of them were bounced almost straight backwards! Rutherford exclaimed, "It was the most incredible event that ever happened in my life. It was . . . as if you had fired a 15-inch shell at a piece of tissue paper and it came back and hit you!" There must be a great amount of empty space in the atom, or most of the positively charged particles and electrons would not pass through. There must also be a very dense, charged portion in each atom that deflected some of the particles. By 1911 Rutherford had devised an atomic model to account for these facts. He calculated that the positive charge and practically all of the atom's mass were concentrated in a tiny region of space, which he called the **nucleus** (NOO klee us) (plural *nuclei* [NOO klee EYE]).

The nucleus was filled with tiny, positively charged particles called **protons.** Fantastic though it may seem, the diameter of an atom's nucleus is only $\frac{1}{100,000}$ as large as the diameter of the entire atom. If an atomic nucleus were as large as a period on this page, the atom would have a diameter equal to one-half of the length of a soccer field. With this comparison in mind, you can easily see that atomic representations are not drawn to scale!

Rutherford and others completed the atomic model by stating that the electrons whirled around the nucleus. Their high speeds kept them from being pulled into the positively charged nucleus. Later scientists added to Rutherford's model. They found that the mass of the nucleus was more than the mass of all the protons. Therefore, the nucleus must contain something besides the protons. Then James Chadwick discovered **neutrons** (NOO TRAHNZ). These particles gave the nucleus its extra mass. A neutron has no electrical charge and has approximately the same mass as a proton.

Rutherford's model gave us a working picture of the nucleus, but it did not explain the motions of the electrons. How far away from the nucleus were they? How were they arranged? These questions were to be answered by the Danish physicist Niels Bohr (1885-1962).

Democritus

John Dalton

J.J. Thomson

Ernest Rutherford

Niels Bohr

6-7 Men who contributed to the modern atomic model.

Bohr and energy levels

Any respectable fireworks display must have brilliant colors along with its sparks, smoke, and noise. How are these colors produced? In fireworks the color-producing compounds are added to an explosive mixture. The energy from the explosion of this mixture heats the atoms of the color-producing compounds. As these atoms cool, they release energy in the form of visible light. Each element releases light of a different wavelength or color. Sodium compounds, for example, create yellow flames; strontium compounds burn red; barium compounds burn green. Changing the basic color compound alters the hue of the fireworks.

Niels Bohr (BORE) knew that certain atoms gave off certain colors when heated. When he passed these *emissions* (ih MISH unz) through a prism, he was able to identify the specific wavelengths of light given off by each atom. Bohr suspected that these emissions were caused by the electrons in the atoms. He theorized that the electrons must jump farther from the nucleus when they were heated, and then return to their original position when they cooled. As they returned, they gave off light energy; the wavelength of the light depended on how far the electrons jumped. Since different elements gave off different colors when

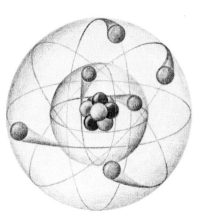

6-8 The Bohr model was the first to have electrons travel in specific energy levels.

113

they were heated, the distance that the electrons jumped must vary from element to element. This meant that each element must have its own unique electron structure!

From the color of an element's emission (or the light wavelength), **Bohr** mathematically calculated the distance of the electrons from the nucleus. He could then develop a model of the atom that explained this color phenomenon. In his model, electrons occupied specific **energy levels.** They could jump to higher energy levels if they were given enough energy, and would return to their original levels when they cooled. Since his model looks like a miniature three-dimensional solar system, we often call Bohr's model of the atom the planetary model.

More sophisticated models of the atom have been developed since Bohr's time. For example, the *quantum* (KWAHN tum) *model* represents the electron energy levels as general regions where electrons most probably exist. Picture an electric fan and a clock sitting side by side. The hands of the clock move so slowly that we cannot see their movement. We can say with confidence exactly where they are at any given point in time.

6-9 The electrons in an atom are traveling so fast that the quantum model portrays their position by a blur or cloud. This "uncertain" location of the electrons was first proposed by Werner Heisenberg in 1925.

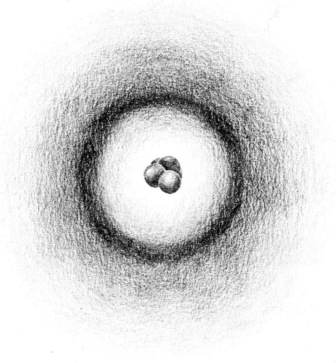

The fan blades, however, are a different story. They move at such a high speed that we cannot see exactly where they are at a given time. We can see only a general region, a blur of blades or "cloud," where the blades are most likely to be located. For the same reason, we cannot assign specific tracks for electrons or pinpoint their exact locations. Because they move at extremely high speeds, we can only designate areas where they will most likely be found. These regions of probable location are called **electron orbitals** (OR bit ulz).

Table 6-10

The History of the Atomic Model		
Man	**Discovery**	**Model**
Democritus	All matter is made of atoms.	
Dalton	Atoms have different masses.	
Thomson	Electrons carry negative charges in atoms.	
Rutherford	A nucleus exists.	
Bohr	Electrons exist in energy levels.	
Heisenberg	The position of the electrons is uncertain.	

The Nuclear Atom

The discoveries of the various subatomic particles have led us to a clearer, more accurate understanding of the structure of atoms. Our atomic model started off as an indivisible core surrounded by an envelope of heat; J. J. Thomson modified it with the addition of electrons; Rutherford and Chadwick gave it a nucleus filled with protons and neutrons; Bohr circled it with electrons in energy levels. Modern atomic physicists have changed our structural model even further. Now the electrons of the various energy levels are better described by orbitals that indicate their probable locations. In this section we will examine the particles of the nucleus in closer detail.

Atomic mass

The two major types of particles in the nucleus of an atom are the *proton* and the *neutron*. A proton carries one unit of positive charge (+1). It is 1836 times as massive as a single electron. A neutron is 1839 times heavier than an electron, but it has no electrical charge. The masses of the proton and neutron are approximately equal; the difference is less than $\frac{1}{10}$ of 1 percent. The actual mass of these particles is approximately 1.6 x 10^{-27} kg, or 0.00000000000000000000000016 kg. An electron is so much lighter than the particles in the nucleus that its contribution to the mass of the atom is extremely small.

How do we calculate the mass of an atom? We must make some basic assumptions to simplify our work. First, since the masses of the protons and neutrons are close to being equal, we can treat them as if they *are* equal. Second, we can disregard the masses of the electrons, because they are so small. Therefore, to find the **atomic mass** we simply add the masses of all the particles in the nucleus.

If scientists used kilograms to measure the mass of atoms, the numbers would be extremely small and difficult to work with. So scientists have chosen a special unit, called the **atomic mass unit,** or the **amu.** An amu is defined as one-twelfth of the mass of a carbon atom that has 6 protons and 6 neutrons. It is roughly the mass of 1 proton or 1 neutron. To find the approximate mass of any atom, simply total the number of particles in the nucleus. For example, a typical sulfur atom has 16 protons and 16 neutrons. Its approximate mass would be 32 amu.

Atomic number

Each element has its own kind of atom, but what makes the atoms of each element unique? Each kind of atom has a certain number of protons in its nucleus. For example, each gold atom has 79 protons in its nucleus. Likewise, all atoms with 79 protons in their nuclei are gold atoms. The number of protons in the nucleus determines the kind of atom. All the atoms of a certain element must have the same number of protons. If a proton were removed from a gold atom, it would no longer be gold. One less

proton would change the atom to platinum, because all atoms with 78 protons are platinum atoms.

The number of protons in the nucleus is called the **atomic number.** Scientists use atomic numbers to identify elements. Hydrogen has an atomic number of 1; oxygen has an atomic number of 8; sulfur has an atomic number of 16. How many protons are in the nucleus of an oxygen atom?

Mass numbers

The sum of the protons and neutrons in the nucleus is called the **mass number.** Except for the simplest hydrogen atom, almost all atoms have both protons and neutrons in their nuclei. (Simple hydrogen is the one exception; it has only a single proton in its nucleus.) Most oxygen atoms have 8 protons and 8 neutrons in their nuclei. Their mass number would be 16 (8 + 8). A carbon atom with 6 protons and 6 neutrons would have a mass number of 12. What is the mass number of a helium atom that has 2 protons and 2 neutrons?

6-11 Elements are identified by their atomic numbers. Lithium, with an atomic number of 3, is a soft, silvery metal that reacts violently with water. It can be sliced easily with a knife. Hydrogen, with an atomic number of 1, is a colorless, tasteless, odorless gas that reacts easily with oxygen. It is so lightweight that it was used to fill giant dirigibles. An atom of lithium has only 2 protons more than an atom of hydrogen, but what a difference those 2 protons make!

117

A typical sulfur atom has a mass number of 32 and an atomic number of 16. The mass number tells you that there are 32 particles in its nucleus. The atomic number tells you that 16 of those particles are protons. You can find the number of neutrons by a simple subtraction operation:

mass number - atomic number = number of neutrons
32 neutrons and protons - 16 protons = 16 neutrons

Some sulfur atoms have a mass number of 33. Since they are sulfur atoms, their atomic number must be 16. Therefore, the difference between these atoms and the more common sulfur atoms is in the number of neutrons that each possesses. The less common type of sulfur has 17 neutrons.

33 neutrons and protons - 16 protons = 17 neutrons

Atoms of the same element that have different numbers of neutrons are called **isotopes** (EYE suh TOAPS). Most elements have several isotopic forms of their atoms. Isotopes of the same element have the same atomic numbers but different mass numbers because they have different numbers of neutrons. An isotope of an element is shown by special notation that indicates both the atomic number and the mass number of the element. The mass number is placed to the upper left of the element's symbol, and the atomic number is placed to the lower left. The isotopes of sulfur would be written $^{32}_{16}S$ and $^{33}_{16}S$. There is another naturally occurring isotope of sulfur that has the notation $^{34}_{16}S$. How many neutrons are in an atom of this isotope?

Scientists read "$^{34}_{16}S$" as "sulfur-34."

6-12 The isotopes of sulfur have different numbers of neutrons.

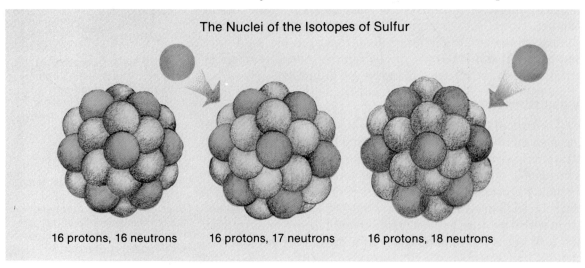

The Nuclei of the Isotopes of Sulfur

16 protons, 16 neutrons   16 protons, 17 neutrons   16 protons, 18 neutrons

Nuclear radiation

The model of Rutherford and Chadwick is like a "photograph" of the nucleus. It is a still picture of the nucleus at a given instant and it answers our questions about what major particles are present. Modern physicists are developing a model that is more like a "motion picture" of the nucleus that will show the arrangement of protons and neutrons and changes in the nucleus. This "film" of the nucleus reveals several surprising facts. Some nuclei are unstable. They tend to break up and emit small particles. Nuclei can be split in two. Occasionally two smaller nuclei join together and release fantastic amounts of energy. This "film" representation of the nucleus is called *nuclear chemistry.*

The study of nuclear chemistry began with the accidental discovery of radioactivity. In 1896 Henri Becquerel found that uranium compounds caused white blurs on photographic plates even though the plates were wrapped in black paper to protect them from light. He found that uranium always gives off some kind of energy. He had observed **radioactivity**—the emission of rays and particles from a nucleus.

His exciting discovery posed many questions about radiation. What is it? What causes it? Is it dangerous? How can it be used? A detailed analysis of radiation was needed. In a classic experiment, researchers aimed a stream of radiation at a photographic plate. The source of radiation was a small piece of uranium

Scientists have collected evidence that over 100 particles besides protons and neutrons can be emitted from the nuclei of atoms. Why should there be so many particles? The atom is a magnificently complex mechanism created by God and completely understood only by Him. As scientists learn more about its workings, they must propose new subatomic particles to account for the existence of the atom.

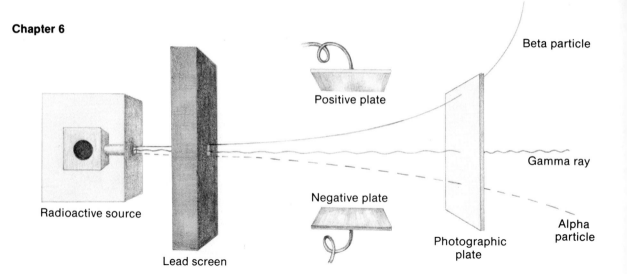

Positive plate

Beta particle

Gamma ray

Negative plate

Alpha particle

Radioactive source

Photographic plate

Lead screen

6-13 Experiment for analyzing radiation.

inside a lead cylinder. (The lead blocked all but a thin stream of radiation.) After it left the cylinder, the radiation passed through magnetic and electric fields. These fields separated the stream into three beams that showed up as spots on the plate.

One beam was deflected slightly. This beam was composed of fairly massive, positively charged particles. These **alpha particles** were each made up of two protons and two neutrons. The particles in the second, or beta (BAY tuh), beam were greatly deflected, but in the direction opposite to the alpha particles. Since the beam was easily bent, the **beta particles** must have been very small; because they were turned in the opposite direction, they must have had a negative charge. Thus it was found that beta particles were free electrons. The third beam was not affected at all by the magnets. These **gamma rays** were not particles; they were electromagnetic waves like radio waves, but with much more energy. Once the stream of radiation had been studied, scientists turned their attention to the changes in the nucleus that were causing all the radiation.

Table 6-14

Three Types of Radiation					
Name	**Symbol**	**Identity**	**Charge**	**Mass**	**Penetration**
alpha	$^{4}_{2}He$	helium nucleus	+2	4 amu	low
beta	$^{0}_{-1}e$	electron	-1	1/1836 amu	medium
gamma	$^{0}_{0}\gamma$	electromagnetic radiation	0	0	high

Nuclear decay

When nuclear changes occur, the nuclei end up with extra energy. They release this extra energy as gamma rays. The release of gamma rays does not change the atomic number or mass number. Gamma rays do cause great changes, however, in anything they hit. Because of their extremely high energy, they slice through almost anything in their way, leaving behind a trail of destruction. Several meters of concrete or a thick plate of lead is required to stop the harmful journeys of gamma rays.

When atoms emit alpha particles, they lose 2 protons and 2 neutrons. This **alpha decay** decreases the atom's mass by 4 amu and transforms the element to the element two atomic numbers below it. Isotope notation is very useful for writing out these reactions in a short form. One type of atom that readily releases an alpha particle is uranium-238 (written $^{238}_{92}U$). The alpha particle is really a helium nucleus, so we write it as ^4_2He. The complete reaction includes the original atom and all the products.

6-15 How an alpha particle is formed.

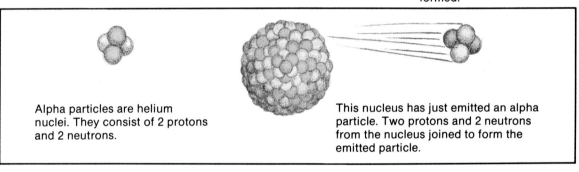

Alpha particles are helium nuclei. They consist of 2 protons and 2 neutrons.

This nucleus has just emitted an alpha particle. Two protons and 2 neutrons from the nucleus joined to form the emitted particle.

6-16 Alpha decay.

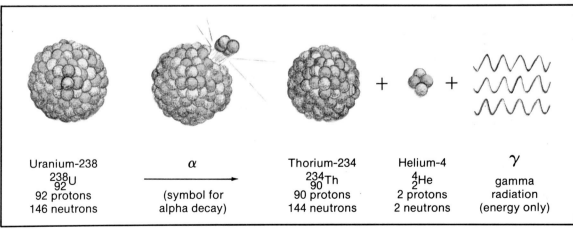

Uranium-238	α	Thorium-234	Helium-4	γ
$^{238}_{92}U$	$\longrightarrow$	$^{234}_{90}Th$	^4_2He	gamma
92 protons	(symbol for	90 protons	2 protons	radiation
146 neutrons	alpha decay)	144 neutrons	2 neutrons	(energy only)

Compare the mass numbers before and after the reaction: 238 = 234 + 4. The sum of the atomic numbers after the reaction is also the same as the original atomic number: 92 = 90 + 2. After the alpha particle is emitted, it quickly grabs electrons from the first thing it hits. Once this helium nucleus has captured two electrons, it is a normal helium atom, and its penetrating power is greatly reduced. It can be stopped by a sheet of newspaper.

Some unstable nuclei release an electron. This nuclear change is called **beta decay.** Electrons cannot normally exist in the nucleus. Then where does this electron come from? It is formed when 1 neutron breaks up to form 1 proton and 1 electron. The electron leaves as beta radiation; the proton remains in the nucleus and elevates the atomic number by one. The overall effect is the emission of an electron and the transformation of the atom into a higher element. The product of the uranium-238 alpha decay is thorium-234. Thorium has a very unstable nucleus

6-17 How a beta particle is formed.

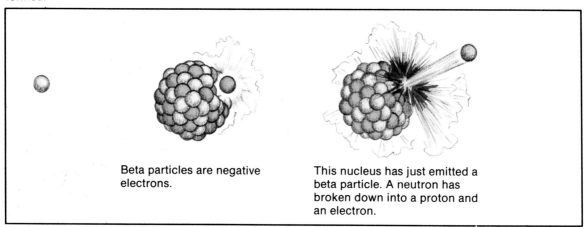

Beta particles are negative electrons.

This nucleus has just emitted a beta particle. A neutron has broken down into a proton and an electron.

6-18 Beta decay.

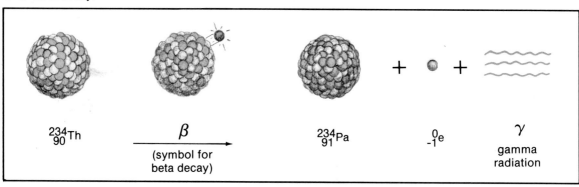

$^{234}_{90}\text{Th}$ $\xrightarrow{\quad\beta\quad}$ $^{234}_{91}\text{Pa}$ $+$ $^{0}_{-1}\text{e}$ $+$ γ

(symbol for beta decay)   gamma radiation

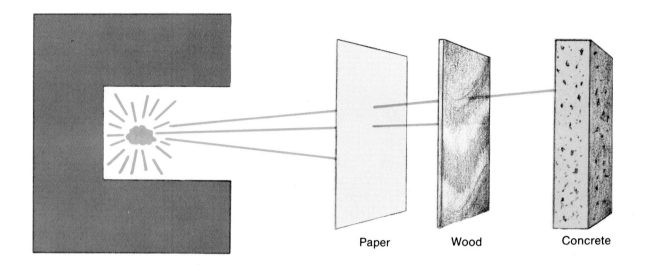

Paper Wood Concrete

and will quickly emit a beta particle to produce protactinium. As in alpha decay, the sums of all the masses and atomic numbers before and after the reaction remain the same: 234 = 234 + 0, and 90 = 91 + (-1). A *free electron* is subject to capture by any atoms that it passes, so this form of radiation can also be stopped easily. It does travel farther than an alpha particle, but it takes only a piece of wood or aluminum to stop the electrons of beta radiation.

6-19 The three types of radiation are emitted by this radioactive sample encased in lead. Can you identify each type on the basis of its penetrating power?

Nuclear changes

Like chemical changes, **nuclear changes** release and absorb energy. However, nuclear changes involve a million times more energy per atom than chemical changes. The nucleus is a tremendous storehouse of energy! Nuclear **fission** (FISH un) occurs when a nucleus is split and energy is released.

In the 1930s scientists found that they could make a nucleus unstable by adding a neutron to it. The unstable nucleus soon broke up to form 2 smaller nuclei and several neutrons. The emitted neutrons could go on to hit other nuclei and cause them to split, releasing immense amounts of energy. This process is called a **chain reaction.**

Where does all the energy come from? When scientists measured the masses of the 2 new nuclei and the neutrons caused by the split, they found that the sum was less than the mass of the original atom. Somewhere, some mass had been lost. What had happened to this matter? Albert Einstein developed the formula

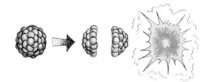

6-20 When a nucleus splits, two smaller nuclei are formed, and energy is released.

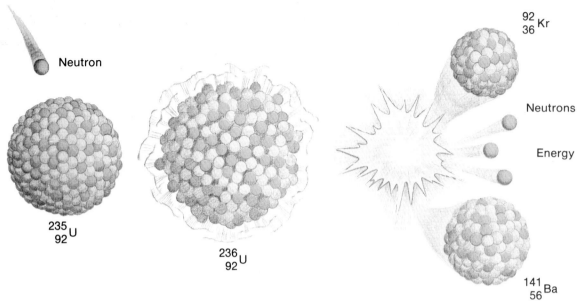

6-21 The process of fission. In the fission of uranium-235, a neutron is fired at a uranium nucleus. This causes the nucleus to become unstable. It splits into two smaller nuclei, emits several neutrons, and gives off a large quantity of energy. What would happen if those neutrons hit other uranium nuclei in the surrounding area?

$E = mc^2$ to answer this question. He showed that mass could be changed to energy. In this equation,

E = energy
m = mass
c = the speed of light

The speed of light is 300,000,000 meters per second. When this number is squared and multiplied by even a minute amount of mass, the resulting quantity is extremely large. Now we can see why a small amount of mass yields fantastic amounts of energy when it is converted. If you could completely convert 1 g of matter into energy, you would have enough energy to send 400 rockets into space—each of them with a mass of 4000 kg!

The process of fission was first used in the two atomic bombs that ended World War II. Now nuclear power plants harness that same type of energy to heat water and run electrical generators. Approximately 13 percent of America's electricity is supplied by fission processes.

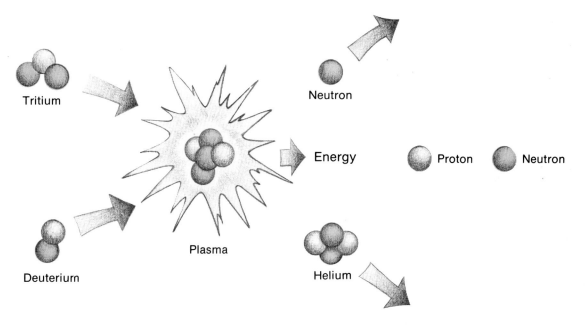

6-22 The process of fusion. In a deuterium-tritium fusion reaction, a tritium nucleus and a deuterium nucleus fuse in the extreme heat of a plasma to form a neutron, helium, and energy.

Nuclear **fusion** (FYOO zhun) is the process that joins smaller nuclei into a larger one. Fusion produces even more energy than fission. Today we think that the sun and stars derive their energy from fusion reactions. The main reaction in the sun is thought to involve the combination of 4 hydrogen nuclei to form a single helium nucleus.

Fusion has rightly been called the energy of the future. It has many compelling selling points. It requires no hard-to-find fuels. The oceans contain all the hydrogen atoms that we would ever need. While fossil fuels produce harmful pollutants and fission produces radioactive wastes, fusion would produce only low-level radioactive products. Such products could be easily handled. The fusion process produces so much energy that power prices could be drastically reduced in the future.

Several obstacles must be overcome before fusion can be controlled and used. For this reaction to occur, the hydrogen nuclei must be under conditions similar to those in stars. The required temperatures and pressures are astronomical! If scientists could reproduce the conditions of the sun on earth, they

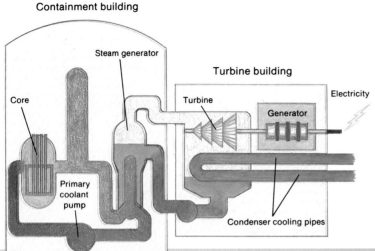

Containment building

Steam generator

Core

Turbine building

Turbine

Electricity

Generator

Primary
coolant
pump

Condenser cooling pipes

6-23 How a nuclear reactor works. The uranium fuel in the core of the nuclear reactor produces very intense heat. The primary coolant water **(red)**, which circulates through the reactor, is heated as it flows around the nuclear fuel. The superheated primary coolant heats a second water system **(blue)** to produce steam. This steam rotates a turbine, which turns an electrical generator. The steam is condensed on cooling pipes which carry water from a nearby lake or stream, and is then recycled through the system.

would run into a second problem: How do you confine such hot plasma? No known container could hold the required materials; the walls would melt or vaporize. Theoretically, the plasma could be held with electrical and magnetic fields. Because putting this theory into practice is difficult, however, sustained fusion is not yet commercially feasible. Nevertheless, physicists are striving to harness this "energy of the future" to meet our present needs.

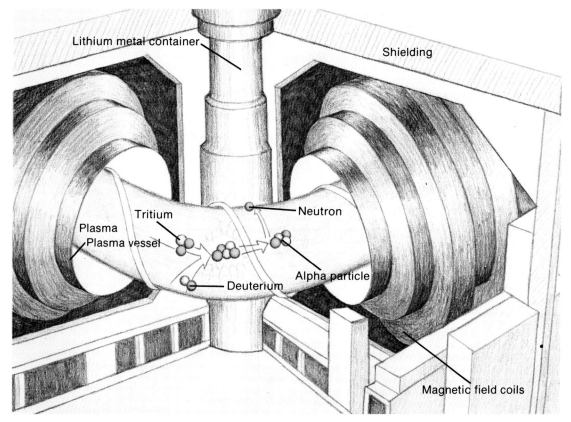

6-24 The tokamak fusion reactor is designed to test the practicality of producing electricity from fusion reactions. A tokamak is a doughnut-shaped reactor in which plasma is confined in a magnetic field. Lasers are used to heat atoms of deuterium and tritium to about 100 million degrees Celsius. At that temperature, the atoms of deuterium and tritium have lost their electrons and become ions, forming the plasma. When the tritium and deuterium nuclei collide, an alpha particle and a very energetic neutron are formed. Scientists hope to tap the energy of this fusion process to produce electrical energy. The neutrons will heat a blanket of liquid lithium metal, which will in turn be used to heat water into the steam needed to drive the turbines in generators.

FACETS
OF BASIC SCIENCE

Clocks with Radioactive Ticks

At the University of Chicago in the 1950s, Willard Libby devised an ingenious way to use radioactive decay as an atomic clock. He noted that cosmic rays from the sun produce a heavy isotope of carbon. This carbon-14, as it is called, has 2 extra neutrons, but its chemical properties are identical to those of carbon-12. Radioactive carbon mixes easily with the rest of the world's carbon supply. In the air, oceans, plants, and animals, 765 out of every 1 billion carbon atoms are C-14. This ratio remains constant in an organism as long as it is alive; but when it dies and no more carbon is taken in, the level of the *radioisotope* (RAY dee oh EYE suh tope) gradually decreases as the nuclei of the C-14 decay at a constant rate.

This decaying process is the ticking of Libby's atomic clock. The number of C-14 atoms that have decayed shows how long ago the material was alive. **Radiocarbon** (RAY dee oh KAR bun) **dating** was initially used on bones, wood, and charcoal. Soon it was used to solve a debate between archaeologists and literary experts over the age of some ancient Bible manuscripts.

In 1947 a band of Arab nomads accidentally discovered a group of small caves on the

northern shore of the Dead Sea. Inside the caves were scores of jars containing Old Testament manuscripts. Were they valuable? How old were they?

Archaeologists said that they were copied about the time of Christ. If so, these manuscripts would prove that all the prophecies about Christ had been written many years before they were fulfilled. Some literary scholars had claimed that the Old Testament was written in the Middle Ages (A.D. 900). They said that the Old Testament prophecies were forgeries written long after Christ. Who was right? Both sides turned to Libby's C-14 clock for some answers.

Libby took a linen covering

from one of the scrolls, burned it into charcoal, and determined the number of C-14 atoms in it. He then calculated that the sample had been losing C-14 atoms for 1917 years, which dated the scrolls at A.D. 33. This date matched the dates on some Roman coins found with the scrolls. The Dead Sea scrolls testified that biblical prophecies were indeed written long before the events they foretold. They also indicated that the Word of God has not changed since the time of Christ.

True science always supports the Bible. The *facts* are always in line with Scripture. Sometimes men misinterpret the facts and form faulty conclusions. This has happened with radiocarbon dating. When men have attempted to use it in situations where it is not valid, they have come up with unrealistic ages for some fossils.

Radiocarbon dating is valid for relatively recent samples. Before Libby published any results, he measured the C-14 contents of many artifacts. Since he knew the age of these artifacts, he could match the C-14 contents to their ages. After measuring the C-14 content of a piece of wood that he knew was 3000 years old, he could safely say that any other wood with the same amount of C-14 was also 3000 years old. In this manner the C-14 scale can be calibrated only for the last 5000 years. Beyond 5000 years the scale is not usable, and men must interpret its results according to their own beliefs. Is it any wonder that they get results that contradict the Bible?

The Electron Levels

An atom of hydrogen has only one electron whirling rapidly about its nucleus. That 1 electron is relatively simple to locate. But an atom of uranium has 92 electrons orbiting its nucleus. How do scientists determine where these electrons are?

The number of electrons in an atom is determined by the number of protons in the nucleus. To be electrically neutral, an atom must have the same number of negatively charged electrons as it has positively charged protons. Scientists have discovered that these electrons are arranged about the proton-containing nucleus in recognizable patterns. This placement is very important, for it determines the chemical and physical properties of the atom.

Energy levels

The electrons orbiting an atom possess different amounts of energy. Neils Bohr calculated that these energies would cause the electrons to orbit at different distances (different energy levels) from the nucleus. The less energetic electrons would orbit close to the nucleus, while the more energetic electrons would orbit in pathways farther away from the nucleus.

Bohr felt that these pathways were definite orbits, but modern researchers have found evidence that the electron moves not in specific paths, but in general regions. Since the electron is moving too fast for them to detect its specific location, they designate "layers" in which the electrons can be found. These "layers" do not have specific boundaries. They represent the regions where an electron with a certain amount of energy is most likely to be found. For convenience, we call these "layers" *energy levels*. The electrons with the lowest amounts of energy occupy the first level, which is closest to the nucleus. Those with more energy locate in higher levels from the second, to the third, all the way to the seventh, which is the energy level farthest from the nucleus. The number of levels depends on the number of electrons in the atom.

Scientists have determined that electrons fill these energy levels in a specific order. For example, the 8 electrons in an oxygen atom fill the first energy level with 2 electrons and the second energy level with the remaining 6. Since it is nearly impossible to draw the energy levels as layers, we can more clearly illustrate the oxygen atom with a Bohr planetary model.

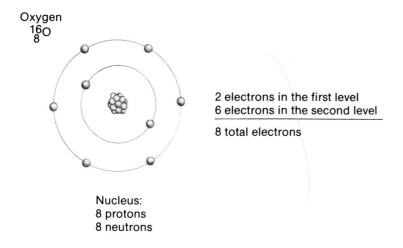

Oxygen
$^{16}_{8}$O

2 electrons in the first level
6 electrons in the second level

8 total electrons

Nucleus:
8 protons
8 neutrons

The 16 electrons in sulfur fill 2 in the first level, 8 in the second level, and 6 in the third level. A Bohr model of sulfur would look like this:

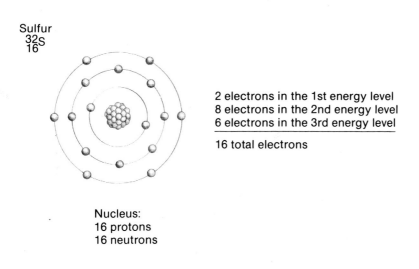

Sulfur
$^{32}_{16}$S

2 electrons in the 1st energy level
8 electrons in the 2nd energy level
6 electrons in the 3rd energy level

16 total electrons

Nucleus:
16 protons
16 neutrons

Filling order

How do the electrons fill the energy levels? The **filling order** is determined by two simple rules:

1. Each of the energy levels has a limit on the number of electrons it can hold. The first energy level can hold only 2, the second can hold 8, the third can hold 18, and the fourth can hold 32.

FACETS
OF BASIC SCIENCE

The Atom: Our Everyday Miracle

Modern science has aimed its most potent experimental weapons at the atom, trying to solve its mysteries. Over the years a progression of atomic models has led up to our present description. On the surface all this knowledge seems very impressive. Dalton's ingenious ideas, Rutherford's exciting experiments, and Bohr's detailed calculations might tempt us to look back in pride and say, "We have it all figured out." Do we really? Stop and take a new look at the atom.

Even though it is extremely small, the atom is wondrously complex. It is so intricate that we have not been able to understand it fully. Its parts work together harmoniously like the pieces of a precision watch. Unlike even the finest watches, however, the atom does not wear out. The parts of most atoms function flawlessly for years, centuries, and millennia.

If we analyze our present theories, we will find that they explain only some situations. They leave several vital questions unanswered. For instance, has it occurred to you that as far as we know, a nucleus is an impossibility? The laws of electricity say that it is impossible for many positive charges to stick together. According to these laws the

protons should repel each other and fly apart with a tremendous release of energy. What holds the nucleus together? No one knows for sure. It seems that the nucleus is governed by rules that we do not fully comprehend. We may not know how these rules work, but we do know their Source. In Colossians 1:16-17, the Apostle Paul gives full credit to Jesus Christ for this act of preservation: "All things were created by him, and for him: And he is before all things, and by him all things consist [hold together]." The Son of God causes the nucleus to be bound together.

Another entity that baffles physicists is the neutron. By itself, it is an unstable particle. It bursts into smaller particles in about seventeen minutes. But, when combined with protons in

the nucleus, it is perfectly stable. Unbelieving scientists can only say *what* happens, not *why* it happens. The Christian knows that it happens because there is an infinitely wise Creator Who planned it that way!

Finally, think about the complex movements of the electron. Its speed and distance from the nucleus are just right to keep it from being pulled into the positively charged nucleus. It can jump to higher energy levels or drop back down, and yet never upset the balance of forces. The atom is truly a complex wonder. Those who recognize the true God can see His hand constantly working in every atom. Through studying the atom, we can see how God has created and is now sustaining the atom, our everyday miracle.

2. The maximum number of electrons in the outermost energy level of an atom is 8. This is called the octet rule. Once 8 electrons have entered an energy level, the next 2 electrons must enter a higher energy level before the lower energy level may be filled.

The way the electrons fill a calcium atom illustrates these rules. Calcium has a mass number of 40 and an atomic number of 20; therefore, it has 20 protons and 20 neutrons. To be electrically neutral, it must also have 20 electrons. These electrons are positioned in this order: 2 in the first energy level (it is now filled), 8 in the second level (it is now filled), 8 in the third level (no more can fill this level until 2 electrons are placed in a higher level), and 2 in the fourth level. The Bohr model would look like this:

Calcium
$^{40}_{20}Ca$

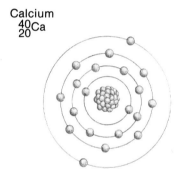

2 electrons in the 1st energy level
8 electrons in the 2nd energy level
8 electrons in the 3rd energy level
2 electrons in the 4th energy level

20 total electrons

Nucleus:
20 protons
20 neutrons

Electron hotel

We can think of the whole arrangement of electron positions as a seven-story hotel. The resident electrons must check in to the lowest floor possible. When one floor is full, all the incoming electrons must go up to the next higher level.

This electron hotel is unique in that the first floor holds only 2 electrons. The second level has room for 8; the third houses 18. The higher we look, the more places we find. The number of electrons that can be found in each level are listed in Figure 6-25. As you can see, there is room for a great many electrons. In fact, there is always room to spare. Even in the most tightly packed atoms, the fifth, sixth, and seventh floors are only partly filled.

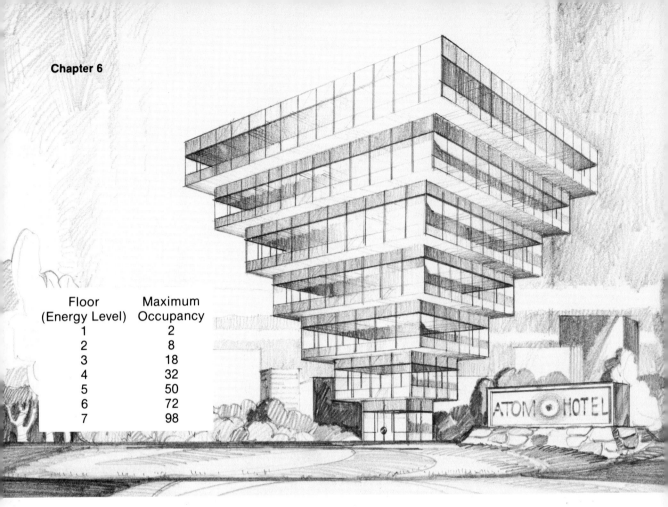

Floor (Energy Level)	Maximum Occupancy
1	2
2	8
3	18
4	32
5	50
6	72
7	98

6-25 The electron hotel.

For example, the 103 electrons in lawrencium fill their energy levels in this order: 2, 8, 18, 32, 32, 9, 2. Levels five through seven have quite a few vacancies.

Can our atom hotel register new guests or check out old ones? For the atom to be electrically neutral, the number of electrons and protons must be equal. When they are not, the atom has an electrical charge. We call these charged atoms **ions** (EYE unz). The number of protons cannot change without changing the kind of atom, but the number of electrons in an atom can change. The addition or loss of electrons usually occurs in the outermost energy level, or the top floor with residents. The change is controlled by the number of electrons already present in the top level and the distance of the top level from the nucleus. For this reason the electrons in the top level have a special name. They are called the **valence** (VAY lunce) **electrons.** The ability of an atom to add or lose valence electrons determines its chemical properties and is a very important key to our further study of matter.

Scientifically Speaking

law of definite proportions
electrons
nucleus
protons
neutrons
energy levels
electron orbitals
atomic mass
atomic mass unit (amu)

atomic number
mass number
isotopes
radioactivity
alpha particles
beta particles
gamma rays
alpha decay
beta decay

nuclear changes
fission
chain reaction
fusion
radiocarbon dating
filling order
ions
valence electrons

Questions to Talk Over

1. Why was the information that Rutherford collected from his experiments "indirect" evidence about the nature of the atom?
2. Why will scientists always have limitations in describing the atom?
3. One of the commonly occurring isotopes of silicon has the notation $^{29}_{14}$Si. What are the atomic number, mass number, and number of neutrons in an atom of silicon-29?
4. Radioactive americium-241 is used in many smoke alarms to ionize the air in the smoke detector. When smoke passes into the detector, the change in charge sets off the alarm. Americium ionizes the air by emitting alpha particles. Describe the nuclear change that takes place.
5. Could an atom fill its energy level in this order: 2 in the first energy level, 8 in the second energy level, 10 in the third energy level, for a total of 20 electrons? Why or why not?

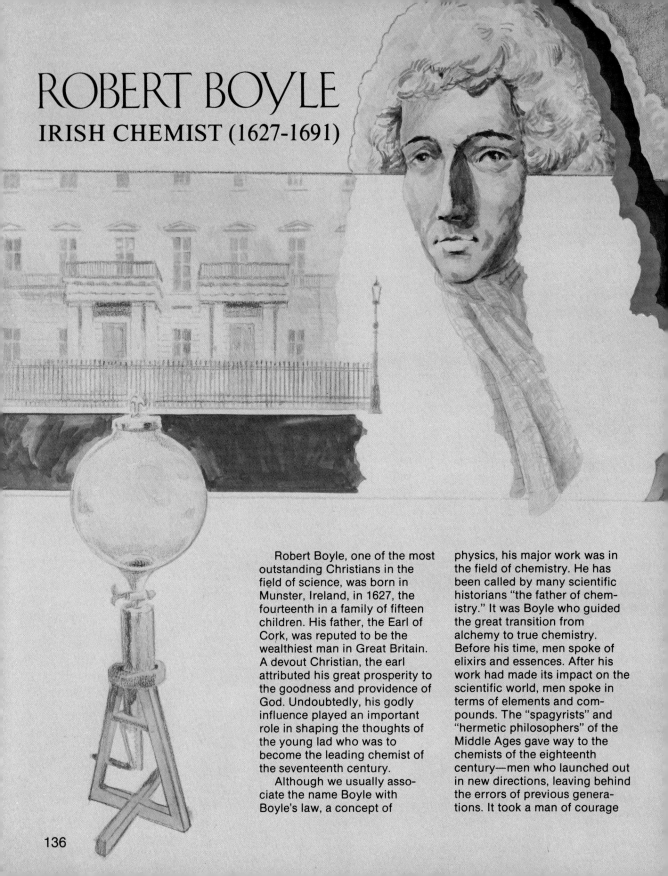

ROBERT BOYLE
IRISH CHEMIST (1627-1691)

Robert Boyle, one of the most outstanding Christians in the field of science, was born in Munster, Ireland, in 1627, the fourteenth in a family of fifteen children. His father, the Earl of Cork, was reputed to be the wealthiest man in Great Britain. A devout Christian, the earl attributed his great prosperity to the goodness and providence of God. Undoubtedly, his godly influence played an important role in shaping the thoughts of the young lad who was to become the leading chemist of the seventeenth century.

Although we usually associate the name Boyle with Boyle's law, a concept of physics, his major work was in the field of chemistry. He has been called by many scientific historians "the father of chemistry." It was Boyle who guided the great transition from alchemy to true chemistry. Before his time, men spoke of elixirs and essences. After his work had made its impact on the scientific world, men spoke in terms of elements and compounds. The "spagyrists" and "hermetic philosophers" of the Middle Ages gave way to the chemists of the eighteenth century—men who launched out in new directions, leaving behind the errors of previous generations. It took a man of courage

THE
SCEPTICAL CHYMIST:
OR
CHYMICO-PHYSICAL
Doubts & Paradoxes,
Touching the
SPAGYRIST'S PRINCIPLES
Commonly call'd
HYPOSTATICAL,
As they are wont to be Propos'd and
Defended by the Generality of
ALCHYMISTS.
Whereunto is premis'd Part of another Discourse
relating to the same Subject.

BY
The Honourable ROBERT BOYLE, Esq;

LONDON,
Printed by J. Cadwell for J. Crooke, and are to be
Sold at the Ship in St. Paul's Church-Yard,
MDCLXI.

to defy the traditions of the alchemists, and Boyle's spiritual make-up afforded him that courage in generous measure.

Robert Boyle studied the Scriptures in their original languages and became familiar with the important theological writings of his day. Converted in his early teens, Boyle dedicated his scientific endeavors to witnessing to God's creation and control of the universe. Boyle wrote on a variety of scientific and religious subjects, and became a powerful force for reproving evil and combatting heresy. His influence continued long after his death. In his will he designated funds for the "Boyle lectures," a series of sermons to be delivered each year. These lectures were to demonstrate that Christianity is intellectually defensible and far more reasonable than the philosophies that oppose it.

Boyle was strictly orthodox in his Christian beliefs. He did his utmost in word and deed to defend the great doctrines of Scripture. He had no patience with preachers who spiritualized or allegorized important portions of the Bible rather than accepting them at face value. Concerning the Lord Jesus Christ, Boyle wrote of "His passion, His death, His resurrection and ascension, and all those wonderful works He did during His stay upon earth, in order to confirm mankind in the belief of His being God as well as man." (L.T. More, *The Life and Works of the Honorable Robert Boyle*, Oxford University Press, 1944, p. 171)

Boyle read the Bible each morning throughout his life in spite of illness, eye trouble, and other difficult circumstances. As a result of his faithfulness and his clear-cut testimony, he was repeatedly offered the highest positions in the Anglican Church. Each time he refused; he believed that his testimony as a layman was a strong, effective ministry of the Christian faith.

During his later years Boyle became intensely interested in world-wide evangelism. A man of considerable means, he supported missionary endeavors in Ireland, Scotland, Wales, India, and North America. In addition, he commissioned translations of the four Gospels and the book of Acts into Turkish, Arabic, and Malayan.

Boyle's greatest burden was for his fellow Irishmen. In spite of great opposition from the Irish clergy, Boyle financed a new Irish translation of the entire Bible, giving the Irish people access to the Word of God. Thousands of these Bibles were distributed throughout the British Isles at Boyle's expense.

When Boyle died in 1691, both the scientific community and the community of believers felt the loss keenly. He had made substantial contributions in both chemistry and physics, and had steadfastly upheld the Faith. Robert Boyle was an outstanding Christian researcher who used his science to exalt the name of the Lord.

FAMILIES OF ATOMS

CHAPTER 7

How would you like to memorize *all* the physical and chemical properties of *every* element? If you were a student taking chemistry in the nineteenth century, you would have to do exactly that. You would need to know what the properties were so that you could predict how the elements would behave, and you would have no way to figure out the properties except by memorizing them. By 1860 scientists had identified a jumble of more than sixty elements, but no one had been able to classify them into a useful order.

Your list of properties would seem endless. There would be some gases, some liquids, and many, many solids. There would be metals and nonmetals, and some elements with characteristics of both. You would have to remember which elements reacted explosively with water, which combined easily with other elements, and which ones refused to react at all. And your task would keep growing, because new elements were being discovered all the time! (We now know of at least 106.) If *only* you had a good way to keep track of them all.

Nineteenth-century scientists knew that they had to find a way to organize the elements. Sorting them into groups of elements that acted alike would make them much easier to study. Finally a Russian scientist named Dmitri Mendeleev (MEN duh LAY ef) succeeded. He organized the elements into a useful chart very much like the **periodic** (PIHR ee AHD ik) **table** we use today. The periodic table has become one of the most useful tools of science. What is a periodic table? How does it help scientists (and students) remember the chemical properties of elements? A good path to understanding the periodic table is understanding how it developed.

7-1 Dmitri Mendeleev produced the first useful periodic table. Although his table did not look like our modern periodic table, it organized the elements in a similar way—by their chemical properties.

The Development of the Periodic Table

A German chemist named Johann Döbereiner (DYOO beh RY nehr) was one of the first to classify elements by their properties. Döbereiner found several small groups of elements with similar properties. Since almost every group contained three elements, he called them *triads*. Unfortunately, not all the known elements fit into Döbereiner's system of triads, and it was not generally accepted by the scientific world.

Classification by Atomic Mass

In 1866 an English chemist named John Newlands proposed another system of classification. He arranged the elements in order of their increasing atomic masses. Newlands pointed out that in most cases every eighth element had similar properties. A musical scale contains seven notes and begins repeating on the eighth note. This interval is called an octave (AHK tiv). Newlands borrowed this term from music to describe his arrangement of the elements. He placed forty-nine of the elements in seven rows of seven each and called his system the *law of octaves*.

7-2 John Newlands organized the elements into octaves similar to the scales on a piano.

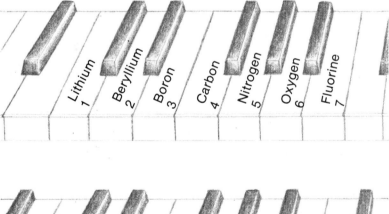

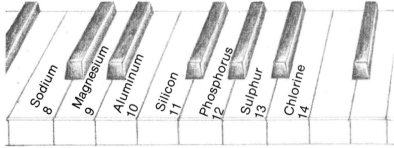

In Newlands's octaves the eighth element had properties similar to the first, the ninth to the second, and so forth. This system worked better than Döbereiner's had, but still not everyone was satisfied.

Just three years after John Newlands proposed his system, Dmitri Mendeleev proposed a similar idea. The Russian chemist also based his classification system on the *atomic masses* of the elements, but he did not believe that the properties of the elements always repeated in every eight elements. He wrote all the elements and their properties on cards and filed them according to their atomic masses. Then he arranged the cards in different ways until he had grouped elements with similar properties in columns, which he then placed next to one another to form rows. Mendeleev placed hydrogen alone in the first row. In the next two rows he placed seven elements, and in the fourth row he placed fourteen elements and three blank spaces.

Mendeleev's table had one important unique feature: blank spaces. As he arranged his cards to group the similar elements, Mendeleev came across elements that did not fit. However, he realized that if he left a blank space and skipped to the next column each time he found a "misfit," all the elements lined up exactly. He predicted that the gaps would be filled by new elements as they were discovered. He even listed their possible chemical and physical properties! Because this arrangement was

7-3 Mendeleev predicted an element he called ekasilicon. The chart below compares Mendeleev's ekasilicon to the germanium discovered by Clemens Winkler in 1866.

Ekasilicon

atomic mass	72 amu
high melting point	
density	5.5 g/cm³
dark gray metal	

Germanium

atomic mass	72.60 amu
melting point	958° C
density	5.5 g/cm³
gray metal	

7-4 This is Mendeleev's early periodic table, which was published in 1872. Notice the blank places in the table. Why did Mendeleev leave these spaces?

TABELLE II

REIHEN	GRUPPE I. — R²O	GRUPPE II. — RO	GRUPPE III. — R²O³	GRUPPE IV. RH⁴ RO²	GRUPPE V. RH³ R²O⁵	GRUPPE VI. RH² RO³	GRUPPE VII. RH R²O⁷	GRUPPE VIII. — RO⁴
1	H=1							
2	Li = 7	Be = 9,4	B = 11	C = 12	N = 14	O = 16	F = 19	
3	Na = 23	Mg = 24	Al = 27,3	Si = 28	P = 31	S = 32	Cl = 35,5	
4	K = 39	Ca = 40	— = 44	Ti = 48	V = 51	Cr = 52	Mn = 55	Fe = 56, Co = 59, Ni = 59, Cu = 63.
5	(Cu = 63)	Zn = 65	— = 68	— = 72	As = 75	Se = 78	Br = 80	
6	Rb = 85	Sr = 87	?Yt = 88	Zr = 90	Nb = 94	Mo = 96	— = 100	Ru = 104, Rh = 104, Pd = 106, Ag = 108.
7	(Ag = 108)	Cd = 112	In = 113	Sn = 118	Sb = 122	Te = 125	J = 127	
8	Cs = 133	Ba = 137	?Di = 138	?Ce = 140	—	—	—	— — —
9	(—)	—	—	—	—	—	—	
10	—	—	?Er = 178	?La = 180	Ta = 182	W = 184	—	Os = 195, Ir = 197, Pt = 198, Au = 199.
11	(Au = 199)	Hg = 200	Tl = 204	Pb = 207	Bi = 208	—	—	
12	—	—	—	Th = 231	—	U = 240	—	— — —

orderly, he thought he could predict these properties from the properties of elements near the "unknowns" on the table.

At first his predictions shocked a skeptical scientific world, but soon investigators began to discover the elements that Mendeleev had foretold. In Mendeleev's chart the elements were arranged by increasing atomic masses. His table clearly showed that the properties of the elements repeat in an orderly pattern. We call his table of the elements a *periodic table* because the properties of the elements repeat in a periodic or recurring pattern, based on their atomic masses. Mendeleev called this principle the *periodic law.*

Classification by atomic number

There was a problem with Mendeleev's table. When the elements were arranged strictly according to their atomic masses, the elements tellurium and iodine seemed to be placed in the wrong columns. However, if their positions were switched, they were placed in columns with elements of similar properties.

Did this inconsistency challenge Mendeleev's system? Did the properties of the elements really vary periodically according to the elements' atomic masses? Could there be a problem with the measurement of their masses? New measurements confirmed the original masses. What caused the switch? Were there exceptions to Mendeleev's periodic law?

Time only added confusion to the issue. Soon scientists discovered several more pairs that seemed to have reversed positions on the periodic table. It was not until 1914 that Henry Moseley (MOZE lee) solved these mysteries. When the elements were arranged according to their *atomic numbers* (the number

7-5 The elements I and Te seemed to fall into the wrong columns when they were arranged strictly according to their atomic masses. But if they were switched, the element I was put in a column with the similar elements F, Cl, Br.

Mass order	
O 15.99	F 18.99
S 32.06	Cl 35.45
Se 78.96	Br 79.90
I 126.90	Te 127.60

Property order	
O 15.99	F 18.99
S 32.06	Cl 35.45
Se 78.96	Br 79.90
Te 127.60	I 126.90

7-6 Henry Moseley was a young man in his twenties when he discovered atomic numbers.

of protons in the nucleus), the order was corrected: iodine followed tellurium and was placed in the appropriate column.

As a result of Moseley's work, the periodic law was revised. It is now based on atomic numbers instead of atomic masses. Today's statement of the **periodic law** is this: *the chemical properties of the elements are periodic functions of their atomic numbers.* When the elements are arranged according to their atomic numbers, the properties of the elements repeat.

Perhaps nowhere else in science is God's purposeful design more evident than in the periodic repetition of the properties of the elements. The scientists of the nineteenth century found a recurring pattern among the elements because it had been placed there by the Creator Himself. The periodic law reflects the orderliness of God.

The authors hope that in your study of science you will see the attributes of God, such as orderliness, in the physical universe. The famous English essayist Francis Bacon wrote that no man "can search too far or be too well studied in the book of God's Word or in the book of God's works." The book of God's Word is, of course, the Bible. In science as well as in all our other studies, His Word must be our base, our underlying guide. The

Atomic number order	
^{8}O	^{9}F
^{16}S	^{17}Cl
^{34}Se	^{35}Br
^{52}Te	^{53}I

7-7 If the elements were arranged by atomic number, they fell into the proper columns.

FACETS
OF BASIC SCIENCE

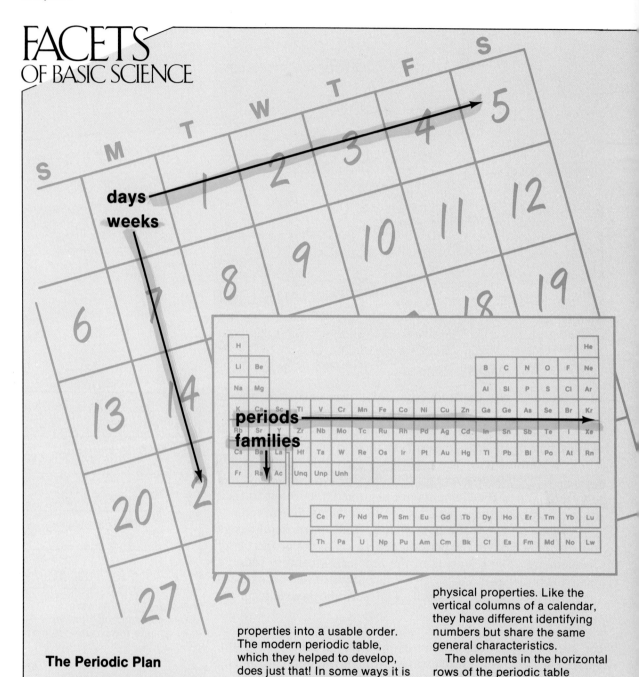

days
weeks

periods
families

The Periodic Plan

Newlands, Mendeleev, and Moseley shared a common goal: to arrange the elements by their properties into a usable order. The modern periodic table, which they helped to develop, does just that! In some ways it is like a calendar. The elements in each vertical column of the chart have similar chemical and physical properties. Like the vertical columns of a calendar, they have different identifying numbers but share the same general characteristics.

The elements in the horizontal rows of the periodic table increase in atomic numbers in the same manner that the days in a week increase in date.

book of God's works is the world which God has made. We hope that you will see in our study of God's creation the physical evidence He has placed there to testify of His might and power.

Relationships in the Periodic Table

The elements of the periodic table are arranged by increasing atomic numbers. The atomic number of an element reveals two important quantities: the number of protons, *and* the number of electrons in an atom. In Chapter 6 we learned that the protons occupy the nucleus and the electrons fill the energy levels. Just as each element has a certain number of protons in its nucleus, each element has its own special **electron configuration** (kun FIG yuh RAY shun) (the number of electrons in each energy level).

Families

Arranging the elements by increasing atomic number also groups the elements by their electron configurations. All of the elements in a vertical column of the periodic table have the same number of *valence electrons*. Because elements with the same number of electrons in their outermost level act very much alike, each column is called a **family** or **group**. Each family on the periodic table is labeled with a special symbol made up of a Roman numeral and a letter. The IA family, for instance, contains six very active elements: lithium, sodium, potassium, rubidium, cesium, and francium. This family is known as the *alkali* (AL kuh lye) *metals*, and each of them has 1 electron in its outer energy level. Why do these elements have similar chemical and physical properties?

Electron configurations determine the properties of elements. The alkali metals (group IA) have similar properties because each of them has a single valence electron. Because this lone electron can be removed easily, these elements are extremely reactive. If you drop a small piece of an alkali metal into water, it will react violently as it forms a compound. In fact, alkali metals are so reactive that if they are not stored in a container of oil (such as kerosene), they will react with oxygen in the air!

Two of the alkali metals, sodium and potassium, are an essential part of our diet. In the body they control the movement of fluids, transmit nerve impulses, and control muscles. Common table salt (sodium chloride) is the main source of sodium in our diets. Important sources of potassium include bananas, grapefruit, oranges, carrots, potatoes, and celery.

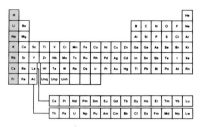

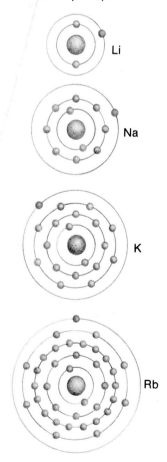

7-8 Each of the elements in a family has the same number of outer-level electrons. The alkali metals (shown on the periodic table above) all have 1 outer-level electron. The first four elements in the family (below) demonstrate the principle.

Li

Na

K

Rb

Elements in Nature

God's creation contains a marvelous blend of utility and beauty. He has displayed many of the elements in very special settings. These photographs will give you a glimpse of several elements as they occur in nature.

a. Two minerals have formed side by side in this crystalline sample from Coahuila, Mexico. The purple crystals are *fluorine*-bearing fluorite. The white crystals are *calcium*-bearing gypsum.

b. Malachite (green) and azurite (blue) are *copper* ores often found together. This sample was found near St. George, Utah.

c. These are pure crystals of the element *sulfur*. Sulfur is found in its pure form much more often than most other elements.

d. The mineral rhodochrosite contains the element *manganese*. This beautiful stone was found at Cape Province, South Africa.

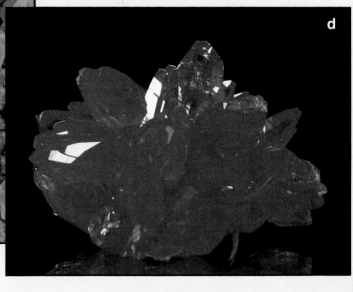

Beryllium, magnesium, calcium, strontium, barium, and radium make up family IIA, the *alkaline-earth metals*. They are close cousins of the IA alkali metals, but they each have 2 valence electrons. This added electron makes them slightly less reactive than the alkali metals, but not stable enough to remain free (uncombined) in nature. Instead, they are found in many common minerals.

Beryllium is used to harden metal alloys. A copper alloy that contains 2 percent beryllium is six times as strong as pure copper. Because it is so light, magnesium is mixed into metals that are used in airplanes. Calcium is also used for structural purposes, in people as well as in building. Teeth, bones, and many modern construction materials (concrete, mortar, plaster, and plasterboard) get their strength from calcium compounds. Calcium is also a vital part of stucco and glass.

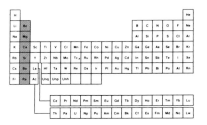

7-9 The alkaline-earth metals (above); the transition metals (below).

Some of the alkaline-earth metals have important medicinal uses. You have probably benefited from milk of magnesia when you needed a mild laxative. This chalky medicine is primarily magnesium hydroxide. When a doctor needs to examine a patient's digestive tract, he orders a series of X rays. The patient drinks a liquid containing barium sulfate. This compound absorbs the X rays and highlights details of the intestines.

Radium compounds are used in the luminescent (glow-in-the-dark) dials of watches and clocks. Strontium compounds give fireworks and flares their brilliant crimson color. This potent chemical can replace its sister element calcium in bones.

The families in the middle of the chart, labeled IB through VIIIB, are sometimes called **subgroups.** They are all clearly from the same clan: they have either 1 or 2 electrons in their outer energy level and have quite similar properties. These strong metals are called the *transition elements.* Very few of these metals are used in their pure form. Pure copper is used in electrical wiring; mercury is used in thermometers and electrical switches; and platinum is used in the pollution control devices on cars. The most common uses of transition metals, however, are metal mixtures called **alloys.** Sterling silver is a mixture of copper and silver; gold in jewelry is a mixture of gold, silver, and copper; and 92 percent of steel is a simple mixture of iron and carbon.

Family IIIA contains such elements as aluminum and boron. These elements have 3 valence electrons. Aluminum is the most abundant metal in the earth's crust. This plentiful element is

7-10 The alloy in this photomicrograph was found in a moon rock. Areas of the different metals that make up the mixture are clearly visible.

7-11 The transition elements have a wide variety of uses. Plated flatware is usually silver electroplated on a copper core.

Galvanized steel is a combination of iron, cobalt, manganese, and zinc. Many new military aircraft have frames made with titanium, an extremely lightweight and strong transition metal.

used for a variety of products, ranging from pots and pans to engine blocks.

Carbon heads the IVA group on the periodic table and gives the family its name; all elements with 4 valence electrons are members of the *carbon family*.

Group VA is headed by nitrogen, the major component of our atmosphere. Air is nearly 79 percent diatomic nitrogen. Both nitrogen and a second member of the VA group, phosphorus, are necessary for plant growth. Both are found in deoxyribonucleic (dee AHK see rye bo noo KLEE ik) acid (DNA), which is the substance of genes.

Group VIA is called the *oxygen family*. Each atom has 6 electrons in its outer energy level. Oxygen is also an element essential for life. Without the oxygen in the atmosphere, most life on earth could not exist. Animals breathe oxygen. The ozone (a triatomic form of oxygen) layer in our atmosphere protects the earth from harmful ultraviolet radiation.

All the elements in the *halogen* (HAL uh jun) *family* (VIIA) have 7 valence electrons. These electrons give the halogens very distinct properties. They are very reactive chemically and exist in their pure form only as diatomic molecules. The atoms of each halogen are larger than the atoms of the one above it in the column, and the physical properties change with the atom's size. As the atomic number of the halogen increases, its color gets darker, and the material becomes denser. Fluorine, the first member of the halogens, is light yellow. Progressing down the family to the larger atoms, we find greenish yellow chlorine, red bromine, and purplish gray iodine. Their physical state also changes with their atomic size. Fluorine and chlorine are gases at room temperature, bromine is a liquid, and iodine is a solid.

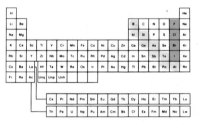

7-12 The halogens.

In strong concentrations halogens are very dangerous. Chlorine was used as a poisonous gas in World War I. In weaker concentrations, however, the halogens can serve us well. Chlorine is dissolved in swimming pools to kill germs in the water. On a larger scale, it is used in city water supplies for the same reason. Before 1900, typhoid fever epidemics raged through cities because of unclean water. Now ½ kg of chlorine in 1,000,000 kg of water kills the harmful microorganisms and keeps city water supplies healthful. Chlorine is not the only halogen that is used to insure good health. Fluorine is added to many community water supplies to help prevent tooth decay. Iodine is an essential nutrient. If it is missing from your diet, a disease known as hypothyroidism could cause the thyroid gland in your neck to

Periodic Table

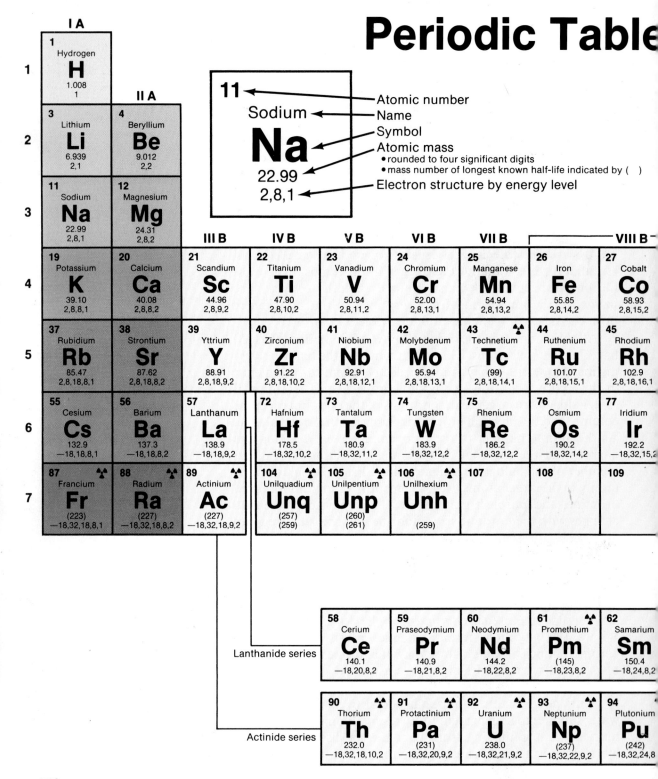

I A

1
Hydrogen
H
1.008
1

Key / Legend:

11 → Atomic number
Sodium → Name
Na → Symbol
22.99 → Atomic mass
 • rounded to four significant digits
 • mass number of longest known half-life indicated by ( )
2,8,1 → Electron structure by energy level

II A

3	4
Lithium	Beryllium
Li	**Be**
6.939	9.012
2,1	2,2

11	12
Sodium	Magnesium
Na	**Mg**
22.99	24.31
2,8,1	2,8,2

	III B	IV B	V B	VI B	VII B	VIII B		
19 Potassium **K** 39.10 2,8,8,1	**20** Calcium **Ca** 40.08 2,8,8,2	**21** Scandium **Sc** 44.96 2,8,9,2	**22** Titanium **Ti** 47.90 2,8,10,2	**23** Vanadium **V** 50.94 2,8,11,2	**24** Chromium **Cr** 52.00 2,8,13,1	**25** Manganese **Mn** 54.94 2,8,13,2	**26** Iron **Fe** 55.85 2,8,14,2	**27** Cobalt **Co** 58.93 2,8,15,2
37 Rubidium **Rb** 85.47 2,8,18,8,1	**38** Strontium **Sr** 87.62 2,8,18,8,2	**39** Yttrium **Y** 88.91 2,8,18,9,2	**40** Zirconium **Zr** 91.22 2,8,18,10,2	**41** Niobium **Nb** 92.91 2,8,18,12,1	**42** Molybdenum **Mo** 95.94 2,8,18,13,1	**43** Technetium **Tc** (99) 2,8,18,14,1	**44** Ruthenium **Ru** 101.07 2,8,18,15,1	**45** Rhodium **Rh** 102.9 2,8,18,16,1
55 Cesium **Cs** 132.9 −18,18,8,1	**56** Barium **Ba** 137.3 −18,18,8,2	**57** Lanthanum **La** 138.9 −18,18,9,2	**72** Hafnium **Hf** 178.5 −18,32,10,2	**73** Tantalum **Ta** 180.9 −18,32,11,2	**74** Tungsten **W** 183.9 −18,32,12,2	**75** Rhenium **Re** 186.2 −18,32,12,2	**76** Osmium **Os** 190.2 −18,32,14,2	**77** Iridium **Ir** 192.2 −18,32,15,2
87 Francium **Fr** (223) −18,32,18,8,1	**88** Radium **Ra** (227) −18,32,18,8,2	**89** Actinium **Ac** (227) −18,32,18,9,2	**104** Unilquadium **Unq** (257) (259)	**105** Unilpentium **Unp** (260) (261)	**106** Unilhexium **Unh** (259)	**107**	**108**	**109**

Lanthanide series

58	59	60	61	62
Cerium	Praseodymium	Neodymium	Promethium	Samarium
Ce	**Pr**	**Nd**	**Pm**	**Sm**
140.1	140.9	144.2	(145)	150.4
−18,20,8,2	−18,21,8,2	−18,22,8,2	−18,23,8,2	−18,24,8,2

Actinide series

90	91	92	93	94
Thorium	Protactinium	Uranium	Neptunium	Plutonium
Th	**Pa**	**U**	**Np**	**Pu**
232.0	(231)	238.0	(237)	(242)
−18,32,18,10,2	−18,32,20,9,2	−18,32,21,9,2	−18,32,22,9,2	−18,32,24,8

of the Elements

| | III A | IV A | V A | VI A | VII A | 2 Helium **He** 4.00 2 |

| 5 Boron **B** 10.81 2,3 | 6 Carbon **C** 12.01 2,4 | 7 Nitrogen **N** 14.01 2,5 | 8 Oxygen **O** 16.00 2,6 | 9 Fluorine **F** 19.00 2,7 | 10 Neon **Ne** 20.18 2,8 |

| 13 Aluminum **Al** 26.98 2,8,3 | 14 Silicon **Si** 28.09 2,8,4 | 15 Phosphorus **P** 30.97 2,8,5 | 16 Sulfur **S** 32.06 2,8,6 | 17 Chlorine **Cl** 35.45 2,8,7 | 18 Argon **Ar** 39.95 2,8,8 |

I B	II B

| 28 Nickel **Ni** 58.71 2,8,16,2 | 29 Copper **Cu** 63.54 2,8,18,1 | 30 Zinc **Zn** 65.37 2,8,18,2 | 31 Gallium **Ga** 69.72 2,8,18,3 | 32 Germanium **Ge** 72.59 2,8,18,4 | 33 Arsenic **As** 74.92 2,8,18,5 | 34 Selenium **Se** 78.96 2,8,18,6 | 35 Bromine **Br** 79.91 2,8,18,7 | 36 Krypton **Kr** 83.80 2,8,18,8 |

| 46 Palladium **Pd** 106.4 2,8,18,18 | 47 Silver **Ag** 107.9 2,8,18,18,1 | 48 Cadmium **Cd** 112.4 2,8,18,18,2 | 49 Indium **In** 114.8 2,8,18,18,3 | 50 Tin **Sn** 118.7 2,8,18,18,4 | 51 Antimony **Sb** 121.8 2,8,18,18,5 | 52 Tellurium **Te** 127.6 2,8,18,18,6 | 53 Iodine **I** 126.9 2,8,18,18,7 | 54 Xenon **Xe** 131.3 2,8,18,18,8 |

| 78 Platinum **Pt** 195.1 −18,32,17,1 | 79 Gold **Au** 197.0 −18,32,18,1 | 80 Mercury **Hg** 200.6 −18,32,18,2 | 81 Thallium **Tl** 204.4 −18,32,18,3 | 82 Lead **Pb** 207.2 −18,32,18,4 | 83 Bismuth **Bi** 209.0 −18,32,18,5 | 84 Polonium **Po** (210) −18,32,18,6 | 85 Astatine **At** (210) −18,32,18,7 | 86 Radon **Rn** (222) −18,32,18,8 |

line of metalloids

Key:

	Active metals			Metalloids
	Alkali			Nonmetals
	Alkaline-earth			Halogens (also nonmetals)
	Transition elements			Noble gases
	Post-transition metals	☢	Radioactive isotopes

| 63 Europium **Eu** 152.0 −18,25,8,2 | 64 Gadolinium **Gd** 157.3 −18,25,9,2 | 65 Terbium **Tb** 158.9 −18,27,8,2 | 66 Dysprosium **Dy** 162.5 −18,28,8,2 | 67 Holmium **Ho** 164.9 −18,29,8,2 | 68 Erbium **Er** 167.3 −18,30,8,2 | 69 Thulium **Tm** 168.9 −18,31,8,2 | 70 Ytterbium **Yb** 173.0 −18,32,8,2 | 71 Lutetium **Lu** 175.0 −18,32,9,2 |

| 95 Americium **Am** (243) −18,32,25,8,2 | 96 Curium **Cm** (245) −18,32,25,9,2 | 97 Berkelium **Bk** (249) −18,32,26,9,2 | 98 Californium **Cf** (250) −18,32,28,8,2 | 99 Einsteinium **Es** (254) −18,32,29,8,2 | 100 Fermium **Fm** (252) −18,32,30,8,2 | 101 Mendelevium **Md** (256) −18,32,31,8,2 | 102 Nobelium **No** (254) −18,32,32,8,2 | 103 Lawrencium **Lr** (257) −18,32,32,9,2 |

Table 7-13

Sources of Halogens	
Halogen	**Source**
Fluorine	The minerals fluorspar (CaF_2) and cryolite (Na_3AlF_6)
Chlorine	Seawater and underground salt beds
Bromine	Seawater
Iodine	Sodium iodide in seaweeds
Astatine	A radioactive decay product of francium-87

swell, forming a goiter. Years ago researchers wondered why people who lived near the sea never had goiters. Eventually their good health was traced to their diets. People who lived in coastal villages often ate saltwater fish that contained large amounts of iodine. Now 1 to 2 percent of potassium iodide is commonly added to table salt to prevent goiters.

The final family of the periodic table has 8 valence electrons. The filled outermost energy levels of these elements make them very unreactive and allow them to exist as pure substances. In fact, they combine with other elements only when forced to do so under high temperature and extreme pressure. This "aristocratic" behavior gives them their family name. Helium, neon, argon, krypton, xenon, and radon are called the *noble gases.* All of these gases are present in the air we breathe, but only in very small amounts. Argon, making up 1 percent of the atmosphere, is the most abundant. Although helium is the second most abundant element in the universe (it makes up a large part of stars), there is very little of it on earth. Some helium is found in the air, but the main source of this extremely light element is natural gas, which is 1 to 2 percent helium. The other noble gases are extremely hard to find.

Although they behave royally, the noble gases do perform some important tasks. In fact, it is their inert (unreactive) qualities that make them useful. When dirigibles (lighter-than-air craft) were first made, hydrogen gas was used to give them lift. The hydrogen gas was very light, but it also burned very easily. The slightest spark could transform the whole dirigible into a

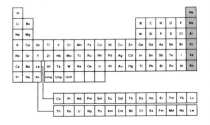

7-14 The noble gases.

seething mass of flames. Helium gas solved this problem. It is also much lighter than air, and it eliminated the chance of fire. Because it is a noble gas, it does not burn. Helium is still used today in airships called blimps.

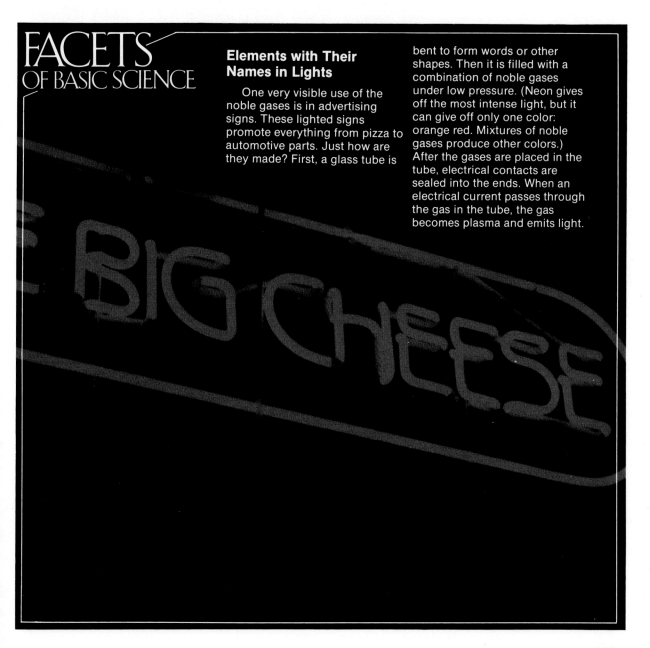

FACETS
OF BASIC SCIENCE

Elements with Their Names in Lights

One very visible use of the noble gases is in advertising signs. These lighted signs promote everything from pizza to automotive parts. Just how are they made? First, a glass tube is bent to form words or other shapes. Then it is filled with a combination of noble gases under low pressure. (Neon gives off the most intense light, but it can give off only one color: orange red. Mixtures of noble gases produce other colors.) After the gases are placed in the tube, electrical contacts are sealed into the ends. When an electrical current passes through the gas in the tube, the gas becomes plasma and emits light.

FACETS
OF BASIC SCIENCE

Hydrogen, the Orphan Element

With 1 proton and 1 electron, hydrogen bears no family resemblance to any group on the periodic table. It is often grouped with the alkali metals, but this clear, odorless gas is anything but metallic. Since the first energy level needs only 2 electrons to be filled, hydrogen needs to gain only 1 electron to be satisfied. This would seem to place it as a distant relative of the halogens, which precede the noble gases on the periodic table.

Hydrogen is the most abundant element in the universe. Astronomers have estimated that 90 percent of all atoms in existence are hydrogen atoms. Yet here on earth hydrogen ranks only tenth in order of abundance and makes up less than $1/1,000,000$ of the volume of our atmosphere.

Periods

The horizontal rows of the periodic table are called **periods,** or **series.** The elements in a period do not have similar properties. They are arranged so that there is a *progression* of properties across each row. On the left side of the periodic table, the elements are metals. As you read across the table, you will notice that the elements are less and less metallic. The elements on the far right side of the table are classified as nonmetals. The electron configurations of the elements in a period show why they progress this way. As you read across a period from left to right, the number of electrons in the outer level increases from 1 to 8.

The number of valence electrons is a major factor in determining the chemical properties as well as many of the physical properties of an element. As the number of outer-level electrons increases, the properties of the elements change from metallic to nonmetallic. When the outer level of an element contains 8 electrons, it is filled. (Helium is the exception; its outer level is completed with only 2 electrons.) Since the outer level is the last one to fill completely, no more electrons can be added to the atom without starting to fill another level. This marks the end of the period. The number of the period is the same as the total number of energy levels being used for electrons. The next electron is added to a higher energy level, and that element starts a new period.

The fourth period on the table begins with potassium. Argon, the element immediately before potassium, has 8 valence electrons in the third energy level. It ends the third period. Therefore potassium adds its last electron to the fourth energy level. With 1 electron in the fourth energy level, potassium is the first member of the fourth series on the periodic table.

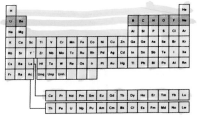

7-15 The second period of the periodic table begins with the element lithium. Each succeeding element in the period has one more valence electron.

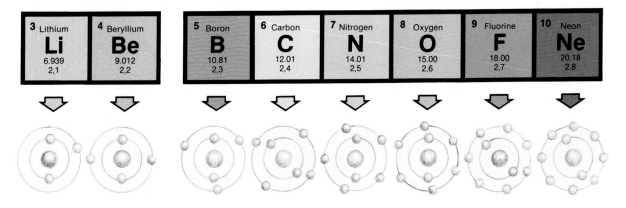

Trends in the Periodic Table

A quick glance at the periodic table tells you that most of the elements are metals, some are labeled nonmetals, and a very few have the distinction of being metalloids (MET ul OYDZ). There seems to be a clear difference among these three classes of elements. Metals are on the left side of the table, nonmetals are on the right side of the table, and the metalloids are neatly in the middle. There also seems to be a clear trend from metals to nonmetals as you cross the periodic table. What causes this trend? What makes metals metallic, nonmetals nonmetallic, and metalloids not quite either?

Metals

Almost three-fourths of the elements are **metals.** We use metals in our cars, bridges, ships, planes, cooking utensils, and home appliances. Our modern way of life depends on metals. Most metals we use are hard, strong, and heavy. And because these metals are most familiar, many people think that all metals have these qualities. Yet many pure metals are so soft that they can be cut with a knife! Some are very weak; some are lightweight. In fact, most metals do not have physical properties anything like the familiar metals that we use every day.

7-16 Alkali metals such as sodium are so soft that they can be cut with a knife.

FACETS
OF BASIC SCIENCE

Manganese—The Metal That Isn't

Manganese, located in the middle of the transition elements, is a very important exception to the general description of metals.

Chemically, manganese is a metal because it has electrons which are easily removed in its outermost energy level. But in its stable form it is a gray-white, brittle substance that is too weak to be used in engineering. Not ductile, not malleable, and without luster, it seems to be an outcast among the transition elements.

Manganese behaves like the other transition elements only when it is alloyed with other metals. Then it adds strength and flexibility. In fact, there are approximately 33 kg of manganese in every metric ton of special structural steel.

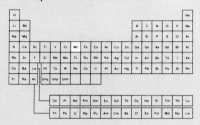

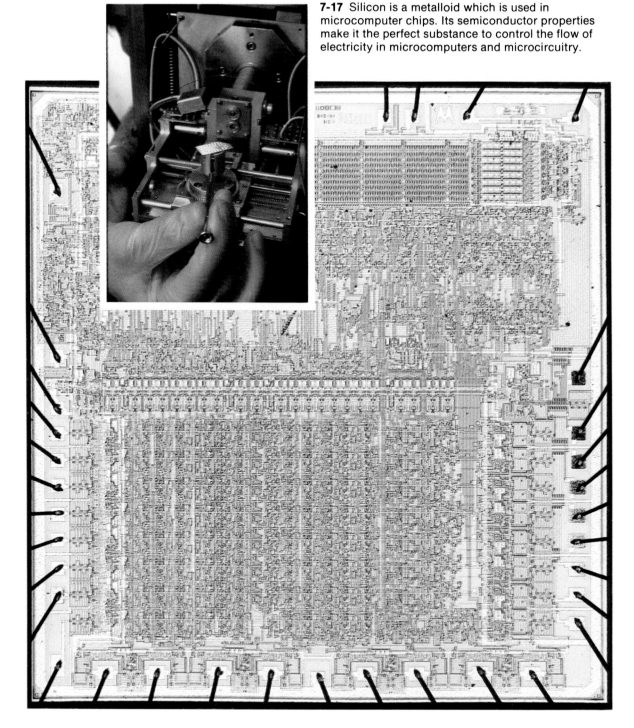

7-17 Silicon is a metalloid which is used in microcomputer chips. Its semiconductor properties make it the perfect substance to control the flow of electricity in microcomputers and microcircuitry.

Then how can we identify metals? They have common properties that give us clues to their identity.

Table 7-18

Common Characteristics of Metals
1. Most metals have a silvery metallic luster if their surfaces are clean.
2. Most metals are solids at room temperature; only mercury (Hg) is a liquid.
3. Most metals are malleable (can be rolled or hammered into shape).
4. Most metals are ductile (can be drawn into wire).
5. Most metals are good conductors of electricity and heat.
6. Metals tend to be reactive; they give up electrons in chemical reactions.

All of these properties are related to where metals belong on the periodic table. Metals belong to families with relatively few electrons in their outer energy level. They do not hold these valence electrons very strongly and can easily give them up. That is why most metals have similar chemical and physical properties. If it were not for these "loose" electrons, metals would not have a silvery **metallic lustre,** be **malleable** (MAL ee uh bul) and **ductile** (DUK til), or conduct electricity.

Metalloids

Across the periodic table from left to right, the properties of the elements become less and less metallic. On the right-hand side of the periodic table, a heavy line divides the metals from the nonmetals. On either side of this line are some elements that have both metallic and nonmetallic properties. These elements are called **metalloids.**

Having properties halfway between metals and nonmetals makes these elements especially useful. Metalloids do not conduct electricity as well as metals, but since they do conduct some, they are called *semiconductors* (SEM ee kun DUK turz). Scientists have learned to use this limited conducting ability to control the amount of electricity that flows through delicate electronic instruments. Without semiconductors, we would not have electronic watches, pocket calculators, or microcomputers.

7-19 Metals have either 1 or 2 valence electrons. These configurations represent sodium, magnesium, titanium, and copper. Can you match the element to its configuration?

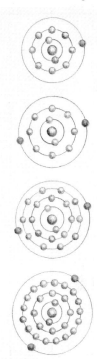

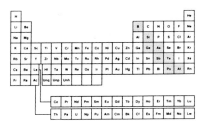

7-20 The metalloids.

FACETS
OF BASIC SCIENCE

Adding to the Periodic Table

In 1939 the periodic table showed only ninety-two elements. Uranium was the most complex element that could be found on the face of the earth, and it held the highest position on the table. No matter how carefully scientists analyzed mineral ores, they could not find any atoms that had more than 92 protons. Had they discovered the limit, or were higher elements possible? They thought that new elements might still be added— and the study of nuclear reactions would be the key.

Scientists knew that neutrons could break up to form a proton and an electron, or beta particle. When this happened, the proton stayed in the nucleus and the electron was emitted. An extra proton in the nucleus would give the atom a higher atomic number and make it a higher element. What would happen if a neutron in a uranium atom split into a proton and an electron (a process called beta decay)? The new proton would raise the atomic number to 93. It might be possible to make an entirely new element this way!

The idea of forming new elements fascinated scientists. But to make uranium emit a beta particle, they had to find a way to upset its nucleus. They could do that by adding extra neutrons

to the nucleus. In 1940 scientists bombarded a uranium sample with neutrons and then painstakingly analyzed the resulting atoms. They found a new element! It had an atomic number of 93, and they named it "neptunium." Only a tiny number of neptunium atoms had been made, but they were a start. The next year, using the same technique, scientists were able to produce an even higher element, plutonium (atomic number 94).

After the first two **transuranium** (TRANZ yoo RAY nee um) ("beyond uranium") **elements** had been made, projectiles bigger than neutrons had to be used. In 1944 helium ions were fired at uranium: americium resulted. When helium ions were aimed at samples of the new transuranium elements, even higher elements were made— curium (1944), berkelium (1949), and californium (1949).

Several years later, groups of

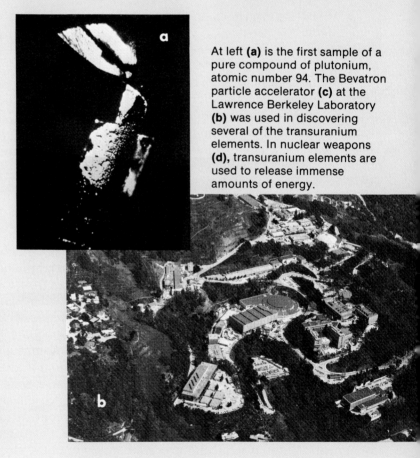

At left **(a)** is the first sample of a pure compound of plutonium, atomic number 94. The Bevatron particle accelerator **(c)** at the Lawrence Berkeley Laboratory **(b)** was used in discovering several of the transuranium elements. In nuclear weapons **(d)**, transuranium elements are used to release immense amounts of energy.

scientists from the University of California at Berkeley and Argonne National Laboratories published sketchy reports about two even new elements. At the end of all the reports, appended notes said that not all the data about the newer elements could be printed. Why had some information been held back? What were the new elements like? How had they been made? All these questions remained unanswered for a full two years.

In 1954 the reason for all the secrecy became obvious. The new elements had been formed inside the fireball of an experimental hydrogen bomb that was exploded in 1952. Until the secrecy that shrouded the test was lifted, only the barest details could be given to the public. It turned out that when tremendous streams of neutrons hit uranium during the explosion, 7 to 8 protons were added to the nucleus. The two elements were named "einsteinium" and "fermium" to honor two great physicists, Albert Einstein and Enrico Fermi.

The quest for new elements is still continuing. Mendelevium, nobelium, and lawrencium have been produced by smashing carbon and boron into einsteinium, curium, and californium. These higher elements are expensive because the small amounts that can be produced decay quickly. One experimental bombardment produced only 17 atoms of mendelevium!

Nonmetals

Hydrogen and the elements on the right side of the periodic table are called **nonmetals.** There are only seventeen of them. These elements hold their electrons tightly, and so their properties are very different from those of the metallic elements. Compare their physical properties with those of the metals.

Table 7-21

Common Characteristics of Nonmetals
1. Nonmetals do not have a silvery luster. They exist in a variety of colors. Sulfur is yellow, bromine is reddish brown, iodine is purple, and carbon is black.
2. Nonmetals exist as solids, liquids, and gases at room temperature, but the gaseous state is the most common. (Eleven of the nonmetals are gases at room temperature.)
3. Solid nonmetals exist as brittle crystals that shatter easily.
4. Nonmetals conduct heat and electricity poorly.
5. The noble gases are nearly chemically inert—they usually do not react.
6. Nonmetals tend to gain or share electrons in chemical reactions.

The periodic table is just a small glimpse of the order that God established to maintain His creation. As we study more about these elements and their combinations, we should remember to praise the Creator for His design. God put the elements with the right properties in the right places in just the right proportions. For instance, God placed the perfect amount of the nonmetal oxygen in the atmosphere to maintain life. If there were less oxygen in the air, less oxygen would be dissolved in the water, and marine life could not survive. Think what would happen to the fish if you turned off the air pump in a large aquarium! A shortage of oxygen would also harm *you.* Your lungs would be forced to work harder, and if you made any physical effort, you would soon be gasping for air! All of the things that burn would be affected, for burning is the chemical combining of a substance with oxygen. In short, life would be very hard and probably very brief.

If there were *more* oxygen in the air, life would be very risky. The added oxygen would make fires blaze out of control. But neither of these situations exists. God has put the perfect amount of oxygen in the air and mixed it with stable nitrogen. The unreactive nitrogen in our atmosphere balances oxygen's strong tendency to combine with other substances.

No other planet that man has observed has such an atmosphere. In accordance with His plan, God created an ideal place for man to live.

Scientifically Speaking

periodic table	series
periodic law	metals
electron configuration	metallic luster
family	malleable
group	ductile
subgroups	metalloids
alloys	nonmetals
periods	transuranium elements

Questions to Talk Over

1. How was Mendeleev able to predict the discovery of new elements?
2. What role does the electron configuration of an element play in determining the element's position on the periodic table?
3. Suppose you discovered a new element that you decided to name sciencium. If sciencium were very reactive—so reactive that you had to store samples of it under oil to prevent it from reacting with the air—and it easily gave up one electron in a chemical reaction, in what family would you place it?
4. Compare and contrast the properties of metals, metalloids, and non-metals.
5. The periodic table is one of man's perceptions of God's order. Why are there exceptions in the order of the periodic table?

FORCES BETWEEN ATOMS

CHAPTER 8

Could any two substances be more different than your skin and a diamond? But both of these substances are mainly carbon. In skin the carbon atoms are linked together with nitrogen in long, flexible chains called proteins. Other elements such as hydrogen and oxygen are attached at various places along the protein molecule. Diamonds are also carbon-based structures. In a diamond the carbon atoms are held together by a complex interlocking framework of extremely strong connections. The pure stone contains carbon atoms only.

What makes these carbon-based substances so radically different? The answer lies in the way their atoms are joined together: their **chemical bonds.** The same substance can bond in different ways. Carbon atoms can link together using one type of bonding to form long, flexible chains. Using similar bonds, the carbon atoms can hold hydrogen, oxygen, and nitrogen atoms to give the complete molecule the special qualities of skin. But the same carbon atoms can bond to one another in a network linkage that makes a diamond one of the hardest substances known. This type of bond excludes other substances, making the diamond crystal pure carbon. Any other elements that slip into the crystal are called impurities and do not join the carbon network.

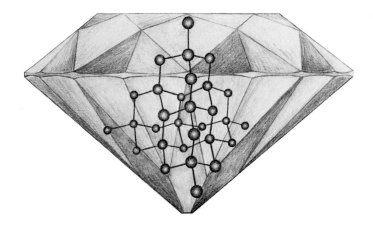

8-1 The interlocking network of carbon atoms in diamonds makes them extremely hard and clear.

What is true of carbon is true of most of the elements. Aluminum can bond to chlorine to make a white, water-absorbing crystal that is the active ingredient in many deodorants (aluminum chlorohydrate). It can also bond with magnesium to form magnalium, a lightweight alloy used in aircraft.

One thing seems clear. When one element joins with another element, their chemical union determines the special characteristics of the resulting compound. Therefore, scientists are very interested in how substances bond. Their studies have led them to conclude that chemical bonds involve mainly the *valence electrons*—those in the outer energy level. The need atoms have for increased stability causes them to bond together. To be stable, they must have a full octet (8 electrons) in their valence level. How does the atom with fewer than 8 fill its valence level? By bonding with other atoms. Compounds are formed when groups of atoms cooperate to fill each other's electron needs.

Atoms use several strategies to get the electrons they want. When certain elements bond together, some atoms forcibly remove electrons from other atoms. The atoms that lose their electrons are content with the full level beneath their lost electrons. In other bonding situations, different atoms share electrons so that they are all satisfied. No matter which method is used, the ultimate goal of bonding is the same. All atoms desire a stable octet of electrons in their valence shell.

Ionic Bonding

Sodium is a soft, silvery metal that reacts explosively with water. Fluorine is a pale, greenish yellow gas that is extremely corrosive. Both are very poisonous and should never be taken internally. Yet when atoms of fluorine and sodium bond, they form a white crystalline compound that is used in toothpaste to prevent cavities. Why do sodium and fluorine change when they bond?

8-2 Toothpaste contains sodium and fluorine, but not as pure elements. They are bonded to form sodium fluoride, a safe and effective cavity preventer.

Sodium and fluorine are bonded together ionically. An **ionic** (eye AHN ik) **bond** forms when 1 or more electrons are transferred from one atom to another. If an atom gains or loses electrons, it is no longer electrically neutral, because the number of electrons is not equal to the number of protons. What do we call such a particle? (See p. 134.) If an atom gains electrons, it will have more electrons than protons. With more negative charges than positive charges, the atom will be negatively charged. A negative ion is called an **anion** (AN EYE un). If an atom loses electrons, it will have more protons than electrons. With more positive charges than negative charges, that atom would be positively charged. A positive ion is called a **cation** (KAT EYE un). Ionic bonds form as a result of the attraction between these two oppositely charged types of particles.

FACETS
OF BASIC SCIENCE

To Share or Not to Share: The Electronegative Question

The strategy that an atom uses to fill its outer level depends on how strongly it holds electrons. This strength is measured as **electronegativity** (ih LEK tro NEG uh TIV uh tee). Electronegativity is a periodic function of the atoms. Atoms that have nearly-filled valence levels tend to have high electronegativities. Those whose outer levels are nearly empty have very low electronegativities.

When atoms of equal electronegativities bond, neither one has the strength to pull electrons from the other, so they must share. When atoms of high electronegativity bond with atoms of low electronegativity, they can easily remove the electrons they need.

Alkali metals
have only 1 valence electron and readily give it up. They have very low electronegativities.

The noble gases
have 8 valence electrons. Therefore, they are balanced and neither give up nor accept electrons.

The alkaline earths
have 2 outer shell electrons. They are stronger than alkali metals but also have low electronegativity.

Halogens
have 7 outer shell electrons and are strong enough to take 1 more. They have very high electronegativities.

The carbon family members
are neither strong nor weak. Possessing 4 valence electrons, they give them up because of moderate electronegativity.

H																	He
Li	Be											B	C	N	O	F	Ne
Na	Mg											Al	Si	P	S	Cl	Ar
K	Ca	Sc	Ti	V	Cr	Mn						Zn	Ga	Ge	As	Se	Br	Kr
Rb	Sr	Y	Zr					Pd	Ag	Cd	In	Sn	Sb	Te	I	Xe
Cs	Ba				Re	Os	Ir	Pt	Au	Hg	Tl	Pb	Bi	Po	At	Rn
Fr	Ra	Ac	Unq	Unp	Unh											

Electronegativity increases in this direction.

Ce	Pr	Nd	Pm	Sm	Eu	Gd	Tb	Dy	Ho	Er	Tm	Yb	Lu
Th	Pa	U	Np	Pu	Am	Cm	Bk	Cf	Es	Fm	Md	No	Lw

167

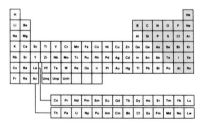

8-3 Ionic bonding occurs when highly electronegative nonmetals take electrons from weakly electronegative metals. Sodium fluoride is a prime example.

Electron transfers in ionic bonds

For electrons to be transferred from one atom to another, they must be pulled. The electronegativities of the atoms help to determine which ones pull and which ones get pulled. *Highly* electronegative nonmetals, such as fluorine, can pull electrons away from *weakly* electronegative elements, such as sodium. For that reason, when highly electronegative nonmetals in the sixth and seventh groups come near weakly electronegative metals in the first or second groups, we can expect electrons to be transferred and ionic bonds to form.

With 7 valence electrons, the outer energy level of the non-metal fluorine is almost full. Consequently, it has a very strong pull for 1 more electron. The metal sodium has only 1 loosely held valence electron. It is easy prey for the very electronegative fluorine.

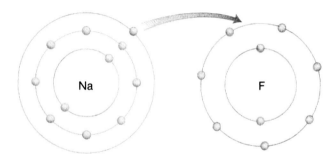

Before: 11 protons, 11 electrons
After: 11 protons, 10 electrons
Sodium becomes a cation.

Before: 9 protons, 9 electrons
After: 9 protons, 10 electrons
Fluorine becomes an anion.

After fluorine takes the electron from sodium, its outer level is full. What happens to the sodium atom? Now it too has a full outer level. After the lone electron in the third level is taken, the 8 electrons in the second level serve as a complete octet. Both atoms are satisfied, and the compound sodium fluoride is formed.

What force holds the compound together? When sodium loses its valence electron, it becomes a cation. Only 10 electrons (11-1) offset 11 protons. When the fluoride atom receives the electron, it also becomes electrically unbalanced. A -1 charge results when 10 electrons (9 + 1) oppose only 9 protons. This is how a sodium ion is bonded to a fluoride ion. The +1 charge on the sodium ion attracts the fluoride ion's -1 charge. This ionic attraction forms a very strong bond.

Illustrating electron transfer

In the first example, Bohr models of the atoms were used to show ionic bonding. Since sketching all the electrons in each atom takes a long time, scientists have developed a shortcut. They illustrate the bonding process much more quickly by showing only the valence electrons. Since the other electrons do not actively participate in bonding, they can be left out. These shortcut representations, called **electron dot notation,** use the element's symbol and a series of dots that stand for valence electrons.

The valence electrons of an element are revealed by its position on the periodic chart. All elements in group IA have only 1 electron in their highest energy level. In electron dot notation, they have one dot beside their symbol. All halogens (group VIIA) have 7 valence electrons. Their symbols are surrounded by seven dots. Look at the electron dot structures for the elements of the third period. Note the placement of the dots for each element.

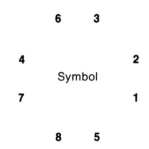

8-4 This is the commonly accepted pattern for placing electrons in electron dot notation. This is not a fixed order. Sometimes the placement of the dots will change to illustrate bonding. The most important thing to note about this representation is that the first two electrons are always paired.

Group	IA	IIA	IIIA	IVA	VA	VIA	VIIA	VIIIA
Valence Electrons	1	2	3	4	5	6	7	8
Bohr model								
Electron dot Structures	Na	Mg	Al	Si	P	S	Cl	Ar

This pattern of filling applies to all elements. Any element with 5 valence electrons receives dots in the same places as phosphorus: two on the right, one on the top, one on the bottom, and one on the left. Any element with 3 valence electrons has a dot structure similar to aluminum's. Now we are ready to write the electron dot structures of sodium and fluorine.

In electron dot notation, the reaction between sodium and fluorine is written this way:

Na $\cdot$:F: $\longrightarrow$ Na $\cdot$:F: $\longrightarrow$ Na$^+$ $\longleftrightarrow$:F:$^-$

| Electron dot structures of atoms | Electron transfer | Electron dot structures of the ions |

It is important to show the charges on the ions. The *kind* (positive or negative) and the *number* of charges on an ion determine which other ions it will react with.

Multiple electron transfers

Sodium fluoride involves one of the simplest electron transfers: a single electron is transferred from a sodium atom to a fluorine atom. Some bonds involve the transfer of 2 or 3 electrons. When magnesium bonds with sulfur, 2 electrons are transferred. Sulfur has 6 valence electrons; it needs 2 more to complete its octet. Magnesium has 2 valence electrons. Its weak electronegativity allows sulfur to take those 2 electrons. Both ions wind up with full octets in their outer level.

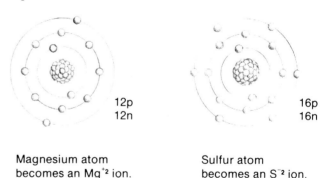

12p
12n

16p
16n

Magnesium atom
becomes an Mg^{+2} ion.

Sulfur atom
becomes an S^{-2} ion.

The electron dot notation of the transfer would look like this:

Mg: $+$ $\cdot$ S: $\longrightarrow$ Mg $+$ S: $\longrightarrow$ Mg^{+2} :S:$^{-2}$

| Electron dot structures of the atoms | Two electrons are transferred. | Electron dot structures of the ions |

Magnesium loses 2 electrons and has a +2 charge. Sulfur gains 2 electrons and has a -2 charge. The 2 ions are held together by their opposite charges.

Ionic bonds can include more than 2 ions. In magnesium fluoride, 2 fluorine atoms meet their need for electrons by each taking 1 electron from a magnesium atom's highest level.

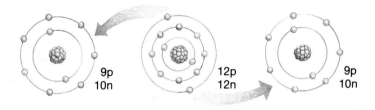

| Fluorine atom becomes a -1 ion. | Magnesium atom becomes a +2 ion. | Fluorine atom becomes a -1 ion. |

The electron dot notation would look like this:

$$Mg \overset{\cdot\cdot}{} + \overset{\cdot\cdot}{\underset{\cdot\cdot}{:F:}} + \overset{\cdot\cdot}{\underset{\cdot\cdot}{:F:}} \longrightarrow Mg \overset{\cdot\cdot}{}^{+} \overset{\cdot\cdot}{\underset{\cdot\cdot}{:F:}} + \overset{\cdot\cdot}{\underset{\cdot\cdot}{:F:}} \longrightarrow Mg^{+2} \overset{\cdot\cdot}{\underset{\cdot\cdot}{:F:}}^{-1} \overset{\cdot\cdot}{\underset{\cdot\cdot}{:F:}}^{-1}$$

For every +2 magnesium ion, there are two -1 fluoride ions. In every ionic bond, the total charges on the anions must be equal to the charges in the cations.

Two metal atoms can yield electrons to a single nonmetal atom. In sodium sulfide, sulfur acquires the 2 electrons it needs from 2 sodium atoms. Each sodium atom donates 1 electron.

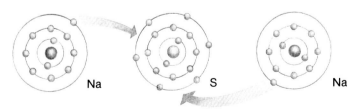

| Sodium atom becomes a +1 ion. | Sulfur atom becomes a -2 ion. | Sodium atom becomes a +1 ion. |

You would write the electron dot representation this way:

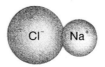

In every case of ionic bonding, highly electronegative non-metals pull electrons away from weakly electronegative metals. Ionic bonding will occur anytime a nonmetal has enough attraction to pull away a metal's electron. Two atoms with similar electronegativities cannot bond ionically, because neither can pull electrons away from the other. Therefore, ionic bonding unites elements from *opposite ends* of the periodic chart.

Structure and properties of ionic compounds

Ionic compounds are formed from vast numbers of ions. In the case of the ionic compound sodium chloride, the sodium atom donated an electron to the chlorine atom. The resulting sodium and chloride ions then attracted each other to form an ionic bond:

This basic unit could join with another unit to form

or three units can form

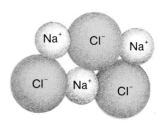

and so on, until an alternating pattern of positive and negative ions is formed. Such a structure is a **crystal lattice** (LAT iss). Most ionic solids exist as crystal lattices of anions and cations.

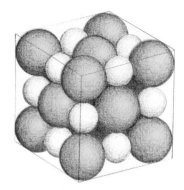

8-5 Sodium chloride lattice.

Since each individual ion in the lattice is bonded to all of its oppositely charged neighbors, the particles of an ionic solid are held strongly in place. This explains the high melting points of ionic compounds. Sodium chloride melts at 801° C; sodium flouride, at 988° C. This structure also explains why we do not call ionic units molecules. Since each ion is bonded to all the ions around it, there is no reason to pick out 1 sodium ion and 1 chlorine ion from their crystal lattice and call them a molecule. As a result, most chemists prefer to use the term **formula unit** to express the basic repeating units of an ionic solid. What is the formula unit of the ionic solid below?

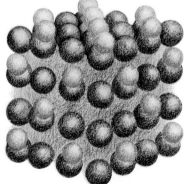

8-6 Calcium chloride lattice.

Most ionic compounds, like table salt, dissolve in water. When an ionic solid is melted or dissolved, it is an excellent conductor of electricity. As a solid, however, it cannot conduct, because the electrons and ions are held in place by the firm grip of the ionic bond.

Covalent Bonding

Suppose 2 atoms with similar electronegativities attempt to react. Both have fewer than 8 valence electrons, and both need to fill their outer levels; but since their pulls are evenly matched, neither one can remove an electron from the other. Ionic bonding is impossible. The only way for both atoms to get a full octet is by sharing valence electrons. A bond that involves sharing electrons is called a **covalent** (ko VAY lunt) **bond.**

Diatomic molecules

Table 8-7
Diatomic Nonmetals

Hydrogen	H_2
Oxygen	O_2
Nitrogen	N_2
Fluorine	F_2
Chlorine	Cl_2
Bromine	Br_2
Iodine	I_2

What combinations of elements put atoms with similar electronegativities together? Obviously, 2 atoms of the same element have identical strengths; they must use covalent bonding. Many gases and vapors exist as **diatomic molecules:** two identical atoms are bonded together. Seven nonmetals form diatomic molecules.

As an example of how 2 atoms bond covalently, visualize how 2 chlorine atoms combine. Both atoms have 7 valence electrons. Each needs 1 more to complete its octet.

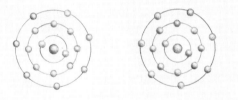

Even if 1 atom could pull an electron from the other, a bond would not form. While 1 atom would have an octet, the atom that lost the electron would have only 6 valence electrons; it still would not have a stable octet. The solution to this apparent dilemma is *sharing*. By contributing 1 electron apiece to form a shared pair, both atoms can have the use of 8 valence electrons. The electron pair spends most of its time between the two nuclei, so both atoms have partial use of a full octet. Now both atoms have attained chemical stability.

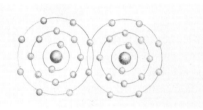

FACETS
OF BASIC SCIENCE

Sayings of Salt

Matthew 5:13 says, "Ye are the salt of the earth: but if the salt have lost his savour, wherewith shall it be salted? it is thenceforth good for nothing, but to be cast out, and to be trodden under foot of men."

Language scholars tell us that the old word *savour* is the same as the word *flavor* in modern English. If this is true, then how can salt lose its flavor?

Salt is sodium chloride. It is made up of a sodium cation ionically bonded to a chloride anion. Scientists believe that the sodium ion gives salt its special flavor.

In biblical times sodium chloride was collected from deserts where sea water had evaporated and left salt deposits. These deposits were not very pure. The salt was mixed with sand, soil, and other impurities.

The traders who collected and sold this salt stored it in cloth bags for the long trip to the marketplace. Sometimes these traders were caught in rainstorms. Since sodium

chloride is an ionic compound, it is very soluble in water. Most of the sodium chloride would be washed out of the mixture, leaving behind the impurities with only a trace of sodium chloride. Without the sodium ions, the salt would "lose its flavor."

Today a similar low-grade mixture of salt and impurities is used to melt ice on streets and sidewalks. It is not useful for anything other than to be "trodden under foot of men."

175

The result of this bond is a greenish yellow gas that is used, among other things, to disinfect swimming pools.

Electron dot notation is also a useful tool to illustrate covalent bonding. The electron dots for elements before bonding follow the pattern you learned earlier. The dot structure of chlorine, which has 7 valence electrons, is this:

$$\overset{\displaystyle\cdot\cdot}{\underset{\displaystyle\cdot}{:Cl:}}$$

To show the *bond* between 2 atoms of chlorine, the symbols of the atoms are written very close together. The shared pair of electrons is represented by the two dots between their symbols. No ions are formed, so no charges are shown.

$$:\!\overset{\cdot\cdot}{\underset{\cdot}{Cl}}\!: \;+\; :\!\overset{\cdot\cdot}{\underset{\cdot}{Cl}}\!: \longrightarrow \;:\!\overset{\cdot\cdot}{\underset{\cdot\cdot}{Cl}}\!:\!\overset{\cdot\cdot}{\underset{\cdot\cdot}{Cl}}\!:$$

Electron dot structures of the uncombined elements	Electron dot structure of the covalently bonded molecule

How can a shared pair of electrons hold 2 atoms together? Look at the diagram of Cl_2. Although the shared electrons can move around both atoms, they apparently spend most of their time between them. Both nuclei attract the electron pair, and the electron pair attracts both nuclei. As in ionic bonding, unlike charges attract each other and hold the atoms together.

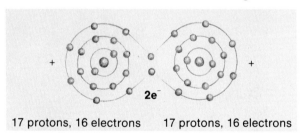

17 protons, 16 electrons   17 protons, 16 electrons

Polyatomic molecules

The electronegativities of nonmetals are all relatively high; therefore, bonds between different nonmetals are also covalent. Since oxygen and hydrogen are both nonmetals, they must bond covalently to form water. Ammonia is made of nitrogen and hydrogen. Since both of these elements are nonmetals, they too must bond covalently. When carbon and hydrogen atoms form methane molecules, covalent bonds are formed because neither element can easily give up its electrons.

A water molecule is formed of 3 atoms: an oxygen atom and 2 hydrogen atoms. The oxygen atom starts out with 6 valence electrons, 2 short of an octet. The 2 hydrogen atoms start with 1 electron apiece (H). Each needs 1 electron to fill its first energy level. After the 3 atoms come together, they all have access to enough electrons to fill their outer energy levels.

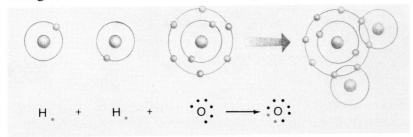

The electrons from 1 atom are no different from another atom's electrons. They are colored differently to show which atom they came from.

Before ammonia (NH_3) is formed, the nitrogen has 5 valence electrons. It needs to gain 3 electrons. To do this, it shares electrons with 3 hydrogen atoms.

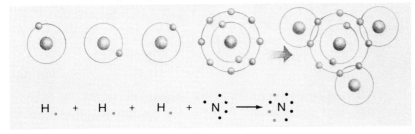

Since carbon has 4 valence electrons, it needs 4 more to attain an octet. Covalent bonds with 4 hydrogen atoms satisfy all 5 atoms.

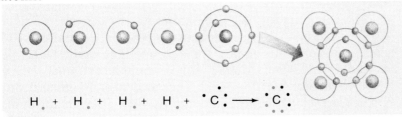

Properties of covalent compounds

The basic unit of an ionic solid is the *formula unit*. The basic unit of a covalent compound is the **molecule.** In ionic compounds the ions attract and hold all their nearest neighbors of the opposite charge.

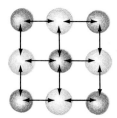

In covalent compounds atoms form single particles called molecules by bonding to a limited number of other atoms. Although there is some attraction between molecules in a covalent solid, these molecules make up the distinct units of the solid.

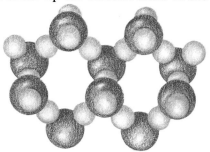

All pure compounds that exist as gases at room temperature are covalent compounds. Most of the compounds that exist as liquids at room temperature are covalent compounds as well. At the seashore two covalent compounds meet as the waves (H_2O) pound the sand (SiO_2) on the beach. But more important than these common compounds are the covalent compounds that make up your body. You consist of proteins, fats, and carbohydrates that are formed when atoms share electrons.

God's design is very evident in the covalent compounds He created to form our bodies. Ionic compounds would be brittle and soluble in water. Metallic solids would be extremely heavy and prevent flexible movement. The covalent compounds in our bodies are strong, lightweight, and flexible. They are insoluble in water and perfectly suited for maintaining the life God gave us.

Metallic Bonding

How do metals "stick together"? What holds the atoms together in pieces of pure aluminum? Each aluminum atom has 3 valence electrons. To form an ionic bond, it would have to give away all 3 of these electrons. But then the aluminum atom that accepted them would have only 6 valence electrons. There is no simple way to imagine aluminum atoms forming ionic bonds with other aluminum atoms.

Would aluminum atoms form covalent bonds? Again, the answer is no. We cannot see any way that aluminum atoms could share electrons with other aluminum atoms so that all atoms end up with stable octets.

Many theories have been developed to handle this problem. The one that works best is called the **free electron theory.** Scientists think that all of the valence electrons in a metal are shared by all of the atoms, since sharing of electrons between individual atoms (covalent bonding) cannot explain **metallic bonds.** This is sharing on a grand scale rather than on the level of 2, 3, or 4 atoms. Positive aluminum ions are embedded in a sea of negative electrons. Many of these valence electrons are free to roam about the entire structure. All the electrons are shared by all the nuclei.

The free electrons account for several properties unique to metals. These electrons allow solid metals to conduct electricity well, because they drift easily with an applied electric force. Most covalent and ionic solids do not conduct electricity, because their electrons are held in bonds. The free electrons also allow metals to conduct heat very well. These unbound electrons give metals their characteristic shiny luster.

8-8 The aluminum in these rolls is held together by metallic bonds.

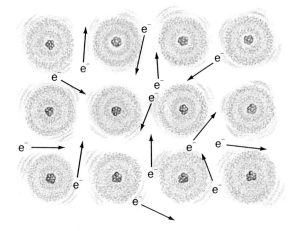

8-9 In metals, positive kernels are surrounded by "seas" of electrons.

179

All three types of chemical bonds give particular properties to the compounds they form. Observing a compound's behavior can reveal its inner structure. It is impossible to "see" the ionic bonds in a compound, but we can still deduce that they are present if that substance acts like other ionic compounds. We cannot see covalent bonds; however, if a material has a low melting point and is insoluble in water, we can assume that it has covalent bonds. We cannot see metallic bonds, but if a material is hard and shiny and conducts electricity, metallic bonds are probably present. An ionic bond that gives metallic properties is just as unlikely as an apple tree that grows watermelons!

Outward actions also show inner conditions in our Christian lives. In the Sermon on the Mount, Christ taught us that "by their fruits ye shall know them" (Matt. 7:20). What people do reveals what they are. Godly people will act godly just as surely as apple trees produce apples and metals conduct electricity.

Table 8-10

Three Types of Bonding		
Ionic	**Covalent**	**Metallic**
1. Transferred electrons	Shared electrons	Free electrons
2. Between elements with very different electro-negativities	Between elements with similar high electro-negativities	Between elements with similar low electro-negativities
3. Between metals and nonmetals	Between nonmetals	Between metals
4. Form solids with high melting points	Form solids with low melting points; liquids; gases	Form solids with relatively high melting points
5. Soluble in water	Usually insoluble in water	Insoluble in water
6. Compounds conduct electricity when melted or dissolved.	Compounds do not usually conduct electricity.	Pure metals and alloys conduct electricity in all phases.

Scientifically Speaking

chemical bonds
electronegativity
ionic bond
anion
cation
electron dot notation
crystal lattice

formula unit
covalent bond
diatomic molecules
molecule
free electron theory
metallic bonds

Questions to Talk Over

1. What effect would having 8 valence electrons have on an element's desire to bond with other elements? Why?
2. Why should ionic compounds be described as formula units instead of molecules?
3. Contrast the way in which ionic and covalent bonds affect the valence electrons of bonding atoms.
4. In the upper atmosphere a layer of triatomic oxygen called ozone protects the earth from harmful ultraviolet radiation. What type of bonding would you expect to be present in ozone molecules? Why?
5. Compare and contrast the physical properties of substances with ionic, covalent, and metallic bonds.

FOUR

THE CHEMISTRY OF MATTER

REACTIONS

CHAPTER
9

Rust cost United States businesses over 25 billion dollars last year. It attacked machinery, trucks, buildings, and cars, turning the strongest steels into piles of useless powder. It may have attacked even your family's car, eating away at its bumpers or fenders. How does this costly villain destroy metals?

Rust is caused by a chemical reaction between metals and moist air. Colorless oxygen from the air combines with the gray iron in a metal to form a brownish red iron oxide called rust. This color change tells us that a chemical change has taken place. Before the reaction, iron and oxygen exist as separate elements; afterward they form a chemical union known as rust.

A chemical change takes place when substances react to form new substances. The rusting of metals is only one example of a chemical change. The burning of fuels and the digestion of foods are chemical changes that are necessary for our survival. Industry uses chemical changes to produce plastics, textile fibers, and a vast array of other materials. Many of these reactions play a vital role in our daily lives.

In a chemical change the participating elements do not change into other elements. Their atoms are simply rearranged. Therefore, a chemical change is really a change in the composition or makeup of the substances involved. When rust forms, the iron and oxygen atoms are not destroyed. Instead, the existing chemical bonds are broken and new ones are made. The result is a totally new substance called iron oxide.

How do we know that a totally new substance was formed? Scientists have a checklist of key signs which confirm that a chemical reaction has occurred:

1. A solid separates from a liquid.
2. A gas is produced.
3. The colors of the chemicals change permanently.
4. The temperatures of the substances change.
5. Light or sound is produced.

Which one of these signs clearly confirms the fact that rust is a chemical change?

Scientists record chemical changes with two very important tools: the chemical formula and the chemical equation. *Chemical formulas* record the composition of substances. *Chemical equations* record the changes that take place in those compositions as the substances react.

Chemical Formulas

A chemical formula is a shorthand way to record the composition of a pure substance. A rust molecule is composed of 2 iron atoms bonded with 3 oxygen atoms. Its formula would be Fe_2O_3. The symbols of the elements tell which kinds of atoms are present. The subscripts (numbers below the line) tell how many of each kind of atom are present. One simple formula completely describes the chemical makeup of rust.

Rust molecules have a definite composition. Each consists of the same arrangement of 2 iron atoms and 3 oxygen atoms. A molecule with any other combination of iron and oxygen would not be rust.

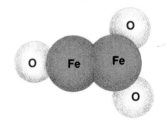

9-1 This representation of a rust molecule shows how the atoms of oxygen and iron are arranged.

185

Oxidation numbers

How do we know that the formula for rust is Fe_2O_3? Why not just FeO or FeO_2? How do we know that each rust molecule has exactly 2 iron atoms and 3 oxygen atoms?

To answer these questions, we could send a sample of rust to an analytical chemist. He would break the sample down, measure the amounts of its individual elements, and give us an exact formula for rust. But this process is time-consuming and expensive. Scientists have developed a shorter, less expensive system that allows them to predict chemical formulas based on the oxidation (AHK sih DAY shun) numbers of the elements. What are oxidation numbers? They tell the number of electrons that an element's atoms gain or lose as they bond to other atoms.

Oxidation numbers may be positive or negative. As you learned in Chapter 7, atoms may gain, lose, or share electrons with other atoms in order to have 8 valence electrons. The atoms of some elements, such as most metals, have weak electronegativity and tend to lose electrons as they bond with other atoms. After losing electrons, these atoms are positively charged. Therefore, these atoms are assigned positive oxidation numbers. Elements whose atoms have strong electronegativities tend to gain electrons. Since gaining electrons gives these atoms negative charges, they are assigned negative oxidation numbers.

How are specific oxidation numbers assigned? A look at the families of the periodic table can help us answer this question. Each of the alkali metals (family I A) has *1 valence electron*. When an alkali metal bonds, it loses this electron and acquires a charge of +1; therefore each alkali metal is assigned an oxidation number of +1. The alkaline earth metals (family II A) each have *2 valence electrons.* Since they readily lose these electrons as they bond, they are each assigned an oxidation number of +2. Aluminum is in family III A. It has 3 easily removed valence electrons. Can you guess its oxidation number?

The noble gases (family VIII A), on the opposite side of the periodic table, have 8 valence electrons—*a complete octet*. They do not normally gain, lose, or share electrons. Therefore, they are each assigned an oxidation number of 0. However, their neighbors, the halogens (family VII A), have a great desire to gain 1 electron in order to complete their valence octet. Strongly electronegative elements like the halogens, which gain control of electrons as they bond, have negative oxidation numbers. When a halogen gains an electron, its oxidation number is -1. The

FACETS
OF BASIC SCIENCE

War on Rust Begins!

Leaders in Detroit say they will fight to stop the latest rust offensive on automobile metals. Thousands of fenders, bumpers, and doors are currently under attack, leaving many of their owners carless.

Automobile makers have promised immediate action. Their first action on the front line of the attack has been to galvanize metal surfaces. This process applies a thin layer of zinc which will sacrifice itself to the enemy. The resulting layer of zinc oxide protects the metal underneath it. The next defensive move is to bind a protective coating to the surface of the car. The body of the car is electrically charged and dipped into a charged vat of special paint. The paint is bound electrochemically to the surface.

The enemy is not defeated, but the battle goes on!

oxygen family (family VI A) has *6 valence electrons*—2 less than a complete octet. What oxidation number would you assign to oxygen?

Some elements have more than one oxidation number. For example, nitrogen (family V A) has *5 valence electrons*. In some compounds it attracts the 3 electrons it needs to complete its octet. In those cases it has an oxidation number of -3. Yet in other compounds, nitrogen shares and loses control of all 5 of its valence electrons. In these chemical unions, nitrogen has an oxidation number of +5.

Iron is another element with *multiple* oxidation numbers. In rust it has an oxidation number of +3. But how do we know this? We can find the oxidation number of any element in any compound by examining the formula of the compound. The formula for rust is Fe_2O_3. The sum of the oxidation numbers of all the atoms in any formula must be 0. Do you remember the oxidation number of oxygen? It is commonly -2. Since there are 3 oxygen atoms in rust, the sum of their oxidation numbers must be -6. In order to produce a total of 0, the oxidation numbers of the iron atoms must total +6. Since there are 2 iron atoms, each has an oxidation number of +3.

What is the oxidation number of iron in $FeCl_2$? Remember that a halogen, such as chlorine, usually has an oxidation number of -1.

Table 9-2

The Oxidation States of the Common Elements									
Metals				**Metalloids**		**Nonmetals**			**Noble Gases**
Periods	Group I A	Group II A	Typical Transition Metals		Group III A	Group IV A	Group V A	Group VI A	Group VII A	Group VIII A
1	H +1 1 -1									He 0 2
2	Li +1 3	Be +2 4			B +3 5	C +4 6 -4 +2	N -3 7 +5	O -2 8	F -1 9	Ne 0 10
3	Na +1 11	Mg +2 12			Al +3 13	Si +4 14	P +5 15 +3 -3	S -2 16 +4 +6	Cl -1 17	Ar 0 18
4	K +1 19	Ca +2 20	Fe +2 26 +3	Cu +1 29 +2	Zn +2 30			As 33		Br -1 35	Kr 0 36
5		Sr 38	Ag +1 47	Cd 48			Sn +4 50 +2		I -1 53	
6		Ba 56	Au 79	Hg 80			Pb +2 82 +4			

This chart shows some of the oxidation numbers of common elements on the periodic table. Note which elements display more than one oxidation number.

Writing formulas

You can determine the formula for a compound if you know the oxidation numbers of its elements. Table 9-2 gives the common oxidation numbers for each element. How would you write the exact formula for-the compound that is formed when magnesium and chlorine bond? First, write the symbols of the two elements next to each other. Always put the *less* electronegative elements first.

MgCl

The metal magnesium has   The halogen chlorine has
weak electronegativity.   strong electronegativity.

Now check Table 9-2 to find the oxidation numbers of the two elements. The oxidation number of magnesium is +2; of chlorine, -1. Write these numbers above the symbols.

+2   -1
Mg Cl

One clue tells us immediately that MgCl is not the correct formula: the sum of the formula's oxidation numbers is not

9-3 Magnesium chloride is used to fireproof cotton fabrics and wood.

189

zero. *In a compound, the sum of all the oxidation numbers must be zero.* To remedy the problem, we must add another chlorine atom. The presence of 2 chlorine atoms is indicated by a subscript.

$$Mg\ Cl_2$$

There is no subscript beside the Mg. This indicates that there is only 1 magnesium atom in the compound. The +2 number of this single magnesium atom is now balanced by the two -1 numbers of the chlorine atoms.

$$+2\ \ 2(-1)$$
$$MgCl_2$$

You can use the same process to write the formula for a compound of aluminum and chlorine.

The symbols:	Al Cl
The oxidation numbers:	+3 -1
	Al Cl
The balanced formula:	+3 3(-1)
	$AlCl_3$

The sum of the +3 from aluminum and the three -1 numbers from the chlorine atoms is 0.

So far we have determined formulas for compounds in which only one of the elements has a subscript. In some compounds, the oxidation numbers of the elements cannot be balanced by simply adding more atoms of one element. In rust, for example, iron (oxidation number +3) is bonded to oxygen (oxidation number -2). After step two of our process, you might run into a roadblock:

The symbols:	Fe O
The oxidation numbers:	+3 -2
	Fe O
The balanced formula:	? ?

Whether you put 2 oxygen atoms or 2 iron atoms into the formula, it still will not balance. You could use the trial-and-error method and place a series of different subscripts into the formula until you find two that work, but that process would be time-consuming and definitely unscientific! Scientists use a common mathematical tool to avoid guesswork. They would use the *least common multiple* of the two oxidation numbers to balance the formula. The least common multiple (LCM) is the smallest number that is a multiple of all the numbers being considered. The LCM of 2 and 3 is 6. Once you have found the LCM of the elements' oxidation numbers, the final step of balancing the formula is short and simple. To find the subscript for each element, divide the LCM by the element's oxidation number. The oxidation number of iron is +3.

$$\frac{LCM}{\text{oxidation number}} = \frac{6}{3} = 2$$

The subscript for iron is 2.

The oxidation number of oxygen is -2. (You can ignore the sign of an oxidation number when finding an element's subscript.)

$$\frac{LCM}{\text{oxidation number}} = \frac{6}{2} = 3$$

You can check the subscripts by totaling the oxidation numbers. Their sum should equal 0.

$$\begin{array}{r} 2(+3) = 6 \\ 3(-2) = -6 \\ \hline 0 \end{array}$$

Since the sum of the oxidation numbers is 0, our formula for rust must be correct.

One of the compounds used in safety matches is composed of phosphorus (oxidation number +5) and sulfur (oxidation number -2). How would you calculate the formula of this compound?

$$\begin{array}{ll} \text{The symbols:} & \text{P} \quad \text{S} \\ \text{The oxidation numbers:} & +5 \quad -2 \\ & \text{P} \quad \text{S} \end{array}$$

The LCM of 2 and 5 is 10 ($^{10}/_5 = 2$; $^{10}/_2 = 5$).

$$\begin{array}{c} \text{The balanced formula:} \quad 2(+5) \; 5(-2) \\ P_2S_5 \end{array}$$

Is this formula correct? Can you check it?

Polyatomic ions

Sometimes several atoms join together and act as a single charged particle. These groups of atoms are called **polyatomic ions.** Polyatomic ions often bond with other ions to form compounds; therefore, they play an important role in many chemical formulas. Table 9-4 lists some common polyatomic ions. Note that the charge on an ion is equal to its oxidation number.

Table 9-4

Name	Formula	Oxidation Number
ammonium	NH_4^+	+1
acetate	$C_2H_3O_2^-$	-1
bicarbonate	HCO_3^-	-1
carbonate	CO_3^{--}	-2
hydroxide	OH^-	-1
nitrate	NO_3^-	-1
phosphate	PO_4^{---}	-3
sulfate	SO_4^{--}	-2
sulfite	SO_3^{--}	-2

Milk of magnesia is a compound that includes a polyatomic ion. This common product consists of magnesium ions and hydroxide ions. Its formula can be found by using our familiar three steps:

$$\text{The symbols: } Mg^{++} OH^-$$
$$\text{The oxidation numbers: } +2 \quad -1$$
$$Mg^{++} OH^-$$
$$\text{The balanced formula: } +2 \quad 2(-1)$$
$$Mg(OH)_2$$

A polyatomic ion should always be enclosed in parentheses when it has a subscript. Also, when the final formula is written, the ions' charges are usually dropped.

Another common product that has a polyatomic ion in its formula is baking soda. Baking soda is the common name for the chemical sodium bicarbonate. Its formula can be determined by our three steps:

The symbols: Na^+ HCO_3^-

The oxidation numbers: $+1$ -1

Na^+ HCO_3^-

The balanced formula: $+1$ -1

$NaHCO_3$

When writing any formula, put first the element or polyatomic ion with the positive oxidation number. Ammonium chloride illustrates this principle. The NH_4^+ (oxidation number $+1$) goes before the strongly electronegative halogen Cl^- (oxidation number -1). The compound's formula, based upon these oxidation numbers, is NH_4Cl. Another compound that contains a polyatomic ion is present in cement. This compound contains both calcium and carbonate ions. Can you find its formula? (Hint: Look up the oxidation numbers of the ions on the charts.)

9-5 Calcium carbonate ($CaCO_3$) is the active ingredient that provides the "glue" in most cements.

Naming compounds

Binary (BY nuh ree) **compounds,** or compounds with only two elements, have both a first and a last name. The first name is simply the name of the first element in the formula (the element with the positive oxidation number). The last name is the name of the second element (the one with the negative oxidation number), with its ending changed to *ide*. How would you name common table salt? Its formula is NaCl. The Na represents sodium; therefore, the first name is sodium. The Cl represents chlorine. In this case, chlorine is the second element of a binary compound. Therefore, its last syllable is dropped and *ide* is added. The last name for NaCl is chloride. Putting both names together, we have *sodium chloride* as the chemical name for table salt.

Table 9-6

Formula	Name
NaF	sodium fluoride
K₂S	potassium sulfide
PbO	lead oxide
ZnBr₂	zinc bromide

Compounds that contain polyatomic ions often have three or more different elements in their formulas. These compounds, called **ternary** (TUR nuh ree) **compounds,** are named much like binary compounds. The first name of a ternary compound is the name of the element or polyatomic ion that begins the formula. The last name is simply the name of the element or polyatomic ion that ends the formula. As usual, an element that forms the last name of a compound must be given an *ide* ending. A polyatomic ion, however, is never changed to add an *ide* ending. The following table gives examples of names of compounds that contain polyatomic ions.

Table 9-7

Formula	Name
NH₄Cl	ammonium chloride
NaOH	sodium hydroxide
K₂CO₃	potassium carbonate
CuSO₄	copper sulfate

Sometimes two elements can combine in more than one way to form more than one compound. Carbon and oxygen can form CO or CO_2. The first compound is a deadly gas that is given off in the exhaust of gasoline engines. If you breathe it, your blood cannot carry life-supporting oxygen throughout your body. The other compound is a harmless gas that plants use as they grow. It is also the gas that bubbles out of soft drinks. Clearly, there is quite a difference between the two compounds.

To prevent confusion, which could in some cases be fatal, a system of prefixes has been developed. A prefix placed before one of the names in a compound indicates how many atoms of that element are present in each molecule of the compound. Prefixes allow us to distinguish easily between the deadly gas carbon _mono_oxide (CO) and carbon _di_oxide (CO_2), the gas in soft drinks. Some common prefixes and examples of their uses are listed in the table below.

Table 9-8

Prefix	Number	Example
mono	1	CO: carbon _mon_oxide
di	2	CO_2: carbon _di_oxide
tri	3	BCl_3: boron _tri_chloride
tetra	4	CCl_4: carbon _tetra_chloride
penta	5	P_2O_5: phosphorus _pent_oxide

Whenever two compounds' names could be confused, it is always best to distinguish the two through the use of prefixes.

Sometimes the common name of a compound is used more often than its scientific name. You very seldom hear water called di-hydrogen oxide! Or have you ever heard someone refer to ammonia as nitrogen trihydride? The common name of a compound does not give us any clues about its chemical formula. Therefore scientists—and students—have to _memorize_ the formulas of common substances, such as water (H_2O), ammonia (NH_3), and rust (Fe_2O_3).

Chemical Equations

Can rust be prevented? Yes, every year millions of dollars are spent to do just that. One of the most common rust-proofing processes is called **galvanization** (GAL vuh nih ZAY shun). Many new cars are protected by this process. Metals are galvanized by coating them with a thin layer of zinc. The zinc combines with oxygen from the atmosphere and forms a coating of zinc oxide that is a barrier against further corrosion. Thus, the zinc bonds to the oxygen and protects the metal beneath.

How could you describe this chemical reaction? Would you use words or pictures? Scientists use chemical equations to describe the changes that take place during a reaction. Do you remember the *law of conservation of matter*? That law states that matter is not created or destroyed during a chemical change. The total amount of matter is *conserved*. That is why chemical reactions can be described by *equations*. The total amount of matter present before a reaction must be *equal* to the total amount of matter present after the reaction.

Word and formula equations

The following equation describes the reaction between zinc and oxygen:

zinc plus oxygen produces zinc oxide

Equations written out in this way are called **word equations.** Word equations can be useful, but they do not show clearly the conservation of matter during a chemical reaction. To illustrate conservation of matter, scientists use **formula equations**. The formula equation for this reaction is written this way:

$$2Zn + O_2 \rightarrow 2ZnO$$

The symbols in a formula equation show how the atoms of each element are rearranged and conserved during the reaction. The formulas on the left side of the reaction represent the substances known as **reactants.** They show the arrangement of the atoms before the chemical change takes place. The formulas on the right side of the equation represent the **products** of the reaction. These formulas show the arrangement of the atoms after the chemical change. The arrow indicates the direction of the change from the reactants to products. The numbers in front of the formulas are called **coefficients** (KO uh FISH unts). They indicate the number of reactants and products needed to balance the equation. According to the law of conservation of matter, the number of atoms of each element must be the same on both sides of the equation. If the number of atoms is not balanced, coefficients can be added. Coefficients are used only to balance equations. *Never change a formula to balance an equation!* The following equation is labeled to show the various parts of a formula equation:

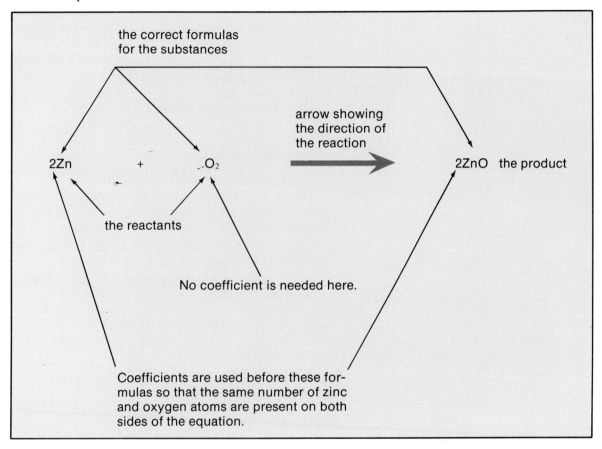

the correct formulas
for the substances

arrow showing
the direction of
the reaction

2Zn   +   O₂   ⟶   2ZnO   the product

the reactants

No coefficient is needed here.

Coefficients are used before these formulas so that the same number of zinc and oxygen atoms are present on both sides of the equation.

Writing formula equations

By following three simple steps, you can write formula equations correctly. Carefully study these steps in the following example.

Carbon reacts with oxygen to produce carbon dioxide. Write the formula equation for this process.

Step 1. Write the word equation for the reaction: carbon plus oxygen produces carbon dioxide

Step 2. Write the formula equation for this reaction. As you write the formula equation, make sure that each formula for carbon is simply C, but that the formula for oxygen is O_2, because free oxygen normally exists as _diatomic molecules_. The formula for carbon dioxide is determined by its oxidation numbers. The oxidation number of oxygen is -2. The oxidation number of carbon is +4. To write a balanced formula, we must add a subscript 2 to the symbol for oxygen.

$$\begin{aligned} \text{The symbols:} \quad &\text{C} \quad \text{O} \\ \text{The oxidation numbers:} \quad &+4 \;\; -2 \\ &\text{C} \quad \text{O} \\ \text{The balanced formula:} \quad &+4 \quad 2(-2) \\ &\text{C} \quad \;\; \text{O}_2 \end{aligned}$$

Now we are ready to write the formula equation:

$$C + O_2 \rightarrow CO_2$$

Step 3. Balance the formula equation with coefficients, _if necessary_. Chemical equations follow the law of conservation of matter; therefore, the same number of atoms of each element must be present on both sides of the equation. Check whether each type of atom is balanced in our equation for the production of carbon dioxide.

There are 2 oxygen
atoms on each side.

$$C + O_2 \rightarrow CO_2$$

There is 1 carbon atom on each side.

This equation is balanced. No coefficients are necessary.

Water is formed by the chemical union of hydrogen and oxygen. What equation describes this chemical change?

Step 1. Write the word equation for the reaction:

hydrogen plus oxygen produces water

Step 2. Write the formula equation for this reaction. Hydrogen and oxygen are diatomic molecules; therefore their formulas are H_2 and O_2. The balanced formula for water is H_2O. Now we are ready to write the equation for this reaction:

$$H_2 + O_2 \rightarrow H_2O$$

Step 3. Balance the formula equation with coefficients, _if necessary_. Is this equation balanced? There are 2 oxygen atoms on the left side of the equation. How many are on the right side? What coefficient must be added to balance the oxygen atoms? Placing a 2 before the H_2O shows that there are 2 water molecules and, therefore, 2 oxygen atoms in the product. This balances the oxygen atoms.

$$H_2 + O_2 \rightarrow 2H_2O$$

Now, are the hydrogen atoms balanced? There are 4 hydrogen atoms in the product, but only 2 in the reactants. Adding the coefficient 2 to the hydrogen in the reactants balances the hydrogen atoms. We now have the balanced equation for the reaction between hydrogen and oxygen:

$$2H_2 + O_2 \rightarrow 2H_2O$$

9-9 Hydrogen is an ideal fuel. It can replace the fuels that are now used in cooking, heating, and transportation. When hydrogen burns, it reacts with oxygen and forms water. The end products and by-products of most energy-producing reactions are pollutants such as the carbon monoxide produced by automobile engines. Hydrogen produces no by-products and only one end product—water.

Review the steps for writing formula equations by determining the equation for the formation of rust. Rust is formed by the chemical action of oxygen on iron. The oxygen bonds with the iron to form the reddish brown compound rust. You can determine the equation that describes this process by applying the three steps that you learned in the previous examples.

Step 1. Write the word equation for the reaction:

iron plus oxygen produces rust (iron oxide)

Step 2. Write the formula equation for this reaction:
Iron is a metal. Its symbol is Fe. Oxygen is a diatomic element; therefore it must be written O_2. The balanced formula for rust was given earlier in the chapter. It is Fe_2O_3. Can you write the unbalanced formula equation for this reaction?

$$Fe + O_2 \rightarrow Fe_2O_3$$

Step 3. Balance the formula equation with coefficients:
This equation is not balanced as it stands. There are 2 oxygens on the left side of the equation, and 3 oxygens on the right side of the equation. To balance these we must use their LCM. The least common multiple of 2 and 3 is 6. Therefore you should place a 3 in front of the O_2 and a 2 in front of the Fe_2O_3.

$$Fe + 3O_2 \rightarrow 2Fe_2O_3$$

Sometimes students try to place the 2 in the middle of the rust formula:

$$Fe_2 2O_3$$

Never break up a formula with a coefficient. Coefficients always go _before_ a formula.

Now you must balance the irons. There is still 1 iron on the left side of the equation, and now there are 4 irons on the right side of the equation. Placing the coefficient 4 in front of the iron on the left side of the equation will balance the irons. Now the total equation is balanced.

$$4Fe + 3O_2 \rightarrow 2Fe_2O_3$$

In these examples we began the operation of balancing the equation by balancing the oxygens. Since balancing the oxygens in an equation often requires the use of a least common multiple, balancing the oxygens is a wise first step.

Types of Reactions

Some chemical reactions combine several substances into one complex compound. Other reactions take apart compounds. Some reactions replace one element in a compound with another element, while still other reactions trade elements between two different compounds. These distinctions are the key to classifying chemical reactions.

Composition reactions

Reactions that combine several substances into one complex compound are called composition reactions. (They are sometimes called synthesis or combination reactions.) A pictorial chemical equation for composition reactions shows two or more reactants, for instance ○ and □, forming one product ○ □.

$$○ + □ \rightarrow ○□$$

The substances that combine can be two elements. For instance, zinc and sulfur combine in an explosive reaction to form zinc sulfide.

$$Zn + S \rightarrow ZnS$$

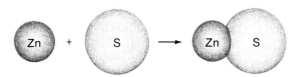

Compounds may also combine in a composition reaction and form a more complex compound. Soft drinks are carbonated by bubbling carbon dioxide through these beverages. Some of the carbon dioxide reacts with the water in the soft drinks and produces carbonic acid.

$$CO_2 + H_2O \rightarrow H_2CO_3$$

The carbonic acid in the soft drinks gives them their sharp taste.

The trademark of all composition reactions is a single product. A composition reaction may begin with two, or three, or even more reactants, but it will always result in only one final compound.

FACETS
OF BASIC SCIENCE

$$2Al_2O_3 \rightarrow 4Al + 3O_2$$

Today we consume over 4,000,000 tons of aluminum each year. But in 1855, aluminum was such a curiosity that a display of 1-kg ingots at New York's Crystal Palace Exhibition caused a sensation. Napoleon III ordered a baby's rattle for Prince Lulu and had one dozen amazingly light spoons manufactured for his wife. The King of Siam was presented with a watch chain of the light metal. The designer of the periodic table, Dmitri Mendeleev, received a vase of the rare metal in recognition of his scientific contributions. The architects of the Washington Monument chose a 2.7-kg aluminum cap for America's tallest memorial.

What made aluminum so rare? What change allowed aluminum to become one of the most plentiful metals in the world? We can find the answer by exploring the woodshed of a young chemist named Charles Martin Hall.

Charles Hall was twenty-two. He had just graduated from college and set up a simple laboratory in his woodshed. His college chemistry professor had challenged him to find a cheap way to purify aluminum metal from its ore. Until that time, aluminum had had many potential uses, but it could be separated from its ore only by a costly chemical process that made the metal too expensive to use widely. Hall decided to accept the challenge.

In his search for an inexpensive way to purify aluminum, Hall chose to experiment with electrolysis. Chemists had been able to separate many substances by passing an electrical current through a solution. One of the substances would be attracted to one of the current-producing electrodes.

Others had tried to separate aluminum with electricity. Chemists had melted an aluminum ore called cryolite, but when they passed a current through it, nothing happened. On February 23, 1886, Charles Hall busily prepared to try a new idea. He was going to use the molten cryolite to dissolve another, richer aluminum ore called bauxite. If the bauxite dissolved in the hot cryolite, it would produce aluminum ions that should migrate to one of the electrodes.

Hall slowly added the powdered bauxite to the molten cryolite. It disappeared. Apparently it had dissolved! He then placed two carbon electrodes into the

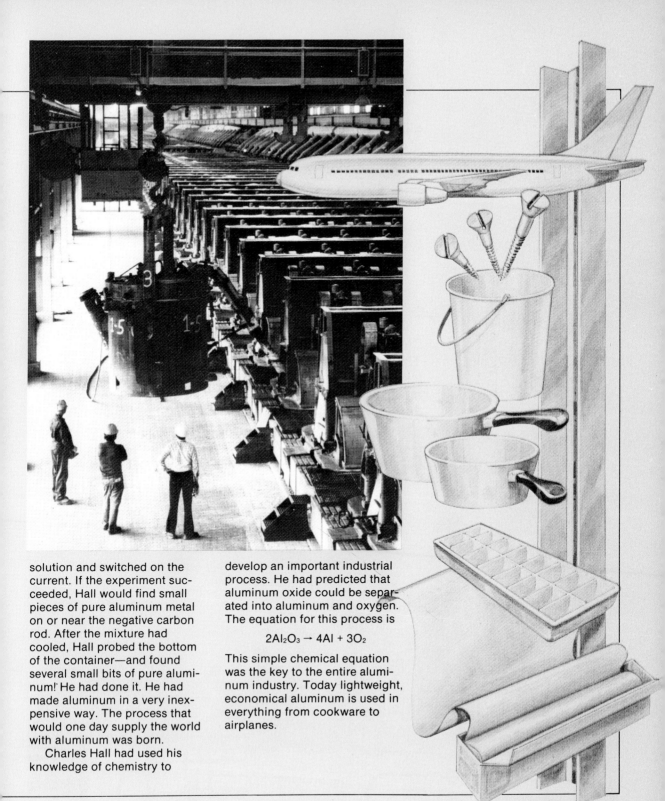

solution and switched on the current. If the experiment succeeded, Hall would find small pieces of pure aluminum metal on or near the negative carbon rod. After the mixture had cooled, Hall probed the bottom of the container—and found several small bits of pure aluminum! He had done it. He had made aluminum in a very inexpensive way. The process that would one day supply the world with aluminum was born.

Charles Hall had used his knowledge of chemistry to develop an important industrial process. He had predicted that aluminum oxide could be separated into aluminum and oxygen. The equation for this process is

$$2Al_2O_3 \rightarrow 4Al + 3O_2$$

This simple chemical equation was the key to the entire aluminum industry. Today lightweight, economical aluminum is used in everything from cookware to airplanes.

Decomposition reactions

Reactions that decompose, or take apart, a molecule are called decomposition reactions. The pictorial chemical equation of a decomposition reaction shows one reactant breaking apart to form two or more products.

$$\bigcirc\square \rightarrow \bigcirc + \square$$

Usually, energy in the form of electricity or heat is necessary to decompose molecules. A strong electrical force can pull apart the atoms of a water molecule.

$$2H_2O \rightarrow 2H_2 + O_2$$

This type of reaction is called **electrolysis** (ih lek TRAHL uh sis) (electro = electricity; lysis = splitting). Heat can also decompose molecules. When limestone is heated strongly enough, it breaks down into calcium oxide (quicklime) and carbon dioxide.

$$CaCO_3 \xrightarrow{\triangle} CaO + CO_2$$

The *delta* ($\triangle$) over the arrow indicates that the reactant must be heated for the reaction to occur.

9-10 Oil refinery.

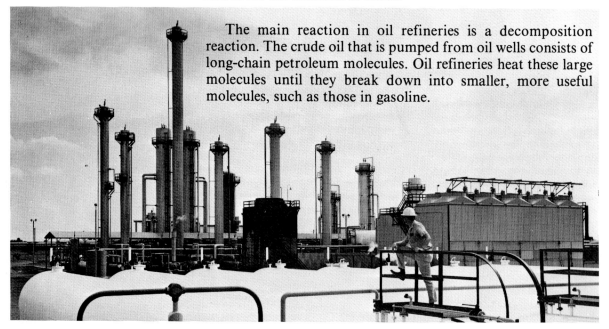

The main reaction in oil refineries is a decomposition reaction. The crude oil that is pumped from oil wells consists of long-chain petroleum molecules. Oil refineries heat these large molecules until they break down into smaller, more useful molecules, such as those in gasoline.

Single-replacement reactions

In a single-replacement reaction, one element in an existing compound is replaced by another element. The general pictorial equation for single-replacement reactions shows this exchange.

$$\bigcirc\square + \triangle \rightarrow \square\triangle + \bigcirc$$

If a piece of zinc is dropped into a beaker of copper sulfate solution, zinc atoms will exchange places with the copper atoms.

$$Zn + CuSO_4 \rightarrow Cu + ZnSO_4$$

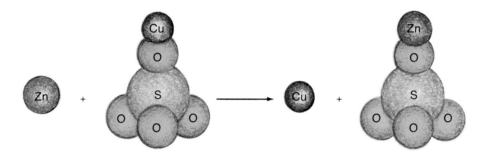

Zinc replaces copper because it is more active than copper. That is, zinc has a stronger desire to be bonded than copper has.

Many metals react with acids because the metal atoms are more active than the hydrogen atoms in the acid molecules. The "stronger" metal atoms quickly replace the "weaker" hydrogen atoms. For example, when the metal magnesium is placed in hydrochloric acid, magnesium atoms take the place of the hydrogen in the acid.

$$Mg + 2HCl \rightarrow MgCl_2 + H_2$$

The hydrogen that is released from the acid is given off in the form of diatomic gas molecules.

Atoms of very active metals, such as sodium and potassium, can even replace one of the hydrogen atoms in a water molecule. (The formula for water, H_2O, can also be written HOH.)

$$2Na + 2HOH \rightarrow 2NaOH + H_2$$

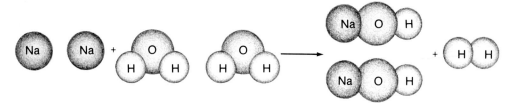

Again, hydrogen is given off as a gas.

Nonmetals can replace one another in compounds just as metals do. For example, when chlorine gas is bubbled through a solution of sodium iodide, the more active chlorine atoms take the place of the iodine atoms.

$$Cl_2 + 2NaI \rightarrow 2NaCl + I_2$$

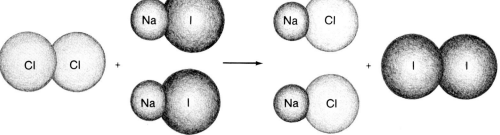

This reaction forms sodium chloride and free iodine.

Double-replacement reactions

In double-replacement reactions, two compounds divide and swap parts with each other. The general pictorial equation for a double-replacement reaction shows how the compounds might trade parts.

$$\bigcirc\square + \triangle \bigstar \rightarrow \bigcirc \bigstar + \triangle\square$$

In one double-replacement reaction, sodium chloride and silver nitrate exchange parts to become sodium nitrate and silver chloride.

$$NaCl_{(aq)} + AgNO_3{(aq)} \rightarrow NaNO_3{(aq)} + AgCl_{(ppt)}$$

Double-replacement reactions usually occur in water solutions. In solution the compounds' ions are free to move around and react. The symbol (aq) after a formula indicates that the chemical is in a water solution. *Aq* is an abbreviation of *aqueous,* a modern form of the Latin word for water. The silver chloride product has a (ppt) after its formula. This indicates that the silver chloride is a *precipitate.* **Precipitates** are solids that are insoluble in water and settle to the bottom of a solution. Many double-replacement reactions produce these insoluble solids and are therefore called precipitation reactions.

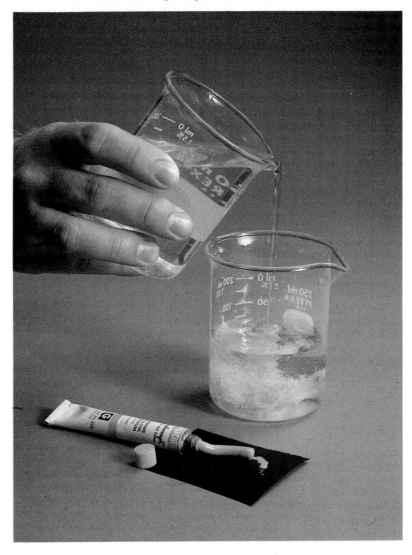

9-11 The precipitation reaction between lead nitrate and potassium chromate forms lead chromate, a brilliant yellow precipitate that is used as a paint pigment.

Exothermic and endothermic reactions

Another way to classify reactions is by whether or not they give off or require energy. Natural gas is used to heat water, dry clothes, cook food, and provide heat in many of our homes. Natural gas provides the energy necessary to accomplish these tasks through a chemical reaction known as combustion, or burning. As natural gas burns, it combines with oxygen to produce carbon dioxide and water. This chemical reaction may be written as the following equation:

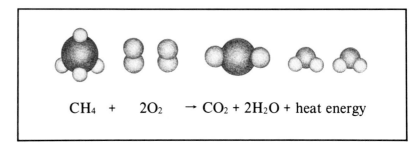

$$CH_4 \; + \; 2O_2 \; \rightarrow \; CO_2 + 2H_2O + \text{heat energy}$$

9-12 An explosion is an exothermic reaction.

This reaction is useful because it gives off large quantities of heat. Reactions that give off heat are called **exothermic** (EK so THUR mik) **reactions.**

The chemical reaction that powers a car is exothermic. So much heat energy is produced by the reaction of fuel with oxygen that cars need radiators to remove excess heat from the engine. Exothermic reactions also maintain your body temperature. Large amounts of heat energy are released as you digest your food. Sweat glands help regulate your temperature by producing sweat when you need to lose some of this heat.

Reactions that absorb energy are called **endothermic** (EN do THUR mik) **reactions**. These reactions occur only if energy is added to their reactants. Most decomposition reactions are endothermic. Baking powder decomposes in the heat of an oven and produces bubbles of carbon dioxide gas. The escaping gas causes cakes, cookies, and breads leavened with baking powder to rise.

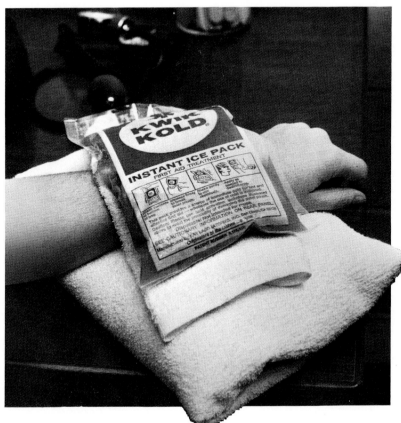

9-13 This special ice pack is cold because of a chemical reaction. Two chemicals in separate compartments of the ice pack are mixed when a seal is broken. As they mix, an endothermic chemical reaction takes place, absorbing thermal energy and making the pack feel cold to the touch.

FACETS OF BASIC SCIENCE

THE MECHANISMS OF REACTIONS

Two nitric oxide (NO) molecules blew out of the exhaust pipe of the passing automobile. They were on a collision path. But at impact they did not simply bounce off each other like millions of particles colliding around them. Instead, the 2 molecules stuck together, forming a clump of 4 atoms. Before they could split apart, an oxygen molecule from the surrounding air slammed into them and broke through some of their electron clouds. For a brief moment all 6 atoms hung together while the electrons from the disrupted energy levels scrambled for new positions. Then it happened: the whole group of atoms split down the middle! With a flash of heat, 2 totally new molecules emerged and then drifted upward to join other nitrogen dioxide (NO$_2$) molecules in the smog above.

This is a fictional account of a possible reaction mechanism. A **reaction mechanism** is an explanation of how individual atoms probably become rearranged during a chemical change. Scientists believe that the way molecules collide plays a key role in the way they react. The speed of the molecules and the angle of collision are the determining factors in whether any chemical reaction occurs.

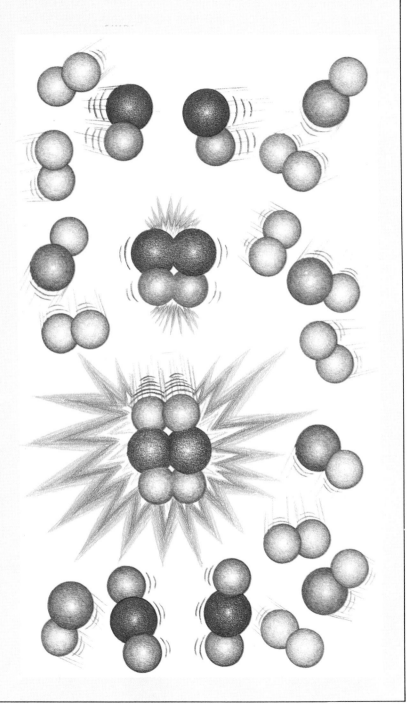

Scientifically Speaking

chemical formula
subscripts
oxidation numbers
polyatomic ions
binary compounds
ternary compounds
galvanization
word equations
formula equations

reactants
products
coefficients
reaction mechanism
electrolysis
precipitates
exothermic reactions
endothermic reactions

Questions to Talk Over

1. Name a chemical change that you depend on to do the following:
   a. keep warm
   b. have energy
   c. get to school
2. Chemical formulas are reliable and useful because chemical compounds have definite composition. What might happen if your food did not abide by this principle?
3. In a certain compound one element has an oxidation number of +8. Why are compounds like this extremely rare? To which family does the element belong?
4. The chemical industry uses the Haber process to produce ammonia. The process follows this chemical equation:

$$H_2 + N_2 = NH_3$$

   This equation is not balanced. How could you balance this equation? What difficulties do the diatomic elements pose?
5. In some reactions, certain ions bond together and precipitate. What happens to the remaining ions? How could you precipitate them from the solution?

SOLUTIONS

CHAPTER

10

Suppose that for homework your teacher gives you these instructions:

"In a *large* container mix 3.6 x 10^{19} kg of salt and 9.0 x 10^{18} kg of other assorted chemicals. Dissolve these in 1.0 x 10^{21} liters of water. Stir well. Add assorted fish and seaweed, stirring well again. Identify this mixture."

You have probably guessed that this is a simplified recipe for the oceans of the world. This record-holding solution is far more complex than most of us imagine. Although the main elements that are dissolved in the oceans are sodium and chlorine (from salt), as many as seventy-one other elements have been found. Even precious metals such as gold are present in sea water!

One element found in sea water is bromine. Its concentration in sea water is very slight, yet the sea is a profitable source of this halogen. The amount in one cubic kilometer of sea water is worth approximately $55,000, and there are over a billion cubic kilometers of sea water! Yet bromine makes up only a fraction of the wealth in the oceans.

In this chapter we will answer some important questions about solutions like the oceans. How do materials dissolve? How much material can dissolve? How can materials be separated from solutions? To begin with, we need to find out what a solution *is*.

True Solutions

To most people, a solution (suh LOO shun) is an answer. To scientists, however, a solution is something that is all mixed up! A true solution is just that—a mixture. But what kind of mixture is it? In Chapter 5 two kinds of mixtures were identified: heterogeneous (appears different in different parts) and homogeneous (appears the same, or uniform, in every part). A solution is a homogeneous mixture of two or more substances. The word *solution* is related to the word *dissolve*. Both words come from the Latin verb *solvere*, meaning "to loosen." In its simplest form, a solution is one substance dissolved in another. The substance that is dissolved is called the solute (SAHL yoot). The substance that does the dissolving is called the solvent (SAHL vunt).

Homogeneous mixtures

Sometimes we mistakenly identify heterogeneous mixtures as solutions. We label milk, orange juice, and even muddy water as "solutions." But these mixtures are not true solutions. The solutes in true solutions do not settle out, nor can the solute be separated from the solvent by filtering. Milk, orange juice, and muddy water can be separated by filtering. They also will eventually settle into distinct layers. What determines whether or not a mixture is a true solution?

You can identify true solutions by the size of the particles dissolved in the solvent. If the solute particles are too large, the solvent will not be able to hold them in solution; the solute will eventually settle out. Such a mixture is called a suspension (suh SPEN shun). In a homogeneous mixture the particle size is very small—often the particles are individual ions or molecules. They

10-1 Scientists find it difficult to explain how all the elements found their way into the oceans. Did streams and rivers carry minerals from the land? Did volcanoes belch out materials into the oceans? The problem is that no process that we can observe today explains the composition of our oceans. No one knows the composition of the oceans when God spoke them into existence, but there is evidence of great changes since their creation. Christians know what changes took place! The Bible tells us of the universal flood which covered the surface of the earth. During the year that the waters were on the face of the earth, many minerals could have been dissolved in the turbulent waters.

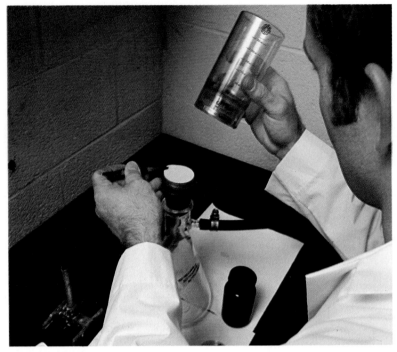

10-2 When scientists analyze a water sample for quality, they first filter out impurities. Particles are trapped in a fine filter, which is then weighed to determine the amount of impurities. Next, chemical tests will reveal what is actually dissolved in the water.

are so small that they can pass right through the pores of a filter. The solvent can hold these tiny particles in solution permanently.

Types of homogeneous mixtures

When you hear the term *solution*, you probably think of liquids. Liquid solutions are the most common type, but solutions can occur in all three states of matter—solids, liquids, and gases. The state of the solution is generally determined by the state of the solvent. If the solvent is a gas, the solution is considered gaseous. If the solvent is a solid, the solution is considered solid.

In *liquid solutions,* the solvent is most often water. The solute may be a solid, a liquid, or a gas. In brine the solute is the solid sodium chloride. Brine solutions, or salt water, are used for everything from packing seafood to gargling for sore throats. In vinegar the solute is a liquid: acetic acid dissolved in water. And in carbonated beverages, the solute is a gas: carbon dioxide dissolved in flavored water.

Although it may seem unusual, it is quite possible to form *solid solutions*. Gases, liquids, and other solids can be dissolved in a solid solvent. Hydrogen gas will dissolve into metals such as platinum (Pt) and palladium (Pd). When hydrogen gas is produced industrially, it is purified with palladium. This metal allows hydrogen gas to pass through it, but stops all other gases. Certain liquids will dissolve in solids. For instance, mercury easily dissolves in gold. This liquid-solid solution is called an **amalgam** (uh MAL gum). Be careful when you work with mercury in the laboratory. The silvery liquid will quickly dissolve into your gold jewelry. It gives a silvery finish that seems attractive but eventually turns black. Most solid-solid solutions are alloys—metals or other substances dissolved in a metal. Most alloys are formed by pouring two molten metals together and letting the mixture cool. Brass is formed by mixing molten copper and zinc.

These metal mixtures are useful because the properties of the alloy often differ greatly from those of the ingredients. An alloy of lead, bismuth, tin, and cadmium is called Wood's metal. All the ingredient metals have melting points above 200° C, but the alloy melts at only 70° C. This unusual alloy plays a vital part in many automatic sprinkler systems. The water valves of the sprinkler system are made from Wood's metal. When a fire heats the alloy, it quickly melts, releasing a shower of water. Many fires have been stopped quickly because of this alloy's unique properties.

Table 10-3

Common Alloys		
Name	**Components**	**Typical Applications**
Brass	copper, zinc	plumbing fixtures, musical instruments
Bronze	copper, tin	ball bearings, gears, valves
Boral	aluminum, boron carbide	neutron absorbers in nuclear reactors
Chromel	nickel, chromium	heat sensors (thermocouples)
Eighteen-karat gold	gold, silver, copper, nickel	jewelry
Dental amalgam	silver, mercury	dental fillings
Monel	nickel, copper, iron	kitchen appliances
Nichrome	iron, nickel, chromium	stove heating coils
Solder	tin, lead	electrical wire connections
Sterling silver	silver, copper	flatware, jewelry
Wood's metal	bismuth, lead, tin, cadmium	automatic sprinklers

10-4 Many chemicals are dissolved in the ocean. One ton of seawater contains 25 kg of sodium chloride (table salt); 1.2 kg of magnesium; .80 kg of sulfur; .36 kg of calcium; .34 kg of potassium; .06 kg of bromine; and even smaller amounts of the elements strontium, boron, fluorine, iodine, iron, copper, lead, zinc, uranium, silver, and gold.

In a *gaseous solution*, both the solvent and solute must be gases. Liquid or solid particles will settle out of a gas. The most common example of a gaseous solution is air. Air is approximately 78 percent nitrogen, 21 percent oxygen, and 1 percent other gases. In any solution the more abundant substance is called the solvent. Therefore, air is a solution of oxygen and other gases (the solutes) dissolved in nitrogen (the solvent).

There are seven simple ways of combining solutes and solvents. The table below has spaces for nine possible combinations, but solid-in-gas and liquid-in-gas solutions do not exist. These seven combinations consist of a single solute in a single solvent, but solutions can be far more complex. Sea water, for example, is a quite complex solution. Hundreds of different solids, liquids, and gases make up the "salt" in the sea!

Table 10-5

		Solvent		
		gas	liquid	solid
Solute	gas	gas-gas O_2 in N_2 (air)	liquid-gas CO_2 in H_2O (carbonated water)	solid-gas H_2 in Pd
	liquid		liquid-liquid CH_3COOH in H_2O (vinegar)	solid-liquid Hg in Ag (dental amalgam)
	solid		liquid-solid NaCl in H_2O (brine)	solid-solid Zn in Cu (brass)

Solvent Action

Of all the substances that God created, water comes closest to being a *universal solvent*. In fact, water dissolves so many materials that pure water is extremely rare, if not totally impossible to find. Even a beaker of "pure" water distilled in a laboratory has a minute amount of dissolved glass in it! Rain may begin pure, but as it plummets through the sky it dissolves atmospheric gases. As it soaks into the ground or runs off rocks, roads, and structures, it dissolves still more substances. By the time that water reaches the sea, almost every element has been added to the solution we call the ocean.

10-6 Soil is so soluble in water that large amounts of dirt can be carried off in a single rainfall. In areas where the soil is not protected by plant life, rapid erosion can occur, leaving behind a devastated landscape.

217

Water is also the solvent for the solution we know as our blood. Our bodies depend on the staggering array of substances that are dissolved and transported by the watery plasma of our circulatory system. Proteins, minerals, sugars, amino acids, vitamins, hormones, and gases are just a few of the major categories of substances that are dissolved in our blood.

The water molecule

Water succeeds so well as a solvent because of its unique molecular structure. Each water molecule consists of 2 hydrogen atoms covalently bonded to a central oxygen atom. But since covalent bonds are not unique to water, and many substances contain hydrogen and oxygen, what makes water special?

Water's unmatched performance as a dissolver is due to the unique shape of its molecules. Water molecules are *lopsided*. The two hydrogen atoms are held on one side of an oxygen atom at an angle of approximately 105° to each other.

The hydrogen atoms are bound to the central oxygen atom by pairs of shared valence electrons. These electron pairs, however, are not shared equally. The slightly more electronegative oxygen atom pulls the shared electrons closer to itself. This unequal sharing causes the molecule to have electrical poles. Remember, electrons are negatively charged particles. In ionic bonding, atoms that take electrons from other atoms acquire a negative charge. In covalent bonding, atoms share electrons. If these electrons are shared unequally, however, there is an unequal distribution of the negative charges. In water the oxygen atom holds the negative electrons more closely than the hydrogen atoms do. Therefore, the oxygen atom gets a slight negative charge, and each hydrogen atom gets a slight positive charge.

The resulting molecule is a **dipole** (DY pole)—not unlike a bar magnet—with two oppositely charged ends. Here is where the lopsided shape of water molecules plays a key role. If these molecules were not bent, the charge would be distributed evenly about the oxygen. It would be like a bar magnet with two north ends and a south center. But the bend in the molecule creates a positive pole and a negative pole. Such polar molecules react to charges just as a bar magnet reacts to magnetic fields. Its negative side (the oxygen atom) will be attracted to positive charges, and its positive side (the hydrogen atoms) will be attracted to negative charges. These attractions play a key role in the dissolving action of water.

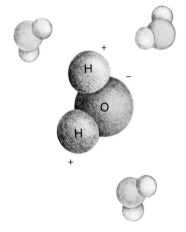

10-7 The water molecule is a dipole.

10-8 (opposite) The polarity of the water molecule allows it to pull ions out of a crystal by orienting one of its polar ends toward the ion. The water molecule uses its positively charged end to pull negative ions from the crystal lattice and its negatively charged end to pull positive ions from the crystal. In solution, the ions are completely surrounded by water molecules.

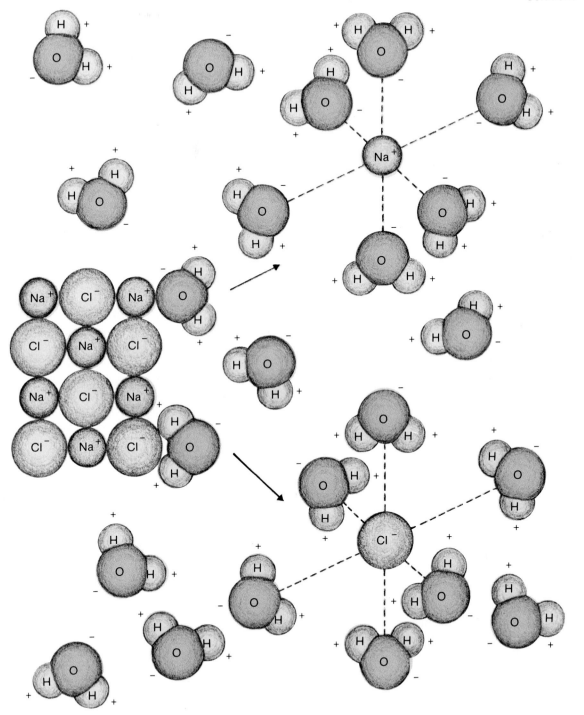

The solution process

When water dissolves a substance, it literally picks the solute apart! Consider what happens when an ionic solid such as table salt (sodium chloride) is dissolved in water. Ionic solids are simply alternating patterns of positive and negative ions. To dissolve the solid, water must break apart this pattern, for only individual ions can remain in solution. Larger particles will

FACETS
OF BASIC SCIENCE

Desalting the Sea

Because Israel's geography and climate severely limit its water resources, this nation has launched an impressive effort to turn her barren deserts into fertile farm land. To accomplish this tremendous task, Israel has developed a plan to double its water supplies by 1990. One of the technologies being used to meet this challenge is flash distillation.

Along the Mediterranean coast and at Israel's southernmost town on the Red Sea, flash distillation plants have been constructed to turn salty seawater into fresh water for agriculture. In a flash distillation plant the salt water is pumped directly from the ocean. The seawater is then pushed through a series of condenser coils in the giant evaporators on its way to a gas furnace where it is heated to 121° C—21° above the normal boiling point of water! How can water be heated to that temperature without boiling away? This superheating is accomplished by keeping the seawater under high pressure. In the next step of the

Flash distillation

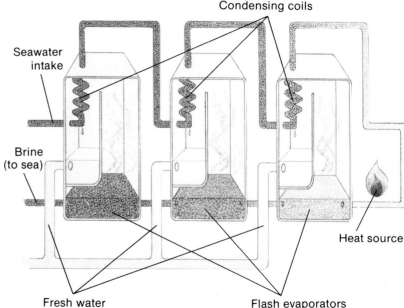

Condensing coils
Seawater intake
Brine (to sea)
Heat source
Fresh water
Flash evaporators

process, the high-pressure, superheated salt water is released into low-pressure evaporation chambers. As soon as the pressure is reduced, the water "flashes" into steam and is collected beneath large condenser coils, leaving salt and other impurities behind. This fresh water is pumped to storage tanks and then used to turn desert into farmland.

Recently other methods of desalting seawater (desalination) have been researched. In the United States, the Du Pont company has led the way in a new technology called reverse osmosis (ahz MO siss). Du Pont's "Permasep" permeator (PUR mee ATE ur) system uses fine, hollow fibers encased in a fiberglass pipe. When salt water is forced through the pipe, the settle out. Somehow, the water molecules must pull the individual ions of the ionic solid apart.

Water does this with its electrical poles. A water molecule's positive pole can pull the negative ions out of a solid, while the negative pole of a water molecule can pull the positive ions out of the solid. This breaking-up process is called *dissociation* (dih so see AY shun).

fibers separate out the salt and allow the fresh water to pass through. Reverse osmosis technology is used to provide fresh water for the Florida Keys, the capital of Saudi Arabia, and the entire island of Malta!

More and more the world is turning to the oceans as a source of fresh water. Since 1977 the world's desalination capacity has almost tripled, and has reached almost 11 billion liters per day. In the years to come, such technologies as flash distillation and reverse osmosis may play an increasingly important role in your life. Thirsty?

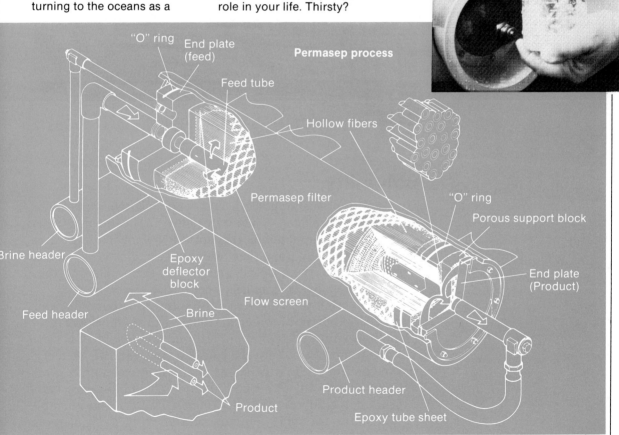

Permasep process

"O" ring
End plate (feed)
Feed tube
Hollow fibers
Permasep filter
"O" ring
Porous support block
Brine header
Epoxy deflector block
Flow screen
End plate (Product)
Feed header
Brine
Product header
Product
Epoxy tube sheet

221

Keep in mind that the molecules of a liquid are in constant, random motion. When moving water molecules collide with a solid, some of them will be in exactly the right position (positive pole to negative ion or negative pole to positive ion) to lure the ions out of the solid. Once the ions are pulled free, the water molecules surround them in a process called **hydration** (hye DRAY shun). This keeps the ions from rejoining the solid. The moving water molecules then distribute the hydrated ions throughout the solution to make it a homogeneous mixture.

Water solutions play an important role in the diet of plants. Have you ever wondered how plants eat? Most of the nutrients necessary for plants are water soluble (dissolvable). As water passes through soil, it dissolves the many different minerals on a plant's daily menu. The plant feeds on these delicacies through its root system and transports them in solution to its stems and leaves. If these substances were not in solution, plants could not eat.

Since a water solution of minerals is the basic meal for a plant, can plants grow without soil? They certainly can! Scientists are studying ways to grow plants by immersing their roots in special feeding solutions. Using this technique, vegetables and other important plants could be grown in very small areas—perhaps even in a colony in space! This special type of gardening is called **hydroponics** (HYE druh PAHN iks).

Solubility

A substance is soluble (SAHL yuh bul) when it can be dissolved by a solvent. When water molecules come in contact with water-soluble materials, they act like cowboys cutting calves from a herd. They force their way between clusters of solute particles, break them apart, and "rope" them. That is, they surround the particles and keep them from regrouping.

Water's ability to dissolve substances is astounding. One hundred milliliters of water at $100°C$ can dissolve 871 g of ammonium nitrate, a common fertilizer. This capacity is measured in terms of solubility. **Solubility** (SAHL yuh BIL uh tee) is the maximum amount of solute that will dissolve in a given amount of solvent. For water solutions, solubility is usually expressed in grams of solute per 100 ml of water. Here is a table of solubilities for some common substances in water at room temperature.

Table 10-9

Solubility of Common Substances		
Name	**Formula**	**Solubility**
		(g solute/100 ml of H_2O at 25°C)
Baking soda	$NaHCO_3$	9.2
Calcium carbonate (chalk)	$CaCO_3$	0.0015
Carbon dioxide (gas)	CO_2	0.17
Ethyl alcohol (liquid)	C_2H_5OH	infinitely soluble
Sugar (sucrose)	$C_{12}H_{22}O_{11}$	210
Table salt (sodium chloride)	$NaCl$	36

The limits of solubility

Some substances are infinitely soluble in each other. In the chart above, ethyl alcohol is listed as being infinitely soluble in water. This is a very interesting case, for something unusual happens when water and alcohol mix. If 100 ml of ethyl alcohol are mixed with 100 ml of water, the total solution should measure 200 ml. But the photograph below shows a resulting solution of only 198 ml. Where did the missing 2 ml go?

10-10 If 100 ml of alcohol and 100 ml of water are mixed, the resulting solution should measure 200 ml, but it doesn't! How can this be? When water and alcohol mix, the nonpolar alcohol molecules can actually fit between the water molecules. The resulting substance is very compact and occupies less space than the two substances separately.

223

The rule that governs the solubility of substances is *like dissolves like*. This means that a substance will dissolve another substance if they have similar structures. Examine the structures of water and ethyl alcohol. They both have a special oxygen-hydrogen combination.

Water

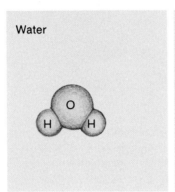

Ethyl alcohol

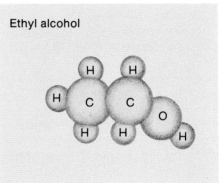

FACETS
OF BASIC SCIENCE

How to Get Squeaky Clean

Why do we use soaps to get things clean? The answer lies in a basic principle of solution chemistry: like dissolves like. Water is a **polar** (POH lur) **molecule.** Dirt and greasy oils are usually **nonpolar molecules.** They will have nothing to do with water. Since water cannot dissolve them, these oils and dirt would remain on us and our clothing unless there were a go-between that could dissolve them and yet be soluble in water. Soap is the perfect middleman for the job!

Look at the structure of a typical soap molecule, sodium stearate.

The molecule itself resembles both polar and nonpolar molecules. It is actually slightly related to a fat molecule (oils are fats). In fact, your great-great-grandmother probably made soap by mixing beef fat and a sodium compound called lye in a giant kettle over a blazing kitchen fire! The part of the molecule that is like oils and dirt is the long chain of carbons. This nonpolar end pulls the dirt and oils off your skin and clothes. The opposite end has ionic charges. These charges make this end polar, and therefore soluble in water. Once the nonpolar end grabs the dirt and oils, all we have to do is swish the soap molecules away with the water!

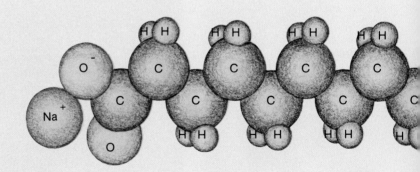

This similarity allows them to flow freely over each other and mix completely. In fact, water molecules can pack between the alcohol molecules. This arrangement is more tightly packed than the molecules of the alcohol alone. That is why the volume of the total solution is less than the sum of the volumes of the water and the alcohol. The property which allows two liquids to dissolve in each other is **miscibility** (MISS uh BIL uh tee).

Most substances have a limit on how much they can be dissolved. This limit is based on the characteristics of both the solute and the solvent. Some substances, like the fertilizer

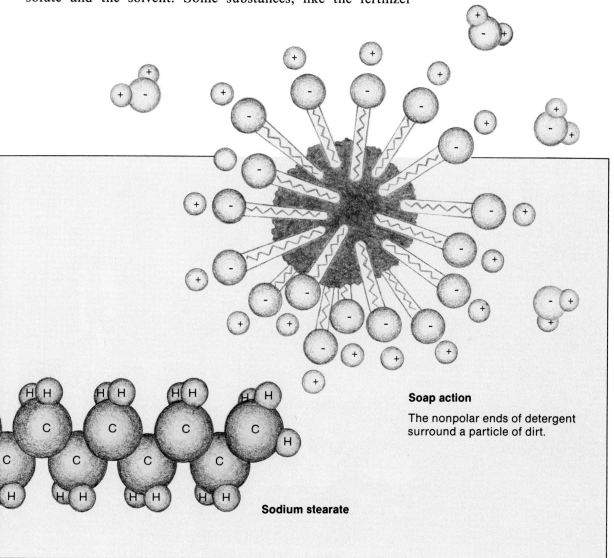

Soap action

The nonpolar ends of detergent surround a particle of dirt.

Sodium stearate

ammonium nitrate, dissociate very easily. It does not take much effort for water to separate the ammonium and the nitrate ions and keep them in solution.

Other substances tend to regroup and must be held at bay. Sodium chloride is less soluble than ammonium nitrate because the sodium and the chloride ions hold a stronger attraction for each other than do ions in ammonium nitrate. If water does not keep them surrounded, they will group together and form a **precipitate** (prih SIP uh tate) (an insoluble solid that sinks to the bottom of the solution). This characteristic makes the water molecules work to keep the ions apart and limits the number of sodium and chloride ions that a certain number of water molecules can handle.

Certain substances cannot be broken apart by water molecules. Because these will not go into solution, they are said to be insoluble. Look up the solubility of calcium carbonate in the chart on page 223. It has a solubility of 0.0015 g per 100 ml of water at 25° C. This amount is so slight that calcium carbonate is considered insoluble. You can test it. Take a piece of chalk (with your teacher's permission, of course!) and place it in a glass of water. No matter how hard you stir, you will not be able to get the calcium carbonate to dissolve.

10-11 Water may be a nearly perfect solvent, but it will not dissolve a rubber duck.

JOHNNY, GO AHEAD AND TAKE YOUR BATH...
YOU WON'T **DISSOLVE**!

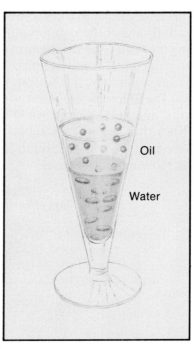

10-12 The nonpolar oil molecules form a distinct layer on top of the denser water molecules.

When a liquid is insoluble in another liquid, it is said to be **immiscible** (ih MISS uh bul). A common combination of insoluble liquids is salad dressing. In oil-and-vinegar salad dressings the nonpolar oil molecules cannot mix with the polar water molecules of vinegar. The rule that like dissolves like is in full play. Shake the mixture and it appears for a few moments that the oil and vinegar have mixed, but the unlike liquids will soon separate into two distinct layers.

Factors that affect solubility

At 0° C, 100 ml of water can dissolve 118 g of ammonium nitrate, while 100 ml of boiling water can dissolve 871 g of the same fertilizer. *Temperature* obviously affects solubility! Most solids become more soluble in liquids as the temperature increases. In our study of solids we discussed the kinetic theory. According to the kinetic theory, the disruptive forces in a solid increase as temperature increases. The weakened structure produced by heating the solid solute is more easily broken apart by the liquid solvent.

The solvent action is also stepped up as the temperature increases. As the solvent's molecules move faster, they can act on more solute particles. Sweetened tea is often prepared by dissolving sugar in a hot solution. The energetic water molecules rapidly attack the sugar, pulling the crystals apart and distributing the molecules throughout the solution. When sugar is added to cooled tea, it will not dissolve as well, and a large amount of sugar remains at the bottom of the glass.

The following chart shows the relationship between temperature and solubility in water for several common substances. Note that one of the substances is only slightly affected by temperature, while the solubility of others increases dramatically as the temperature rises.

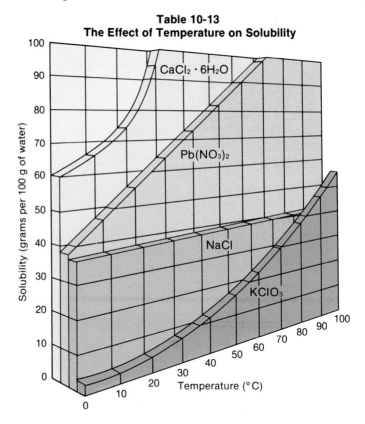

Table 10-13
The Effect of Temperature on Solubility

Generally, solutions of two liquids follow the same trend. But when gases are dissolved in liquids, an increase in temperature has the opposite effect. When a cold bottle of a carbonated drink is uncapped, almost all of the carbon dioxide stays dissolved in the solution. But if you open a *warm* bottle of soft drink, you will have a mess on your hands—literally! As the gas escapes rapidly from the warm solution, it causes the liquid to

10-14 Both of these soft drinks have just been poured. Which one would you choose? If you apply the principle that cold liquids hold gas solutes in solution better than hot liquids, you will choose the glass on the left. The CO_2 gas escaping from the glass on the right tells an observer that this drink is lukewarm.

bubble out of the bottle. As the temperature increases, the solubility of the carbon dioxide in water decreases; the gas remained in the solution only because the bottle was sealed. Once the seal is broken—fizz! The carbon dioxide escapes and you are left with a "flat" tasting soda.

Another factor that affects the solubility of a gas in a liquid is the *pressure* of the air or other gases that are touching the liquid. This relationship was studied by William Henry. In 1801 he formulated a law that we now call **Henry's law** in his honor. It states that the greater the pressure on a liquid, the greater the mass of the gas that will remain dissolved at any given temperature. That is why the gas remains in the soft drink while it is sealed. But as soon as the pressure is released, the gas escapes.

Table 10-15

Factors That Affect Solubility
The nature of the solute and the solvent 　　All solutions: Like dissolves like. The more alike 　　　　the solute and the solvent, the more soluble 　　　　they will be. Temperature 　　Solids in liquids: Solubility increases with 　　　　temperature 　　Liquids in liquids: Solubility increases with 　　　　temperature 　　Gases in liquids: Solubility decreases with 　　　　temperature Pressure 　　Gases in liquids: Solubility increases with 　　　　pressure

Look back at the chart comparing solubilities and temperature on page 228. In lukewarm water (30° C), 100 ml of water will hold about 65 g of lead nitrate [Pb(NO₃)₂]. If you were to add any more lead nitrate to the solution, it would not dissolve because the solution is already saturated. A **saturated** (SACH uh RAY tid) solution contains all the solute that the solvent can normally hold at a specific temperature. If this lead nitrate solution were heated to 60°, it could then hold 90 g of solute. The solution would be saturated no longer, since 25 g of solute

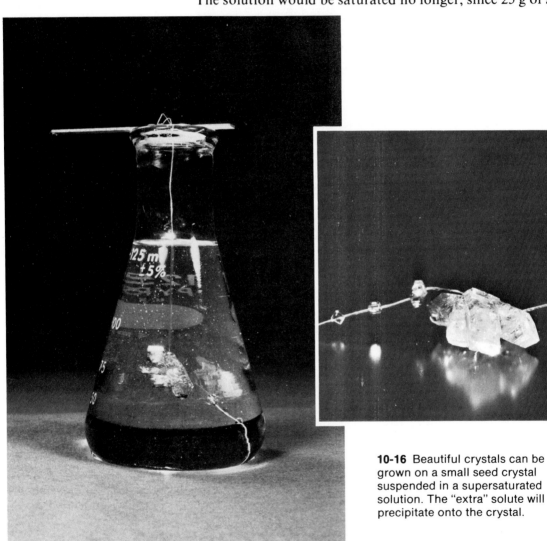

10-16 Beautiful crystals can be grown on a small seed crystal suspended in a supersaturated solution. The "extra" solute will precipitate onto the crystal.

could still be dissolved. The term **unsaturated** describes a solution in which more solute can still be dissolved.

Suppose that the 25 extra grams of lead nitrate were dissolved in the solution and the solution then cooled back to 30° C. If this cooling occurred very slowly and the solution were not jarred in any way, all 90 g of solute might stay dissolved. When a solution contains *more* solute than it normally can, it is *supersaturated*. Supersaturated solutions are very unstable. A speck of dust settling into the solution or even a scratch on the side of the container might provide a site for the "extra" solute to precipitate. This is one way that scientists grow pure crystals. They immerse a small seed crystal of the solute in a supersaturated solution. The excess solute precipitates onto the seed crystal and causes it to "grow."

Concentration

Have you ever been served a glass of Kool-Aid that was too weak? Or perhaps you have been served lemonade that was too strong. Generally speaking, we could say that the Kool-Aid was *dilute* and the lemonade was too *concentrated*. You use these terms every day, but do you understand what they mean? When you make orange juice you dilute the frozen concentrate; when you make lemonade you dilute the lemon juice; and when you make a powdered drink you add water to the powder.

But what tells us if the substance is dilute or concentrated? Generally these terms refer to the number of solute particles that are in solution. If there are just a few dissolved particles, the solution is dilute. If the solution is close to its saturation point, it is concentrated. As you can see, these terms are not very precise. They are all "ball park" terms that help us to differentiate between solutions. Scientists need a more precise way to measure the concentration of a solution.

Concentration measurements

Scientists can specify the concentration of a solution in several ways. One is called **percentage by mass**. This method is especially helpful if you need to prepare a solution yourself. If your teacher asked you to prepare a "5-percent sucrose solution," you would know to dissolve 5 g of sucrose in 95 g of water. This would yield 100 g of solution. The 5 g of sucrose would be exactly 5 percent of the total mass of the solution.

Another way to indicate the concentration of a solution is by **specific gravity**. Chemical manufacturers list specific gravities on product labels to specify the concentration of a prepared solution. Concentrated sulfuric acid, a very caustic chemical that is used in laboratories and industry, is labeled with a specific gravity of 1.84. What does this number mean? Specific gravity is the ratio of the density of the solution to the density of water. The mathematical formula to calculate specific gravities is

$$\text{specific gravity} = \frac{\text{density of the substance}}{\text{density of water}}$$

The density of water is easy to remember. It is 1.00 g/cm^3. Therefore calculating specific gravity is a very easy mathematical operation. It is simply dividing the density of the solution by one! Concentrated sulfuric acid has a density of 1.84 g/cm^3. The specific gravity of the acid is

$$\text{specific gravity} = \frac{1.84 \text{ g/cm}^3}{1.00 \text{ g/cm}^3} = 1.84$$

Note that the units (g/cm^3) cancel. A specific gravity is not expressed in units. It is simply a number that tells how many times denser than water a solution is. The higher the specific gravity, the denser (more concentrated) the solution.

Mechanics use specific gravity to test car batteries. They use a device called a hydrometer to suck up a certain volume of acid from the battery. Inside the hydrometer is a floater, which rises to a certain mark if the battery is charged. The specific gravity of the solution in a charged battery is high enough to make the floater rise. When the battery is *not* charged, the acid goes out of solution, lowering the specific gravity of the fluid and making it unable to support the floater.

Concentration effects

Boiling point elevation Putting salt into water makes the water boil at a higher temperature. This relationship is true for all solid solutes and many liquid solutes. A few liquid solutes such as alcohol actually *lower* the boiling point of water.

How can we understand the phenomenon of **boiling point elevation**? First, consider what happens when a liquid boils.

FACETS
OF BASIC SCIENCE

The Shocking Story of Electrolytes

If pure water does not conduct electricity, then why are water and electricity such a dangerous combination? Why are we warned to keep radios, hair dryers, and other electrical appliances safely away from bathtubs and sinks? True, *water* cannot conduct electricity, but some of the solutes in it *can*. These substances are called **electrolytes** (ih LEK truh LYTS). Electrolytes break up into ions (ionize) as they are dissolved. These ions act as ferryboats to transport electrical charges through a nonconducting solvent.

The strength of an electrolyte can be tested by a conductivity apparatus such as the one pictured. The two electrodes can complete an electrical circuit only if the solution between them can conduct electricity. When the circuit is complete, the light bulb glows.

If a substance does not ionize in solution, it cannot conduct electricity. Such substances are classified as **nonelectrolytes** (NAHN ih LEK truh LYTS). Sugar is an example of a nonelectro-

lyte. Substances that do ionize are classified according to the number of ions they produce: the more ions there are, the more electricity will be conducted through the solvent. Substances that ionize thoroughly to produce many ions are called strong electrolytes. The light bulb in the conductivity apparatus glows brightly when its electrodes are immersed in such a solution. Table salt is a good example of a solute that ionizes well; sodium chloride is a very strong electrolyte. If the bulb

glows dimly when the electrodes are immersed in a solution, we can conclude that the solute does not ionize thoroughly. Vinegar is a good example of such a solution. Vinegar is composed of acetic acid dissolved in water. Since acetic acid does not easily break up into ions, it is classified as a **weak electrolyte.**

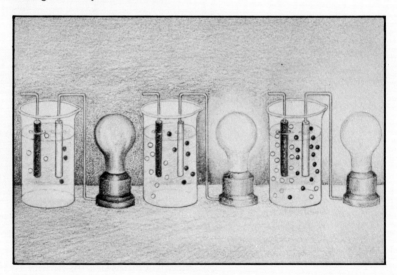

Remember that liquids have molecules that are in contact but free to roll over one another. At low temperatures the molecules "crawl over" one another rather lazily. A few at the surface may be able to escape into the air. At higher temperatures the motion becomes more vigorous, and a great many more molecules escape from the surface. If enough heat is supplied, the liquid will reach its boiling point, the temperature at which the upward pressure of the escaping molecules equals the downward pressure of the atmosphere, and the liquid boils.

Now, what will be the effect of placing molecules or ions of solute between the water molecules? Very simply, the solute particles will get in the way and hinder the motion of the water molecules. More heat must be supplied to boil the mixture, giving it a higher boiling point.

Freezing point depression Another effect of solution concentration is **freezing point depression**. You probably have added salt to an ice-cream freezer to lower the freezing point of the water surrounding the canister of ice cream. The greater the concentration of salt, the more the freezing point was lowered.

10-17 Why do you add salt to the ice in an ice-cream freezer?

The explanation for this is similar to the explanation of boiling point elevation. When water freezes, the molecules must move into certain definite locations to form crystals of ice. Solute molecules or ions hinder the water molecules from getting to their proper places. The greater the concentration of the solute, the greater the hindrance, and the more the solution must be cooled to make it freeze.

The antifreeze used in cars is an important application of the freezing point depression principle. Adding antifreeze to the water in a radiator produces a mixture that has a considerably lower freezing point than water alone. The engine's coolant is now in no danger of freezing, expanding, and damaging the engine block when a car is left outside in below-zero weather.

Scientifically Speaking

solution	miscibility
solute	precipitate
solvent	Henry's law
suspension	saturated
amalgam	unsaturated
dipole	supersaturated
dissociation	percentage by mass
hydration	specific gravity
hydroponics	boiling point elevation
soluble	freezing point depression
solubility	electrolytes
polar molecule	nonelectrolytes
nonpolar molecules	weak electrolyte

Questions to Talk Over

1. Make a list of everyday solutions in which water is the solvent. List as many as you can, including substances you may find in the kitchen, the medicine cabinet, and even the car.
2. Have you ever heard some hardy soul say, "Don't worry, I won't melt!" as he went out into the rain without an umbrella? What did the person really mean? What is the difference between melting and dissolving?
3. Scientists sometimes say that "like dissolves like," meaning that similar substances will mix with each other. Some substances, such as oil and water, do not mix. Why?
4. Which solution of each pair is more concentrated? Explain your answers.
   a. weak coffee or strong coffee
   b. water in a mountain stream or water in a lake
   c. iced tea the way you sweeten it or iced tea the way your mother sweetens it

ACIDS, BASES, AND SALTS

CHAPTER 11

Have you ever wondered what gives foods their distinctive flavors? Some foods are sour, others are bitter, and many are salty. Scientists tell us that foods like lemons, grapefruits, and green apples taste sour because they contain acids. Raw almonds and unsweetened chocolate taste bitter because they contain bases. Salty foods taste salty because of salts, of course! But did you know that acids and bases can combine to form many *different* salts that are used to season many different foods?

In the first two chapters of this unit, we have studied how substances in general react and how they dissolve in solutions. In this chapter we will study three specific types of substances—acids, bases, and salts—and how to identify them by the unique ways they react in solutions.

Many years ago, a scientist named Arrhenius discovered that solutions of certain substances conduct electricity. He called these substances *electrolytes* because of this property. Arrhenius concluded that electrolytes conduct electricity because of the ions that they produce in solutions. Today scientists classify these electrolytes into acids, bases, and salts because of the type of ions each group produces in solutions.

Acids

What makes a bee sting hurt? The painful irritation is caused by an **acid**. When a bee stings you, it injects formic acid under your skin with its stinger. As the formic acid dissolves in the water of your cells, its molecules produce a special type of ion. These ions irritate the cells and cause the bee sting to hurt.

The acid ion

What makes formic acid an acid? Like most acids, formic acid (HCOOH) has ionizable hydrogen in its structure. Ionizable hydrogen atoms can separate from a molecule and form hydrogen ions in a process called **ionization** (EYE uh nih ZAY shun).

When formic acid dissolves in water, its ionizable hydrogen atom breaks away from the rest of the formic acid molecule. During the split, positive and negative ions are formed. The less electronegative hydrogen atom loses the electron it donated to the molecular bond and becomes a positive ion. The remainder of the acid molecule attracts the electron from the hydrogen atom and becomes a negative ion.

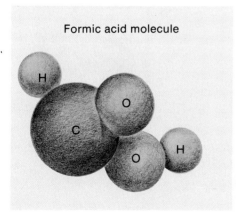

Formic acid molecule

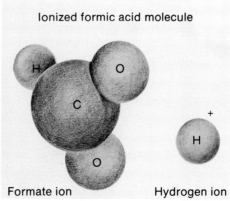

Ionized formic acid molecule

Formate ion   Hydrogen ion

A POSH RESTAURANT SNUGGLED IN DOWNTOWN GREENVILLAGE

I'M **STARVED**... LET'S ORDER

GOOD, I'LL HAVE THE CHEF'S SUPER DELUXE SPECIAL

I'LL HAVE THE.... NO, I'D BETTER STICK TO MY DIET... I'LL TAKE A GLASS OF GRAPEFRUIT JUICE

A HAPPY COUPLE ORDERS THEIR MEAL

WHICH IS PROMPTLY DELIVERED

WAIT SUSAN! DON'T DRINK THAT!

STEWART, YOU JUST SPILLED MY GRAPEFRUIT JUICE!

I KNOW IT DOES. IT'S A TASTY "COMBO" OF CITRIC AND ASPARTIC ACIDS

WHAT!? YOU DRINK ACIDS?

FWAPP

YOUR DRINK...CONTAINS... **ACIDS!**

OF COURSE...

BUT **ACIDS** ARE **DANGEROUS!** AT THE FACTORY THEY USE **HYDROCHLORIC ACID** TO EAT THROUGH METALS. EVERYWHERE THERE ARE SIGNS WARNING YOU ABOUT HOW **DANGEROUS** AND **CAUSTIC** THE ACID IS!!!

OH STEWART, THAT'S A **STRONG** SOLUTION OF HYDROCHLORIC ACID. YOU HAVE A DILUTE VERSION IN YOUR STOMACH.

I DO!?

YES! AND WE USE OTHER MILD ACIDS EVERY DAY. YOU GOT UPSET OVER NOTHING!

WOW, I SURE FEEL STUPID NOW. I'VE GOT A SPLITTING **HEADACHE**

238

NO PROBLEM. I HAVE SOME **ACETYLSALICYLIC ACID** TABLETS IN MY PURSE...

...ASPIRIN

A positive hydrogen ion is very reactive. A hydrogen atom normally has one proton and one electron; losing an electron during ionization leaves it with a lone proton. Can a proton exist by itself? That question intrigued the Danish chemist J. N. Brönsted (BRUN ste*th*). Brönsted believed that a proton would be too reactive to exist alone in solution and would be immediately *donated* to a water molecule.

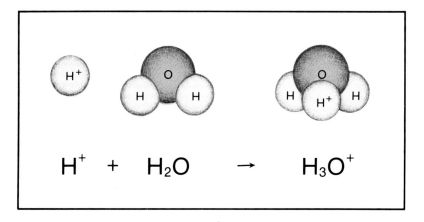

$$H^+ \ + \ H_2O \ \rightarrow \ H_3O^+$$

The ion (H_3O^+) that is formed by this donation is called a **hydronium** (hye DRO nee um) **ion.** Hydronium ions are powerful irritants. Bee stings hurt because formic acid produces hydronium ions in the water solution of your cells.

Brönsted's ideas about acids were not unique. In England, a chemist named T. M. Lowery developed a similar theory about

11-1 Brönsted defined an acid as a proton donor.

239

the same time that Brönsted did his work. Both men's theories defined an acid as any substance that can donate protons. Today we give both men credit for defining acids and call their theory the **Brönsted-Lowery theory of acids.**

You may have seen a product called muriatic acid in a hardware store. The scientific name for this cleaning agent is hydrochloric acid. Its formula is HCl. Hydrochloric acid has many industrial uses. It is used to clean metals, refine sugar, and to produce corn syrup. Your body uses it about three times a day (more if you eat snacks!). How? Hydrochloric acid is a key ingredient in your digestive juices.

Is hydrochloric acid an acid by the Brönsted-Lowery definition? Can it donate protons? When hydrochloric acid molecules dissolve in water, they ionize into hydrogen ions (protons) and chloride ions. The hydrogen ions immediately attach themselves to water molecules to form hydronium ions, while the chloride ions remain in solution. This equation describes the process:

$$HCl + H_2O \rightarrow H^+ + Cl^- + H_2O \rightarrow H_3O^+ + Cl^-$$

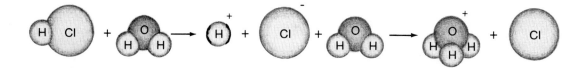

Judging by this reaction, would you call hydrochloric acid a Brönsted-Lowery acid?

Table 11-2

Acids in Common Substances	
Acid	**Substance**
acetic acid	vinegar
citric acid	citrus fruit
ascorbic acid	vitamin C
carbonic acid	soft drinks
lactic acid	milk
formic acid	bee stings
oxalic acid	rhubarb

Strengths of acids

The sulfuric acid in a car battery can corrode painted surfaces and eat holes in clothing. Yet we touch and eat other acids every day. The aspirin that you take for a headache is an acid; the sharp flavor of soft drinks is caused by an acid; and many of the vitamins that you take are actually acids. What makes some acids strong and caustic and other acids weak and harmless?

Acids are classified as strong or weak according to the number of hydronium ions that they produce in a water solution. What governs how many hydronium ions an acid produces in solution? One factor is the *number* of ionizable hydrogen atoms in each molecule of the acid. Sulfuric acid (H_2SO_4) is a strong acid because each of its molecules has 2 ionizable hydrogen atoms which can combine with water to produce 2 hydronium ions.

Phosphoric acid (H_3PO_4) has 3 ionizable hydrogen atoms. It seems that phosphoric acid should be even stronger than sulfuric

Table 11-3

The Strengths of Some Important Acids			
Chemical name	**Formula**	**Ability to produce hydronium ions in solution**	**Strength**
perchloric acid	$HClO_3$	very good	very strong
hydriodic acid	H I	very good	very strong
hydrobromic acid	HBr	very good	very strong
hydrochloric acid	HCl	very good	very strong
nitric acid	HNO_3	very good	very strong
sulfuric acid	H_2SO_4	good	strong
sulfurous acid ($SO_2 + H_2O$)	H_2SO_3	good	strong
phosphoric acid	H_3PO_4	medium	moderate
hydrofluoric acid	HF	poor	weak
nitrous acid	HNO_2	poor	weak
benzoic acid	$HC_7H_5O_2$	poor	weak
acetic acid	$HC_2H_3O_2$	very poor	very weak
carbonic acid ($CO_2 + H_2O$)	H_2CO_3	very poor	very weak
hydrogen sulfide	H_2S	very poor	very weak
boric acid	H_3BO_3	very poor	very weak
hydrocyanic acid	HCN	very poor	very weak

acid. Yet it is classified as a moderate-strength acid. Phosphoric acid is weaker than sulfuric acid because of a second factor that affects acid strength: the *degree* of ionization of the acid. Phosphoric acid molecules hold their ionizable hydrogen atoms more strongly than sulfuric acid molecules hold theirs. Therefore, phosphoric acid's hydrogen atoms cannot ionize easily, and phosphoric acid produces fewer hydronium ions than does sulfuric acid.

Citric acid ($H_3C_6H_5O_7$) has 3 ionizable hydrogen atoms. It is also a very weak acid. Do you think its hydrogen atoms are easily ionized?

Properties of acids

What taste is common to lemons, grapefruits, and dill pickles? *Sourness*. Each of these foods tastes sour because it contains an acid. Grapefruit and lemons contain citric acid, and dill pickles contain acetic acid which they absorb from the vinegar used to pickle them. Sourness is the typical taste of an acid.

Acids have a number of other characteristic properties. One of the first properties of acids to be discovered was the ability of acid solutions to conduct electricity. All acids are electrolytes. Do you realize that starting a car depends upon this property of acids? The sulfuric acid solution in a car battery stores and conducts the electricity needed to start the car.

One of the best-known properties of acids is their ability to corrode metals. Again, the ionizable hydrogen of acids plays the leading role in the reaction of acids with metals. The corrosion reaction is actually a *single replacement reaction*: the metal switches places with the hydrogen in the acid.

11-4 Acid is used to clean sheet metal before it is rolled and stored.

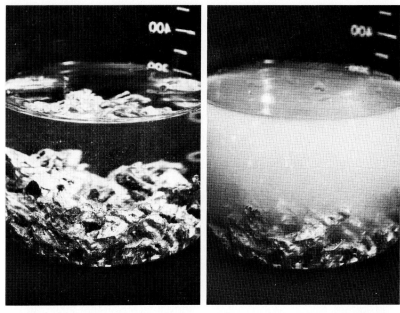

11-5 Zinc metal reacts rapidly with hydrochloric acid. What are the bubbles produced on the metal?

Consider the reaction between zinc metal and hydrochloric acid. The chloride ion and the hydronium ions from the acid pull zinc atoms from their metallic bonds, ionize them, and keep them in solution. As more zinc atoms are pulled into solution, the metal appears to be "eaten away." The hydrogen ions from the acid join in pairs and are given off as diatomic hydrogen gas.

$$Zn + 2HCl \rightarrow ZnCl_2 + H_2$$

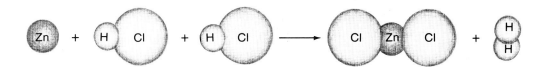

Proverbs 10:26 describes a metal-acid reaction that will set your teeth on edge! Solomon warns, "As vinegar to the teeth, and as smoke to the eyes, so is the sluggard to them that send him." Why did the writer use this analogy to illustrate the folly of employing a lazy man? Perhaps the answer lies in the effect of the acetic acid in vinegar on the calcium metal in teeth. The acetic acid attacks the calcium in the enamel of the teeth, leaving a gritty sensation in the mouth. This irritation grates on the nerves until it cannot be ignored. Do you realize that you have the same effect on your teachers and your parents when you appear to be lazy?

FACETS
OF BASIC SCIENCE

The King of Chemicals

Chemical companies in the United States produce more sulfuric acid than any other single chemical. Production of sulfuric acid in America began in Philadelphia thirty-one years after the signing of the Declaration of Independence. By the time of the Civil War, sulfuric acid had become one of the most important chemical products of our nation.

Today this acid is used in almost every industrial process. In fact, economists consider sulfuric acid so essential to industry that they sometimes measure the economic condition of a country by how much sulfuric acid it uses. Generally, when a nation's usage of sulfuric acid drops, its whole economy is headed for a downturn.

You can easily understand why sulfuric acid is often referred to as the "king of chemicals." Its properties make it extremely useful. A dense, oily substance with a high boiling point, concentrated sulfuric acid is highly caustic and can eat through metals in a matter of minutes! Most importantly, sulfuric acid can react with numerous other chemicals to produce thousands of useful products. More than 40 percent of the sulfuric acid used in the United States goes into the manufacture of phosphate fertilizers. Without these fertilizers the Midwest could be nobody's breadbasket! The second largest consumer of sulfuric acid is the chemical industry. Chemists use sulfuric acid to produce paints, dyes, plastics, fibers, and a vast array of other chemical products.

Modern acid-production equipment

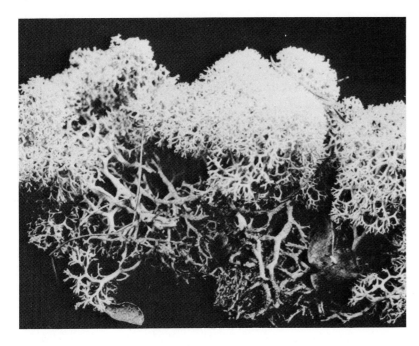

11-6 Litmus is obtained from lichen. (Courtesy Carolina Biological Supply Company)

A property of acids that is useful to scientists is their ability to affect indicators. **Indicators** are organic compounds that show a definite color change when they react with acids or bases. Litmus, a common indicator, is obtained from a lichen that is native to California. In its natural state, litmus is a bluish chemical, but it turns red when it touches an acid. How do scientists use indicators? To test a solution for acidity, special paper that has been soaked in a litmus solution and then dried is touched to the solution. If the solution is acidic, the blue litmus paper turns red.

Acids are also able to cancel the chemical action of bases. When equal strengths of acids and bases are combined, they can *neutralize* each other. The resulting solution is neither acidic nor basic.

Bases

A variety of **bases** are lurking in your kitchen! Many of the floor cleaners, window cleaners, and oven cleaners that are commonly stored under kitchen sinks contain the base ammonium hydroxide (hye DRAHK side). Another base that you may keep near the sink is lye, or sodium hydroxide. The commercial preparations used to open clogged drains usually contain lye.

There is a good chance that bases are concealed in your bathroom as well. Milk of magnesia, which is used as an antacid, a laxative, and a remedy for burns caused by strong acids, is a water suspension of the base magnesium hydroxide. Other antacid products such as Maalox, Di-Gel, and Mylanta contain bases that neutralize stomach acids.

The base ion

All three bases mentioned so far have one thing in common: the **hydroxide ion** (OH^-) is part of their structure.

NH_4OH
Ammonium hydroxide

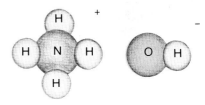

NaOH
Sodium hydroxide

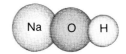

$Mg(OH)_2$
Magnesium hydroxide

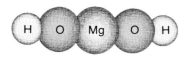

When these bases dissolve in water, they break up, or dissociate, into positive ions and negative hydroxide ions. The hydroxide ions are known as base ions.

Hydroxide ions are very reactive. Their structure includes 1 *extra* electron that they took from the positive ion of the base.

hydroxide ion (OH⁻)

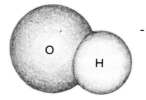

Hydroxide ions are excellent proton *acceptors*. When a proton-carrying hydronium ion comes in contact with a hydroxide ion, the negatively charged hydroxide attracts the positively charged proton from the hydronium ion. What would you guess is the product when the proton and hydroxide ion combine? Look closely at the following equation to see what happens in this reaction.

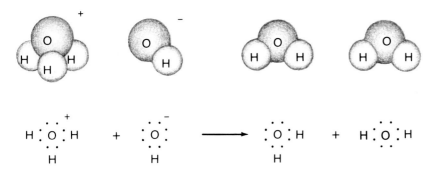

Properties of bases

If you have ever had your mouth washed out with soap, you know that bases taste bitter. You can distinguish between the bitter taste of a base and the sour taste of an acid by noting where you sense the two tastes on your tongue. The taste buds on the tip of your tongue taste acids, while those on the sides of your tongue sense the bitter taste of bases.

Bases not only taste bitter, they also feel slippery. Never touch or taste a base or acid unless you are instructed to do so by your teacher, or unless the chemical's label states that it is safe to do so. Many strong acids and bases can cause severe burns; and if eaten or drunk, they can act as poisons!

Bases also affect indicators. We noted before that acids turn blue litmus paper red. If this paper is allowed to dry, the red color will remain. The red litmus paper will turn blue again when it is placed in a base.

Just as acids can neutralize bases, bases can neutralize acids. When an acid and a base combine to produce a salt and water, the reaction is called **neutralization** (NOO truh lih ZAY shun).

Even though a solution of hydrochloric acid can corrode metal, and a solution of sodium hydroxide can eat holes in clothing, a mixture of the two could be safe to drink! When the hydrochloric acid was dissolved in water to form the solution, its molecules ionized. The hydrogen ions that were produced combined with water and formed hydronium ions.

$$H_2O + HCl \rightarrow H_2O + H^+ + Cl^- \rightarrow H_3O^+ + Cl^-$$

The sodium hydroxide solid also split into ions when it was dissolved.

$$H_2O + NaOH \rightarrow Na^+ + OH^- + H_2O$$

When the acid and base solutions are mixed, all 4 ions suddenly meet in the same solution. The hydroxide ions immediately pull the single protons from the hydronium ions to form water.

$$Na^+ + OH^- + H_3O^+ + Cl^- \rightarrow Na^+ + Cl^- + 2H_2O$$

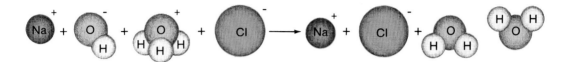

This reaction is the heart of the neutralization process. As an acid donates protons, a base in the same solution immediately accepts them. Research has shown that the other ions present during a neutralization reaction do not actually participate in the reaction. They do not combine with each other or with the hydroxide or hydrogen ions. For this reason they are referred to as **spectator ions**. In the reaction between sodium hydroxide and hydrochloric acid, the sodium ions and chloride ions are spectator ions. They are present as ions in solution both before and after the reaction takes place. To extract crystals of sodium chloride (NaCl) from the solution, it would be necessary to evaporate the water.

Strengths of bases

Bases have varying strengths just as acids do. There are strong bases that ionize completely in solution and produce many hydroxide ions, and there are weak bases that do not ionize easily and produce few hydroxide ions in solution. A substance that produces a large amount of hydroxide ions can be very corrosive. For this reason, strong bases should be handled with great care; if they are misused, they can cause severe burns.

What kinds of substances act as strong bases? Scientists have found that when the alkali metals and the alkaline earth metals combine with hydroxide ions, the resulting compounds are capable of releasing large amounts of hydroxide ions in solution. Compounds such as sodium hydroxide (NaOH), potassium hydroxide (KOH), and calcium hydroxide [Ca(OH)$_2$] readily dissociate into metal ions and hydroxide ions. Apparently, the bond between hydroxide ions and these active metals can easily be broken, making these compounds strong bases.

Weak bases tend to hold on to their hydroxide ions. One important weak base is ammonium hydroxide (NH_4OH). In the beginning of this section, we mentioned its use as a cleaning agent. This weak base often appears in cleaning products because its mild action makes it relatively safe to use.

What makes ammonium hydroxide a weak base? Generally, the strength of a base is measured by the number of hydroxide ions the base releases in a solution. In ammonium hydroxide the bond between the ammonium ion (NH_4^+) and the hydroxide ion (OH^-) is relatively strong. Since in a solution the ammonium ion will not easily release the hydroxide ion, ammonium hydroxide is a weak base.

Table 11-7

The Strengths of Some Common Bases			
Chemical name	Formula	Ability to produce hydroxide ions in solution	Strength
sodium hydroxide	NaOH	very good	strong
calcium hydroxide	$Ca(OH)_2$	very good	strong
potassium hydroxide	KOH	very good	strong
ammonium hydroxide	NH_4OH	poor	weak
aluminum hydroxide	$Al(OH)_3$	very poor	very weak

Other Bases

Brönsted and Lowery defined a base as any substance that will accept a proton. Hydroxide ions are powerful bases because they readily accept protons. However, by this definition, hydroxide ions and the compounds that contain them are not the only bases. For example, ammonia (NH_3) is considered to be a base under the Brönsted-Lowery definition. Its unique structure causes it to attract protons strongly. In an ammonia molecule, the 3 hydrogen atoms that surround the central nitrogen atom leave a pair of electrons available for bonding.

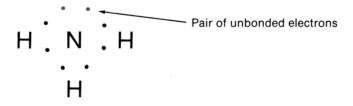

Pair of unbonded electrons

This unbonded pair of electrons is very electronegative. Consequently, it makes an ideal *proton acceptor*. When an ammonia molecule accepts a proton, it becomes an ammonium ion.

$$H \overset{\bullet}{\underset{\bullet}{\bullet}} N \overset{\bullet}{\underset{\bullet\bullet}{\bullet}} H \underset{H}{} + H^+ \longrightarrow H \overset{\bullet}{\underset{\bullet\bullet}{\bullet}} N \overset{\bullet}{\bullet} H$$

Salts

Table salt, sodium chloride, is only one of a large class of compounds known as **salts**. You are familiar with many salts in the form of seasonings that we use in our foods. Do you like oriental foods? If so, you probably like the taste of monosodium glutamate. This salt gives a meaty flavor to many Chinese dishes.

Salts are made up of a negative ion (anion) that comes from an acid, and a positive ion (cation) that comes from a base. Sodium chloride is made up of chloride (Cl^-) anions from hydrochloric acid and sodium (Na^+) cations from sodium hydroxide. Monosodium glutamate has the same cation (Na^+), but its anion, glutamate ($C_5H_8O_4^-$), comes from glutamic acid.

11-8 What salt gives Chinese foods their characteristic flavor?

FACETS OF BASIC SCIENCE

Color-coding Chemicals

Acids and bases are color-coded by substances called indicators. You already know of one indicator—litmus. Litmus turns red in acids and blue in bases. But litmus is only one of many indicators that scientists use to distinguish acids and bases.

Most indicators are organic chemical compounds. That is, their basic structures consist of long chains of carbon atoms. These indicators change colors when they react with acid and base ions. Each displays one color when it combines with hydronium ions and another color when it combines with hydroxide ions. Some indicators even change colors according to the strengths of acid or base solutions.

All water solutions of acids or bases contain both hydronium (H_3O^+) and hydroxide (OH^-) ions. In a strongly acidic solution, there are many H_3O^+ ions but few OH^- ions; in a neutral solution there are equal amounts of H_3O^+ ions and OH^- ions; and in a strongly basic solution there are many more OH^- ions than H_3O^+ ions. Scientists have used these facts to develop a special scale that measures the strengths of acids and bases. The **pH scale** (from "per hydronium") is based on the relative concentration of hydronium ions in various solutions. The scale's values range from 0 to 14: the lower the number, the higher the concentration of hydronium ions. A pH of 1 indicates a high concentration of hydronium ions, and therefore a strongly acidic solution. A pH of 14 indicates just the opposite—a low concentration of hydronium ions and a strongly basic solution. A pH of 7 is exactly in the center of the scale. Therefore, a solution with pH 7 has an equal number of hydronium and hydroxide ions. Such a solution is neutral.

The indicator bromothymol blue changes color at exactly pH 7. When molecules of this indicator react with hydroxide ions, they turn blue. The same molecules turn yellow when they react with hydronium ions. In a solution at pH 7, bromothymol blue is in the presence of equal amounts of acid and base ions. What color—blue or yellow—would you expect to see? If you guess *both,* you were correct. Half the bromothymol blue molecules react with hydronium ions, and half react with hydroxide ions. Therefore, both yellow and blue indicator molecules are present in the neutral solution. Since a mixture of blue and yellow appears green, bromothymol blue appears to turn green in a solution at pH 7.

Other indicators have distinctive color changes at other pH values. Some of the most useful products available for testing the pH of a solution consist of strips of paper that have been treated with several different indicators. Since each indicator changes color at a different pH value, such a product can be used to measure many different hydronium and hydroxide concentrations. The paper strips treated with one of these products turn red when they touch a solution with a pH of 1. As they are touched to solutions with increasingly higher pH values, they change color from yellow, to green, and then finally to blue at a pH of 14. These treated strips make it very easy for scientists to color-code a solution and determine whether it is strongly acidic, strongly basic, or some strength in between.

Bromothymol blue indicator

Base   Neutral   Acid

The pH Scale

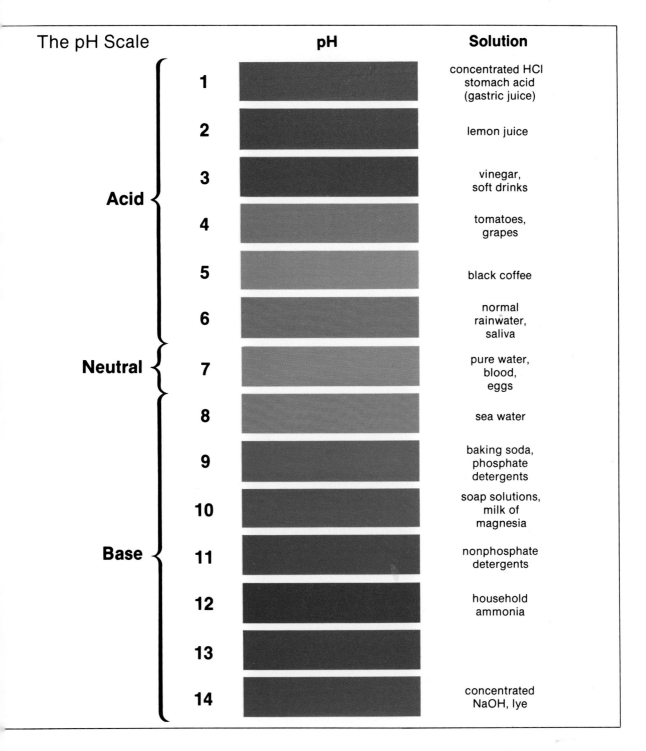

	pH	Solution
Acid	1	concentrated HCl stomach acid (gastric juice)
	2	lemon juice
	3	vinegar, soft drinks
	4	tomatoes, grapes
	5	black coffee
	6	normal rainwater, saliva
Neutral	7	pure water, blood, eggs
Base	8	sea water
	9	baking soda, phosphate detergents
	10	soap solutions, milk of magnesia
	11	nonphosphate detergents
	12	household ammonia
	13	
	14	concentrated NaOH, lye

Making salts

When an acid dissolves in water, it ionizes into positive and negative ions. For instance, nitric acid splits into a positive hydrogen ion (cation) and a negative nitrate ion (anion). The hydrogen ion (proton) is immediately donated to a water molecule to produce a hydronium ion.

$$HNO_3 + H_2O \rightarrow H^+ + NO_3^- + H_2O \rightarrow H_3O^+ + NO_3^-$$

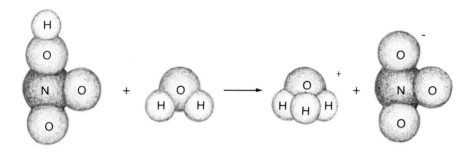

When a base dissolves in water, it dissociates into positive and negative ions. The base potassium hydroxide breaks up into a positive potassium ion (cation) and a negative hydroxide ion (anion).

$$KOH + H_2O \rightarrow K^+ + OH^- + H_2O$$

When an acid and a base are mixed together, they neutralize each other. The products of a neutralization are water and salt. The acid cations and base anions neutralize each other to form water.

$$H_3O^+ + OH^- \rightarrow HOH + HOH$$

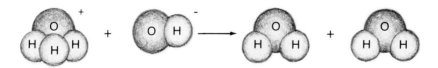

FACETS
OF BASIC SCIENCE

Acid Rain

What is the pH of rain? You would probably expect pure rain-water to be neutral, but that is not the case. Under normal conditions, rain and snow are slightly acidic because of the carbon dioxide dissolved in them. They usually have a pH of about 5.6. Scientists know that this has been the order of things for thousands of years because they have measured the pH of snows deep within glaciers.

That is, until now. In the past twenty years the snow and rain in certain parts of the world have been getting more and more acidic. Scientists in Sweden, Canada, and the northeastern United States have recorded precipitation with pH levels from 5 to 2. As much as two-thirds of the entire North American continent is now receiving *acid rain.*

Acid rain? English scientist Robert Angus Smith coined the term in 1872. Smith measured the pH of the precipitation in the industrial region near Manchester, England. He found that as more industry moved into the area and increased its sooty output of air pollutants, the pH of the rainwater fell. His was the first scientific report to draw a relationship between air pollution and acid rain.

Today scientists are gathering evidence that links acid rain to the sulfur oxides and nitrous oxides dumped into the air by plants that burn fossil fuels. In 1982, western nations ejected almost 100 million tons of sulfur dioxide into the atmosphere. These pollutants cause acid rain by mixing with the moisture in the atmosphere. When the two meet, they form a chemical called sulfurous acid. In the presence of oxygen from the atmosphere and with a little energy from sunlight, this chemical can be oxidized into sulfuric acid.

The results can be disastrous. Acid rain has been accused of killing the fish in more than one-third of the lakes in New York's Adirondack region. Acid rain measuring pH 2.7—as acid as vinegar—has fallen on Kane, Pennsylvania, and rain with a pH of 1.5—stronger than lemon juice—has hit the town of Wheeling, West Virginia.

The problem of cleaning up acid rain is the price. Faced with tremendous clean-up costs, industry officials claim that no study has yet produced a direct link between air pollution levels and damage to wildlife. However, many environmentalists, aided by the concern of other North American governments, are pressuring the United States to immediately cut back the amount of sulfurous pollutants that are dumped into the air. As more and more areas of the world begin to suffer the effects of acid rain, the issue is sure to grow. No, a few dead fish will not bring an end to the world, but any trend that affects an increasing number of lakes and streams is of increasing concern to scientists.

What position should a *Christian* take on environmental issues like this one? The Bible pictures man as the steward of God's physical creation.

In the Old Testament God commissioned Adam to subdue the earth (Gen. 1:28). He blessed the children of Israel when they built the temple. And He sent Nehemiah to oversee the reconstruction of Jerusalem after it was destroyed because of their sin. Man was given a commission by God to alter his physical environment.

Today there are those (including some Christians) who feel that nature is best when it is left completely alone. They are "protectionists" who insist that we should not alter nature for any reason. Yet the Bible pictures man as a "manager" of the physical universe. Management may include protection, but it is not limited to that. We cannot shut down all of the industries that produce sulfur oxides simply because they affect the environment. Man's authority, however, does not give him the right to abuse the earth.

In Deuteronomy 22:6-7 God taught His people an important lesson in conservation. When they hunted birds for meat, they were to take either the bird *or* its young, but never both. In this way the population of the birds would not be destroyed.

Today man needs to learn how to make such wise choices. We need the products of the industries that dump sulfur oxides into the air. And we also need to conserve the environment for future generations. Man should not selfishly take what he wants and leave a depleted world. *Balance* is necessary. We must have production, *and* we must work to find ways to produce without destroying our environment.

(Each hydronium ion from the acid can combine with one hydroxide ion from the base to form two water molecules.)

In most cases, the *acid anions* and the *base cations* remain in solution. If the water in the solution is evaporated, these ions associate—join together—to form an ionic compound. This compound is *salt*. In our original example, the nitrate anion combines with the potassium cation.

$$K^+ + NO_3^- \rightarrow KNO_3$$
(base cation + acid anion → salt)

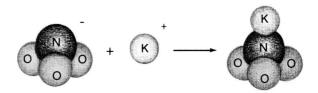

Properties of salts

Since there are many different acids and many different bases, thousands of different salts can be produced from acid-base reactions. Theoretically, any acid could react with any base to produce a unique salt. The table below lists three acids and three bases. Notice the nine different salts that could be produced from their reactions with one another.

Table 11-9

Salts from Sample Acid-Base Reactions			
	Bases		
	*Na*OH sodium hydroxide	*K*OH potassium hydroxide	*Mg*(OH)$_2$ magnesium hydroxide
Acids H*Cl* hydrochloric	NaCl sodium chloride	KCl potassium chloride	MgCl$_2$ magnesium chloride
H*NO*$_3$ nitric	NaNO$_3$ sodium nitrate	KNO$_3$ potassium nitrate	Mg(NO$_3$)$_2$ magnesium nitrate
H$_2$*SO*$_4$ sulfuric	Na$_2$SO$_4$ sodium sulfate	K$_2$SO$_4$ potassium sulfate	MgSO$_4$ magnesium sulfate

To study salts more effectively, scientists classify them according to whether they have properties similar to acids, to bases, or to neither. Salts that are chemically neutral (neither acidic nor basic) are called **normal salts**. Normal salts are produced when an acid completely neutralizes a base. Some common normal salts are sodium chloride (from hydrochloric acid and sodium hydroxide), sodium sulfate (from sulfuric acid and sodium hydroxide), and potassium nitrate (from nitric acid and potassium hydroxide). Another neutral salt is calcium sulfate. Can you guess which acid and base produce this salt when they react?

$$H_2SO_4 + Ca(OH)_2 \rightarrow Ca^{++} + SO_4^{--} + 2H_2O$$

Salts which contain hydrogen are called **acid salts.** When an acid salt dissociates, its negative ion holds on to one or more hydrogen ions. Does the formula for baking soda give any hint as to why it is called an acid salt?

$$NaHCO_3$$

11-10 In the heat of an oven, baking soda decomposes, producing the carbon dioxide which causes a cake to rise.

FACETS
OF BASIC SCIENCE

Why Is pH Important?

The pH of swimming pools is carefully regulated. If the pH drops below 6.8, the pipes in the filters may become clogged with mineral deposits.

Manufacturers of hair products carefully test the pH of their products to make sure they are safe. If the pH of a hair permanent were too high, the permanent would dissolve rather than curl the hair.

Testing the pH of a urine sample can give a doctor important information about his patient. Urine with normal pH is slightly acid. If the pH test shows that urine is too acid or too base, the patient may have a serious medical problem. When pH is abnormal, crystals can form in the urine. These crystals may lodge in the kidneys to form painful stones. Doctors sometimes treat kidney stones with special diets. They select foods with acid or base properties to adjust the pH of the urine and dissolve the crystals.

Baking soda contains the positive sodium ion from a base and the negative hydrogen carbonate ion from an acid.

$$Na^+ \qquad HCO_3^-$$

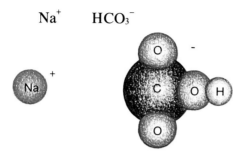

When baking soda is dissolved in water, it ionizes into a positive sodium ion and a negative hydrogen carbonate ion.

$$NaHCO_3 + H_2O \rightarrow Na^+ + HCO_3^- + H_2O$$

The hydrogen carbonate ion indicates that baking soda is an acid salt.

How are acid salts formed? An acid salt results when the acid in an acid-base reaction is not completely neutralized. Baking soda, for instance, forms when carbonic acid is incompletely neutralized by sodium hydroxide. Study the following reaction:

$$NaOH + H_2CO_3 \rightarrow Na^+ + OH^- + H^+ + H^+ + CO_3^{--} \rightarrow$$
$$NaHCO_3 + HOH$$

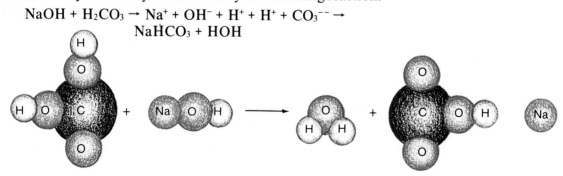

Since the amount of sodium hydroxide in the solution is limited, there are not enough OH^- ions to completely neutralize the acid's H^+ ions. The H^+ ions that are not neutralized are incorporated into the negative ions of the salt. Because each negative ion of the salt contains at least one hydrogen ion, it is classified as an acid salt.

What kind of salt would contain hydroxide ions? A **basic salt.** Basic salts contain hydroxide ions left over from the incomplete neutralization of a base. One basic salt, malachite $[Cu_2CO_3(OH)_2]$, is used to make the bursts of green light in fireworks.

11-11 Different salts produce the brilliant colors in fireworks.

Scientifically Speaking

acid

ionization

hydronium ion

Brönsted-Lowery theory of acids

indicators

bases

hydroxide ion

neutralization

spectator ions

salts

normal salts

acid salts

basic salts

pH scale

Questions to Talk Over

1. If a young animal stumbles over a nest of fire ants, the colony will immediately launch what may be a fatal attack. These feisty little insects can inject formic acid under the skin of their victims. A swarm of fire ants can attack and kill a calf! What properties of acids like formic acid make them so potentially dangerous?

2. The formula for carbonic acid is H_2CO_3. Even though its formula indicates that it could be a very strong acid similar to H_2SO_4 (sulfuric acid), carbonic acid is present in soft drinks. Why are solutions of this acid relatively safe to drink?

3. Why would you rinse an acid burn with a weak base? Is it essential that this base be weak?

4. Milk of magnesia contains magnesium hydroxide [$Mg(OH)_2$]. Your stomach contains hydrochloric acid (HCl). What type of reaction takes place when you take milk of magnesia? What salt is formed?

5. Why do manufacturers balance the pH in shampoos?

FIVE

THE MOTION OF MATTER

MACHINES
CHAPTER
12

In 215 B.C. the Roman navy besieged the port city of Syracuse on the southeast coast of Sicily. The attackers thought they had an easy prey, but the tiny nation turned out to be a worthy opponent. It kept the entire Roman navy at bay for over three years. How did the defenders succeed for so long? Mostly by using the ingenious machines of the scientist Archimedes (AHR kih MEE deez).

As the Romans first entered the harbor, they were greeted by a hailstorm of rocks launched from catapults along the shore. When the ships neared the shoreline, Archimedes' men lowered large hooks from long poles called booms. They embedded the hooks in the wooden hulls, hoisted the ships into the air, and plunged them into the sea. The stubborn Romans sent more ships to conquer the city. This time, as the Roman ships entered the harbor they mysteriously burst into flames. Archimedes had directed the defenders of Syracuse to use their polished shields as mirrors to focus the rays of the hot Mediterranean sun on the sails of the Roman ships. The intense heat ignited the cloth sails, causing the Romans to abandon their ships. The Roman commanders hated and feared Archimedes so much that the instant they took Syracuse they put the scientist to death!

Did Archimedes possess some magic that his enemies did not? No, what Archimedes possessed was knowledge and a great ability to apply his knowledge. Scientists before his time had used mathematics in the description of nature, but Archimedes applied his mathematical ideas for the practical control of everyday events. He contributed to the development of levers, pulleys, and other simple devices we still use today. In this chapter we will explore these simple machines and the forces that make them work.

Forces

Walking, talking, breathing, eating, brushing your teeth, and most of your other daily activities involve the application of forces. We define a **force** as a push or a pull acting *on* an object. Think of all the different pushes and pulls that you use to clean up your room. (You may have been told that you do not use enough, often enough!) You *pull* your games, books, and clothes off the floor and *push* them into their appropriate boxes, shelves, and drawers. You *push* and *pull* the sheets, pillows, and blankets as you make your bed. You *push* the vacuum cleaner forward and *pull* it back as you clean the carpet. Because contact must be made to apply these forces, they are called *contact forces*. There are several different types of contact forces; the two that we will study are *tension* and *friction*.

Tension

In a tug-of-war, the pull of each team is transferred by a rope. Inside the rope, the opposing pulls tug at the individual fibers. The force that holds the rope fibers together is called **tension** (TEN shun). Tension plays a supporting role in many different engineering designs. Tension forces act along the cables of suspension bridges to keep the highway and its traffic from plunging into the water below. Tension is present in the ropes that hold the mountain climber, in the cables of a ski lift, and in the cords of a hang glider's harness.

12-1 How does the tension in a ski-lift cable change as the lift is operated?

The amount of tension that a rope or cable can bear depends on the material from which it is made. Some ropes hold together under tremendous strain; others snap under much less force. Scientists have found that synthetic ropes (such as the nylon ropes used in waterskiing) can be very dangerous under too much strain. Natural hemp ropes slowly unravel, but synthetic ropes suddenly burst apart when the tension becomes too great!

Friction

When the brakes are applied, frictional forces bring a car to a stop. **Friction** (FRIK shun) is a type of force that opposes the motion of an object. It occurs when surfaces rub against each other. In a typical disc brake, for instance, a pad is pressed against a rotating disc to supply the friction that stops the car. Friction also affects the engine of a car, but there it is not useful. The valves, pistons, and other moving parts must *overcome* friction, or they cannot function.

12-2 This cut-away drawing shows how oil lubricates an engine. The lubricant is pumped from the oil pan, through a filter, and over each of the moving parts.

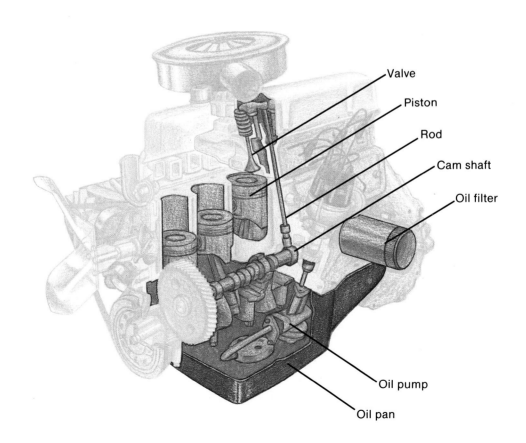

Valve

Piston

Rod

Cam shaft

Oil filter

Oil pump

Oil pan

One method of reducing friction is to smooth surfaces. That is why car manufacturers carefully machine and polish each piston and cylinder in an engine. But even very smooth surfaces will stick together under high temperatures and high pressures. In fact, the heat produced by friction can weld surfaces together. To prevent this, the moving parts of an engine are lubricated. **Lubricants** (LOO brih kunts) are friction-reducing substances with special molecular structures that allow their particles to slide over each other easily. These substances may be either liquids or solids. In most cars, a motor oil is used to lubricate the moving parts. The long, straight chains of carbon atoms in oil glide over each other with very little friction. Some new synthetic oils use a solid lubricant called graphite. The graphite is kept in a fluid suspension so that it can flow through the car's lubricating system. The carbon atoms in graphite join together to form flat plates that can slip over each other with relative ease. When a person "checks the oil" in his car, he is making sure that its engine is protected against friction.

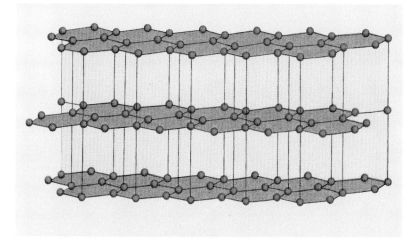

12-3 The structure of graphite shows the flat layers of molecules that slide over each other to reduce friction. If graphite's structure were changed so that these layers interlocked tightly, could this carbon form still be used as a lubricant?

Not all the effects of friction are bad. Have you ever tried to walk down an icy sidewalk? The slippery ice reduced the friction between your shoes and the sidewalk. The chances are that your frictionless stroll met with a painful end! Friction between automobile tires and the road is essential for control of a car. In the winter, cars slip and slide over ice-covered roads because the tires cannot grip the surface. Scientists believe that the ice turns partially to water under the pressure of the shoe or tire. The water then lubricates the connection and allows *too much* movement.

FACETS
OF BASIC SCIENCE

Buoyancy

What keeps you afloat in a swimming pool? The **buoyant** (BOY unt) **force.** This is the same force that pushes up on boats, barges, beach balls, buoys, and everything else that floats in water. Archimedes is given credit for discovering it. One day while he was bathing in a public bath, Archimedes noticed that some force caused his body to seem lighter. He hypothesized that his body caused this force by displacing some of the water, and that the force would be equal to the weight of the water that had been displaced. In his honor, we call the principle of buoyancy **Archimedes' principle**. A harbormaster uses this principle to tell how much cargo a ship is carrying. By reading a scale painted on the hull of the ship, the port authorities can determine how much water has been displaced and, therefore, how much cargo is on the ship.

Measuring forces

One of the simplest ways to measure a force is to use a spring scale. How does a spring measure force? The more force there is on a spring, the more the spring will expand. If the spring expands in direct proportion to the amount of force applied to it, it can be easily calibrated (marked at measured distances to represent certain forces). This relationship is called **Hooke's law:** the force on a spring is directly proportional to the stretch of the spring.

Spring scales are calibrated in SI units called *newtons* (N), the unit of force named in honor of Sir Isaac Newton. An apple exerts about $1\frac{2}{3}$ N on the palm of your hand as you hold it. This book exerts about 10 N on the desk top. You would exert roughly 450 N as you sat on a horse's back, yet a horse would exert over 6000 N if he sat on you!

I DUNNO. I THINK THIS APPLE WEIGHS MORE THAN ONE AND TWO-THIRDS NEWTONS.

Work

What is **work**? Have you ever been told that you do not know what that word means? Perhaps you do *not* know—at least, not what a scientist means by it. The term *work* has many meanings. Work may be physical effort, a job such as mowing a lawn or weeding a garden. It may be an artistic accomplishment such as a musical composition or a painting. Both of these definitions are valid, but neither can serve as the scientific definition of the term. Scientists must deal with measurable quantities. They define work in terms of measurable conditions that must be met for *work* to be accomplished.

Force and position

When an object moves under the influence of a force, work is done. Therefore the two conditions that define work are a *change in position* and an *applied force.* When a weight lifter lifts a barbell above his head, he does strenuous work. But once the barbell is in position, he is no longer working. He is exerting force to hold the barbell in place, but the force is not causing motion. Since there is no change in position, no work is being done.

A weight lifter can change the amount of work he does by adding mass to the barbell. If he adds 10 kg to each side of the

12-4 These two weight lifters are lifting equal masses; yet, one is doing more work than the other. Can you tell which one is doing more work? Why?

Military press

Snatch

barbell, he increases the amount of work he must do to accomplish the lift. Even though he is lifting the barbell the same distance, he is using more force to lift the increased mass.

Two weight lifters are lifting the same amount of mass. The first is doing a military press. He pushes 100 kg from his chest to the full extension of his arms. The other is doing a snatch. He must pull the 100 kg from the floor and push it over his head in one continuous motion. Which lifter is doing more work? Consider both the force and the change in position. Is the force the same? Yes, both are lifting 100 kg. Is the distance the same? No, the lifter doing the snatch must pull and then push the barbell over a greater distance. Therefore, he is doing the greater amount of work.

Can position be changed without a force? Would work be accomplished? Consider this special case. In deep space, interplanetary probes such as *Voyager II* glide without added thrust from their rockets. There are practically no gravitational forces to pull a spacecraft and slow it down. If no force is being applied to *Voyager II* as it coasts through space, is work occurring? No. Where there is no applied force, there can be no work. In most cases motion *is* linked directly to some force. Even when you coast downhill on your bike, a force is being applied. The earth's gravity pulls both the bike and you, the rider.

12-5 This computer simulation shows *Voyager II* gliding through space past Saturn. Are there any forces that might act on a space probe as it passes near a planet?

FACETS
OF BASIC SCIENCE

Keeping the Body Moving

God designed the human body to use lubricants effectively. If your bones met surface-to-surface each time you moved, they would produce tremendous amounts of heat and friction. Your joints would eventually wear out! To avoid this, God covered the ends of the bones with a very smooth material called cartilage and filled the joints with a friction-reducing lubricant called *synovial* (suh NO vee ul) *fluid.* Together the cartilage and fluid allow the body to move with very little friction. However, this system can break down. Arthritis, a disease of the joints, attacks cartilage, causing it to become rough and stiff. The increasing friction in the joint makes movement more and more difficult.

God's friction-reducing design also plays an important role in the heart. The heart mus-cle contracts over 86,000 times each day. If the friction of this movement were not reduced, the heart would quickly wear out. The heart is surrounded by two layers of tissue that form the *pericardium* (PEHR uh KAR dee um). The outer layer is a tough, resilient film that protects the heart. The thin inner membrane is a delicate layer of tissue that covers the heart itself. Between these two layers is 10 to 15 ml of pericardial fluid; this lubricating fluid allows the two pericardial layers to slide effortlessly over each other. This ingenious system allows the heart to function, free from damaging friction.

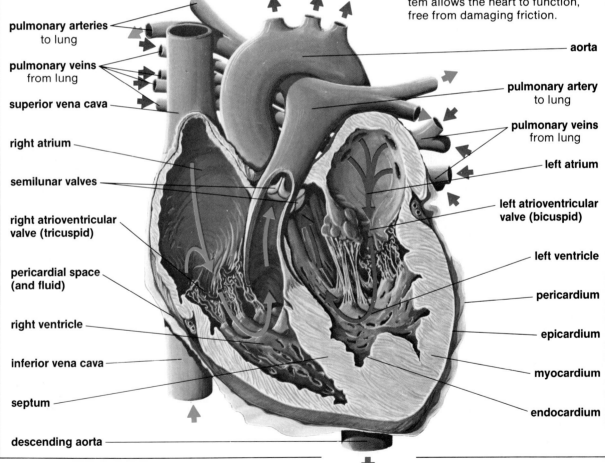

pulmonary arteries
to lung

pulmonary veins
from lung

superior vena cava

right atrium

semilunar valves

right atrioventricular
valve (tricuspid)

pericardial space
(and fluid)

right ventricle

inferior vena cava

septum

descending aorta

aorta

pulmonary artery
to lung

pulmonary veins
from lung

left atrium

left atrioventricular
valve (bicuspid)

left ventricle

pericardium

epicardium

myocardium

endocardium

Work depends on both force and distance. For this reason scientists define work as the amount of force applied on an object multiplied by the distance the object moved.

$$\text{work} = \text{force} \cdot \text{distance}$$
$$W = F \cdot d$$

For example, if 20 N of force is required to slide a cooler from one end of a picnic table to the other (a distance of 2 m), the amount of work accomplished would be: 20 newtons · 2 meters or 40 newton·meters (N·m). If the cooler were full of ice, more force would be necessary. Suppose 40 N were applied to move the cooler the 2 m. The total work done on the cooler would be 40 N · 2 m or 80 N·m. In the SI system, the newton·meter has been given a special name. It is called a **joule** (JOOL) **(J).**

$$\text{one newton·meter} = \text{one joule}$$
$$1 \text{ N·m} = 1 \text{ J}$$

Work and motion

Frequently work changes not only the position of an object, but its motion as well. In soccer, each kick changes the motion of the ball. The first kick changes it from a state of rest (motion-lessness) to a state of motion. Each force (kick) that follows changes the ball's direction and the speed of its motion. The

12-6 The work accomplished by kicking a soccer ball depends on both the force of the kick and the distance through which that force is applied.

12-7 Could the goalie stop this ball if the force of the kick were doubled?

work done during each kick depends on the force and the distance through which the force is applied. If the force of two kicks is the same, which kick would give a ball more energy (do more work): a sweeping kick that contacts the ball for a long distance or a quick, sharp kick that contacts the ball for only a fraction of the foot's swing?

When you expend energy to do work on a soccer ball, the ball gains energy. This increase in energy shows up as an increase in speed. The more work is done on the ball, the more energy it has, and the faster it moves.

Similarly, the more energy an object has, the more work that object can do. In this case, the soccer ball's energy is in the form of motion. A ball shot at 5 meters per second (m/s) can do so much work on a goalie's outstretched hands. But if the ball is shot at 10 m/s, it might have enough energy to force the goalie's hands back into the goal.

Work and power

Karen and Paul Wilkins are a fiercely competitive pair. This brother and sister are always challenging each other to contests. One day at the lake, Karen shouted to Paul that she would race

him to a buoy about 100 m from the shore. She even offered him a head start! Puzzled by her generosity, but determined to show her that he could outswim her, Paul dived into the water and stroked toward the marker. Meanwhile, Karen calmly stepped into the family's boat and started the engine. As she sped past him, Paul shouted, "You can't use the boat. That's not fair!"

"I didn't say *how* I'd race you to the buoy!" Karen called back to him.

The same amount of work was performed to get each of them to the buoy, even though they got there by different means. Karen got there faster because she applied the principle of power. **Power** is the rate at which work is done; that is, the amount of work done in a period of time. Written as an equation, power = work ÷ time.

$$\text{power} = \frac{\text{work}}{\text{time}}$$

$$P = \frac{w}{t}$$

The more quickly work is done, the more power is needed to do it. Machines such as the Wilkinses' boat can help to increase the rate at which work is done. Some machines are more powerful than others. For example, if he had known that Karen was challenging him to a boat race, Paul might have borrowed a more powerful boat. Of course, either boat would be far more powerful than a person's arms and legs!

The unit of power in the SI system is the **watt (W)**. One watt is the amount of power produced by 1 joule (newton·meter) of energy in 1 second. How much power would you use as you run up a flight of stairs? Suppose you weigh 550 N and the stairway is 5 m high. If you can run up the stairs in 10 s, the amount of power used is 275 N·m/s, or 275 watts. Note how the amount was calculated.

$$P = \frac{work}{time} \quad = \frac{(550 \text{ N}) (5 \text{ m})}{10 \text{ s}} \quad = \frac{2750 \text{ N·m}}{10 \text{ s}} \quad =$$

12-8 The appliances that make life easier in our homes consume a large amount of power. The power consumption of these devices is measured in joules per second, or watts.

$$275 \text{ N·m/s} \quad = 275 \text{ J/s} \quad = 275 \text{ watts (W)}$$

Levers

A simple **lever** is a rigid bar capable of turning about a fixed point called a **fulcrum** (FUL krum). The lever appeared in Old Testament marketplaces in the form of equal-arm balances, which were used to measure silver and gold for trading. A pan was attached to each end of a rigid bar, which was equally divided by a fulcrum. The pans held the precious metals which were used as the standard for comparison. Dishonest traders were known to adjust their balances so that they no longer had "equal arms." In Proverbs 11:1, God's children are admonished to avoid such practices: "A false balance is abomination to the Lord: but a just weight is his delight."

Although levers were applied throughout the ancient world, Archimedes was the first to mathematically determine the principle by which they work.

12-9 An ancient Egyptian balance.

The law of moments

Imagine a seesaw, a light boy, and a heavy boy. Your job is to balance the boys on the seesaw. You might guess that the heavy boy should sit closer to the fulcrum than the light boy. But how *much* closer should he sit? The best way to solve this problem is to perform an experiment, gather data, and then analyze the data. First, weigh both boys. Suppose the heavy boy weighs 450 N, twice as much as the lighter boy, who weighs 225 N. Let the boys get on the seesaw, and have them move until they balance it. They can take a number of different positions to balance the

lever. For example, when the 450-N boy sits $\frac{1}{2}$ m from the fulcrum, the 225-N boy can balance him by sitting 1 m from the fulcrum. When the 450-N boy sits 1 m from the fulcrum, the 225-N boy can balance him by sitting 2 m from the fulcrum. Also, with the heavy boy at 1½ m, the light boy must be 3 m from the fulcrum. This table summarizes the data:

Meters from fulcrum in order to balance	
450-N boy	225-N boy
½	1
1	2
1½	3

After he arranges his data in a table, the physicist usually looks for a pattern that ties the data together. With enough "head scratching," the physicist sees a general principle at work. In this case, the weight of the heavy boy multiplied by his distance from the fulcrum is equal to the weight of the light boy multiplied by his distance from the fulcrum:

$$(450 \text{ N}) (½ \text{ m}) = (225 \text{ N}) (1 \text{ m})$$
$$(450 \text{ N}) (1 \text{ m}) = (225 \text{ N}) (2 \text{ m})$$
$$(450 \text{ N}) (1½ \text{ m}) = (225 \text{ N}) (3 \text{ m})$$
$$(\text{weight}_1) (\text{distance}_1) = (\text{weight}_2) (\text{distance}_2)$$

This relationship seems to work, at least for these two boys. Trying this experiment again, this time with different boys, might yield the following data:

Meters from fulcrum in order to balance	
600-N boy	200-N boy
⅓	1
⅔	2
1	3

Again, the products of the weights and the distances are equal in each case:

$$(600 \text{ N}) (\tfrac{1}{3} \text{ m}) = (200 \text{ N}) (1 \text{ m})$$
$$(600 \text{ N}) (\tfrac{2}{3} \text{ m}) = (200 \text{ N}) (2 \text{ m})$$
$$(600 \text{ N}) (1 \text{ m}) = (200 \text{ N}) (3 \text{ m})$$

Would this principle also hold true for inanimate (in AN uh mit) (non-living) objects? Substituting sacks of flour or kegs of nails for each of the boys would settle this question. After

enough testing, this principle can be confidently applied to all kinds of objects. Only weights of the objects and their distances from the fulcrum are important. This principle can be summarized by this equation:

$$w_1 \, d_1 = w_2 \, d_2$$

In this equation, the first weight (w_1) multiplied by the first distance (d_1) is equal to the second weight (w_2) multiplied by the second distance (d_2). This principle is called the **law of moments.** It applies to all levers. The distances must be measured from the fulcrum to the exact point where the weight is applied on the lever arm for the calculations to be correct.

You may use this equation to find unknown values in a lever system. If you know three of the quantities, you can calculate the fourth value. For example, how far from the fulcrum of a seesaw would a 300-N girl sit to balance a 450-N boy who is sitting 1 m from the fulcrum? The first weight is 300 N; the first distance is

not given. The second weight is 450 N, and the second distance is 1.0 m. Place these values in the equation.

$$300 \text{ N} \cdot d_1 = 450 \text{ N} \cdot 1.0 \text{ m}$$

Now divide both sides by 300 N (w_1).

$$\frac{\cancel{300 \text{ N}} \cdot d_1}{\underset{\text{cancel}}{\cancel{300 \text{ N}}}} = \frac{450 \cancel{\text{ N}} \cdot 1.0 \text{ m}}{\underset{\text{units cancel}}{300 \cancel{\text{ N}}}}$$

The 300-N value on the left side and the newton units on the right side cancel, leaving meters as the unit for d_1.

$$d_1 = 1.5 \text{ m}$$

First-class levers

Some 1500 years before Christ, early Britons labored to build the astronomical observatory we now call Stonehenge. The gray sandstone slabs that make up the main ring of the observatory were quarried on the Marlborough Downs and hauled 39 km south to the Salisbury Plain. These ancient men must have been excellent engineers and craftsmen. Even with modern construction equipment the things they did would be difficult, but the Britons accomplished them using only *simple machines.*

The **first-class lever** played an important part in constructing Stonehenge. With first-class levers, a push **(effort)** is applied to one end (the **effort arm**) of the lever in order to move a weight **(resistance)** at the opposite end (the **resistance arm**). The fulcrum is located between them. Using simple arrangements of timbers and boulders as levers and fulcrums, the ancient builders maneuvered massive 40-ton stones and arranged them with great precision.

You can use the law of moments to calculate the effort needed to move an object with a first-class lever. Suppose you had to move a stone (much smaller than the stones at Stonehenge!). Note the measurements in the drawing below:

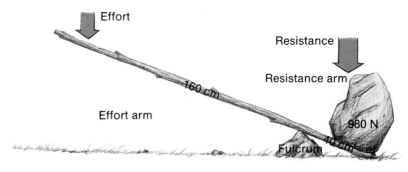

FACETS OF BASIC SCIENCE

Mechanical Advantage

Simple machines give the user a **mechanical advantage.** The term mechanical advantage may be misleading. In the problem of moving the stone, you found that you could save effort, but that the saving was not "free." You had to pay for it by applying the effort over a greater distance. This hidden cost is an example of the *distance principle:* what is saved in effort is paid for in distance.

One way of expressing how much an effort is magnified by a simple machine is the mechanical advantage (M.A.). It can be calculated in three different ways.

$$M.A. = \underset{1}{\frac{\text{resistance}}{\text{effort}}} = \underset{2}{\frac{\text{effort arm}}{\text{resistance arm}}} = \underset{3}{\frac{\text{The distance that the effort is applied}}{\text{The distance that the resistance moves}}}$$

$$= \frac{980\ \text{N}}{245\ \text{N}} = \frac{160\ \text{cm}}{40\ \text{cm}} = \frac{40\ \text{cm}}{10\ \text{cm}}$$

If we apply them to the law of moments, we can solve for the effort needed to lift the stone.

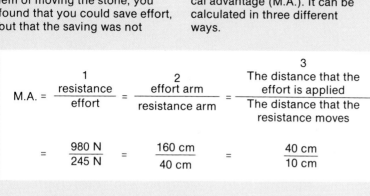

$$w_1 \cdot d_1 = w_2 \cdot d_2$$

effort | effort arm | resistance | resistance arm

First, place the known values into the equation:

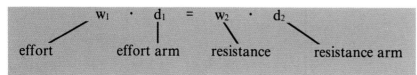

$$w_1 \cdot 160\ \text{cm} = 980\ \text{N} \cdot 40\ \text{cm}$$

the force to be applied (effort) | the length of the effort arm | the weight of the stone (resistance) | the length of the resistance arm

Next, solve for the effort by dividing both sides by the length of the effort arm.

$$\frac{w_1 \cdot 160\ \text{cm}}{160\ \text{cm}} = \frac{980\ \text{N} \cdot 40\ \text{cm}}{160\ \text{cm}} \quad \text{units cancel}$$

$$w_1 = 245\ \text{N (the units of force)}$$

The effort needed to move the stone was only one-fourth of the weight of the stone! Did you actually do less work? Did you somehow "pay" for the reduced effort? Look at the task again.

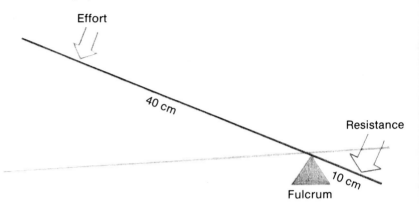

You can see that although you applied one-fourth of the effort, the effort arm moved *four times as far* as the resistance arm.

Second- and third-class levers

With the other two types of levers the resistance, effort, and fulcrum are arranged differently. In a **second-class lever,** the *resistance* is located *between* the fulcrum and the effort. Most doors are second-class levers. The hinges form the fulcrum, the effort is applied at the doorknob, and the weight of the door is the resistance. Another common second-class lever is the wheelbarrow. Where are the effort, resistance, and fulcrum of the wheelbarrow?

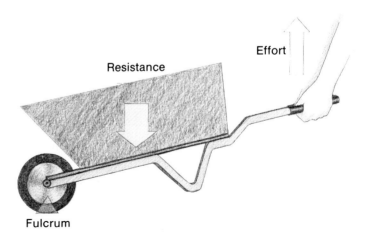

When you carry your tray at a cafeteria, you use a **third-class lever**—your arm! The muscle called the biceps exerts an effort on the bones in your forearm. The fulcrum is your elbow, and the resistance is held in your hand. With third-class levers the *effort* is applied *between* the fulcrum and the resistance. The resistance arm (the distance from the fulcrum to the point of resistance) is longer than the effort arm (the distance from the fulcrum to the point of effort).

The mechanical advantage of third-class levers reveals some interesting facts about the body's design. One of the equations for mechanical advantage was

$$\text{M.A.} = \frac{\text{the distance that the effort is applied}}{\text{the distance that the resistance moves}}$$

When the biceps move the upper forearm 5.0 cm, the hand is moved 30 cm. Therefore, the mechanical advantage is

$$\text{M.A.} = \frac{5.0 \text{ cm}}{30 \text{ cm}} = \frac{1}{6}$$

units cancel

If a mechanical advantage is less than 1, it takes a large effort to overcome a small resistance. Does the action of the forearm seem inefficient?

It will not, if you consider the way this lever functions. As the distance principle states, levers that avoid effort "pay" with large movements of the effort arm and only small movements of the resistance arm. However, third-class levers do not avoid effort. Instead, a lot of effort and a small amount of movement on the part of the effort arm result in a large movement of the resistance arm. If God had designed the human body with first-or second-class levers, it would not have the range or speed of motion that we enjoy.

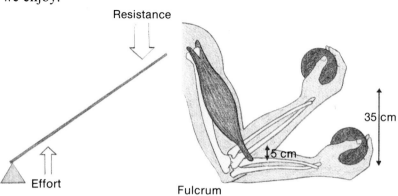

12-10 The biceps in the arm supplies the effort. The resistance is the combined weight of the arm and the ball in the hand. The resistance arm for the ball is the distance from the elbow to the center of the ball. What is the effort arm?

283

FACETS
OF BASIC SCIENCE

Stonehenge

Using simple machines to hoist into place a 25-ton pillar of stone would be no small feat. The builders of Stonehenge placed *thirty* of those stones in a circle 30 m in diameter.

Archaeologists have developed theories about how the main ring was constructed. According to one theory, the builders may have dug a deep pit where each stone was to stand.

To erect a pillar, they rolled it on logs until one-third of its length hung over a pit, then lifted the other end and tilted the stone over the edge. Next, layer by layer, they built a log structure against the side of the leaning stone so that they could use levers to lift the huge column upright. Workers then hurriedly filled in the pit. Scientists still wonder how these early engineers lifted and placed the 4-ton capstones that topped the ring of columns.

After 3500 years, seventeen of the original stones stand today. Ten of them are still capped.

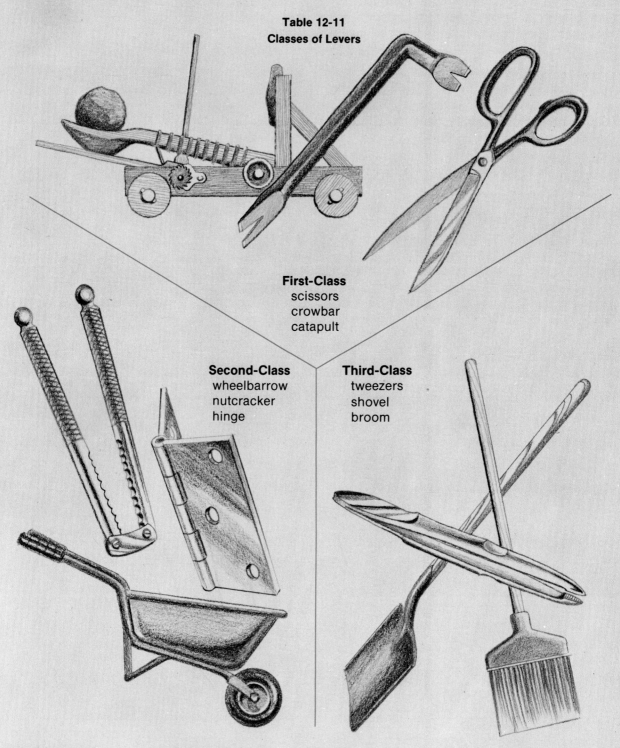

**Table 12-11
Classes of Levers**

First-Class
scissors
crowbar
catapult

Second-Class
wheelbarrow
nutcracker
hinge

Third-Class
tweezers
shovel
broom

Wheels and axles

A simple lever such as a crowbar cannot move the resistance very far. To cover distance, the simple lever must be modified. One such modification is called a **wheel and axle.** The fulcrum of this lever is the center of the axle. The effort arm and resistance arm revolve around the fulcrum, allowing the resistance to be moved continuously. The length of the resistance arm and of the effort arm of a wheel and axle may vary. In the reel of a fishing rod, the effort arm (handle) is longer than the resistance arm (the radius of the spool). Because of this, the mechanical advantage is greater than 1. If you have ever been deep-sea fishing, you know that a large reel can be used to land a very big fish! Yet the savings in effort must be paid for in distance. Each turn of the handle covers a far greater distance than the amount of line it winds on the spool.

The wheel and axle also plays an important role in bicycles. On a bicycle the effort arm (the radius of the axle) is much smaller than the resistance arm (the radius of the tire). Is the mechanical advantage of a bicycle wheel less or greater than 1?

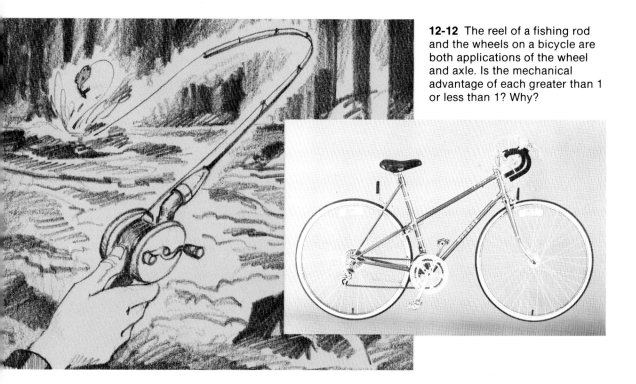

12-12 The reel of a fishing rod and the wheels on a bicycle are both applications of the wheel and axle. Is the mechanical advantage of each greater than 1 or less than 1? Why?

Pulleys

A **pulley** is also a modified lever. The effort arm and the resistance arm of a pulley are the same length. Therefore, the mechanical advantage of a *single fixed pulley* is equal to 1. If a single fixed pulley does not save effort or shorten the distance through which the effort is applied, then how are single fixed pulleys useful? This type of pulley changes the direction of an effort. Sometimes this gives a definite physical advantage. Lifting an object with a single pulley attached to the ceiling allows you to literally put your weight into your effort. This is often much easier than bearing the whole effort with your legs, back, and arms.

A *single movable pulley* has a mechanical advantage of 2. The drawing below illustrates why:

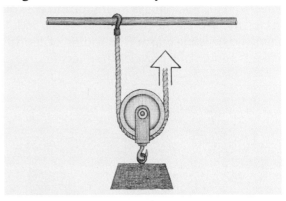

$$\text{M.A.} = \frac{1\text{ m}}{\frac{1}{2}\text{ m}}$$

As the rope is pulled 1 m, the pulley moves upward only ½ m. The motion of the pull is divided in half since two ropes are attached to the resistance.

What is the mechanical advantage of this pulley system?

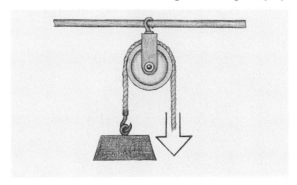

The mechanical advantage is 1. Fixed pulleys change only the direction of the motion. They do not affect the amount of effort needed.

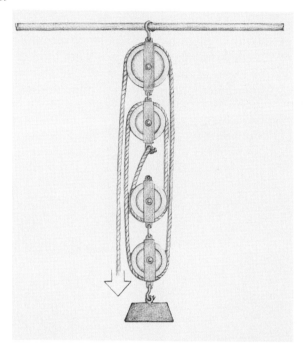

In this pulley system the mechanical advantage is 4. Can you see why? There are four ropes supporting the resistance. Therefore the effort is only ¼ of the resistance, but the rope must be pulled four times the distance that the resistance is moved. This gives us a quick way to calculate the mechanical advantage of pulley systems. The number of ropes supporting the resistance will be the same as the value of the mechanical advantage. Such an arrangement of fixed and movable pulleys is called a **block and tackle.**

Suppose a workman were trying to lift a piano with a six-pulley block and tackle (three fixed and three movable pulleys). If the piano weighs 2400 N, how much effort would be required of the workman?

What is the mechanical advantage of the system? Since six ropes are attached to the resistance, the M.A. is 6. Therefore the required effort is ⅙ of the resistance, or 400 N.

$$\text{Effort} = \frac{\text{Resistance}}{\text{M.A.}} = \frac{2400 \text{ N}}{6} = 400 \text{ N}$$

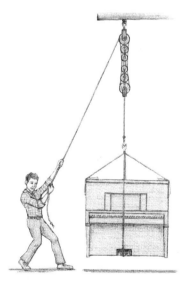

12-13 How does the workman "pay" for the reduced effort he achieves by lifting a piano with a six-pulley block and tackle?

Inclined Planes

Historians tell us that the ancient Egyptians did not have pulleys. This fact makes the construction of the pyramids an even more amazing feat of engineering. The simple machine that was used to move the giant limestone blocks into position was the **inclined plane.** Many earthen ramps were built during the construction process. Lighter stones could be slid up steeper ramps while the heavier stones required long, gradual inclines.

12-13 The huge stones that were used to build the pyramids could not have been moved into place without the mechanical advantage of an inclined plane.

The distance principle applied

An ancient papyrus dating from 1300 years before Christ gives the approximate measurements of one of these inclined planes: 384 m long and 32 m high. If the Egyptian engineers had lifted the stone directly into place 32 m above the ground, the work done would have been equal to the force needed to lift the stone multiplied by the distance (32 m). The work needed to lift a 6000-N block would be calculated this way:

$$W = F \times d$$
$$W = 6000 \text{ N} \times 32 \text{ m}$$
$$W = 192,000 \text{ N·m}$$
$$W = 192,000 \text{ J}$$

By sliding the stone up the ramp, the same 192,000 J of work would be accomplished with much less effort. Of course, the *distance principle* tells you that the savings in effort must be paid for in increased distance. How could the effort needed to slide the block up the ramp be calculated? You know the total work (192,000 J), and you know the distance over which that work will be accomplished (384 m). Therefore you can use the work equation to solve for the force (effort) needed to move the stone.

$$W = F \times d$$
$$192,000 \text{ N·m} = F \times 384 \text{ m}$$

If both sides are divided by the 384 m, you can solve for F.

$$\frac{192,000 \text{ N·m}}{384 \text{ m}} = \frac{F \times 384 \text{ m}}{384 \text{ m}}$$

$$\frac{192,000 \text{ N}}{384} = F$$

$$500 \text{ N} = F$$

Compare the effort needed to push the block up the inclined plane (500 N) with the resistance of the block (6000 N), and you will see why the Egyptians used this simple machine! Can you calculate the mechanical advantage of this incline? One of the ways to calculate M.A. is to divide resistance by effort. The resistance of the block was 6000 N while the effort needed to slide the block was 500 N. The mechanical advantage would be:

$$\frac{6000 \text{ N}}{500 \text{ N}} = 12$$

Different inclined planes have different mechanical advantages. A short, steep ramp has a lower mechanical advantage than a long ramp with a gradual slope. The distance principle indicates that the mechanical advantage of any inclined plane is the ratio of the length of the incline to its height:

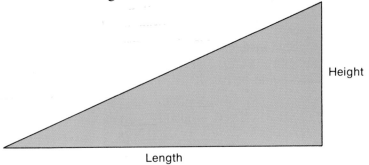

Height

Length

$$M.A. = \frac{\text{length of incline}}{\text{height}}$$

Of course, friction always opposes motion up an inclined plane. For these calculations, we have ignored the effects of this force. This keeps our calculations simple.

Today, inclined planes are fairly common. A stairway is a modified inclined plane. It takes a lot of effort to shinny up a pole or to climb a rope, but walking up a stairway is relatively easy. Steep mountains present a challenge to even the most powerful automobile engines. The force an engine can supply is limited. To overcome this problem, engineers design roads to wind back and forth, sloping gently as they go up a mountain. A smaller force applied over the longer distance is able to pull the car up the hill. Whether the car goes straight up the hill or winds back and forth, the total work done by the engine is the same.

Wedges

Two inclined planes placed bottom to bottom form a **wedge.** Wedges help woodsmen split logs more easily. The pyramid builders split the huge rocks they quarried with wedges. Some common examples of wedges are axes, hatchets, chisels, and knife blades.

Screws

An inclined plane wrapped around a cylinder or cone is a **screw.** Cylindrical screws are called bolts. A bolt is threaded so that it will accept and tightly hold a nut. Conical screws are designed to force their way into wood or other compressible materials.

The distance between two adjacent threads on a screw is called its **pitch.** If the pitch is small, the effort must be applied over a great distance. The screw's penetration is small compared to this distance. Therefore, a small pitch indicates a high mechanical advantage. A large pitch would indicate a low mechanical advantage. That is why screws with small pitches are easy to turn.

Table 12-14

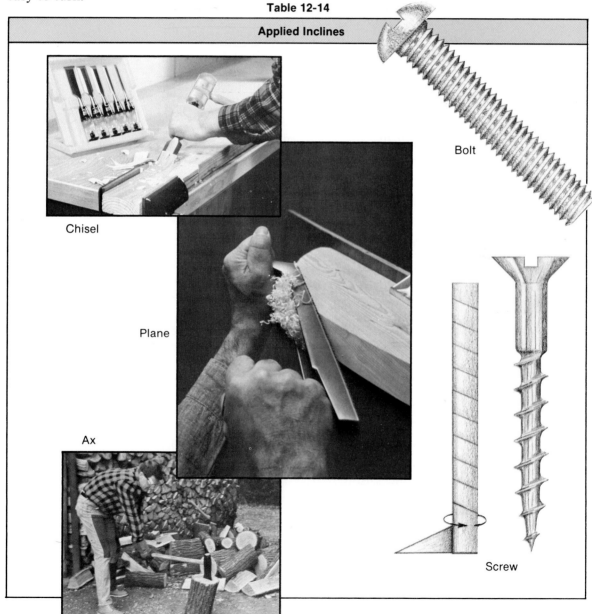

Applied Inclines

Chisel

Plane

Ax

Bolt

Screw

293

Scientifically Speaking

force	effort
tension	effort arm
friction	resistance
lubricants	resistance arm
Hooke's law	second-class lever
buoyant force	mechanical advantage (M.A.)
Archimedes' principle	third-class lever
work	wheel and axle
joule (J)	pulley
power	block and tackle
watt (W)	inclined plane
lever	wedge
fulcrum	screw
law of moments	pitch
first-class lever	

Questions to Talk Over

1. Sledding is popular in areas where winter snows blanket the ground. What allows a sled to overcome friction? Does the same principle apply to other winter sports, such as skiing and ice-skating?
2. Imagine a two-story building with two staircases, one of which is spiral-shaped. If identical twins were given equal loads to carry to the second floor and they were required to use different staircases, would the choice of staircase make any difference? Why?
3. Karen decided to take up isometric exercises. Her first exercise was to press her palms together and push with all her strength. Although Karen may have been improving her physical fitness, was she accomplishing any work? Explain your answer.
4. Make a list of household machines that use levers.
5. At a hydroelectric plant, giant valves control the flow of water through the turbines. Some of the valves are opened and closed by turning a wheel and screw. How do these simple machines enable a man to close these valves in spite of the tremendous pressure of the water?

MECHANICS

CHAPTER
13

In "The Boscombe Valley Mystery," Sherlock Holmes rescued a young man who was falsely accused of murdering his father. Young McCarthey was nearby when his father was murdered and, in the eyes of Scotland Yard's Inspector Lestrade, he had the perfect motive: he would inherit a large fortune! But the inspector had overlooked some very important clues when he made his hasty arrest.

Holmes intervened to show that the real key to the mysterious murder lay in the footprints at the scene of the crime. Yes, the inspector had found the son's footprints near the corpse, but he had missed another set of footprints—very unusual ones! After studying these prints, Holmes concluded that a tall man who limped with his right leg and wore thick-soled hunting boots

13-1 In this case, Holmes has overlooked the obvious!

committed the murder. Lestrade laughed at Holmes's description of the murderer, for it did not fit his prisoner, the young McCarthey, at all. Yet Holmes's careful collection of clues before he jumped to a conclusion had led him to the real murderer. Soon the man Holmes described was captured and a thankful young heir was set free!

In this story, Holmes taught Lestrade the importance of collecting clues before determining motive, a lesson that Lestrade never seemed to learn. In physics, scientists ignored the same lesson for centuries. Early Greek philosophers tried to explain motion by determining the "motive"—*why* things move—before they had collected all of the clues—*how* things move. Of course, this led them to many incorrect conclusions. Aristotle believed that arrows flew through the air because the atmosphere closed behind them and pushed them forward! It was not until Galileo (GAL uh LAY oh) Galilei challenged these faulty notions in the seventeenth century that scientists began rethinking the way things move. Galileo proposed that we should study *how* things move before we conclude *why* they move. Like Sherlock Holmes, he thought it was best to collect clues rather than jump to an immediate conclusion about motive. His work started a revolution in physics that was completed by the English physicist Isaac Newton. The modern study of motion, called **mechanics** (mih KAN iks), grew from Newton's work. Today we split the study of motion into two parts: **kinematics** (KIN uh MAT iks), the description of *how* things move; and **dynamics** (dye NAM iks), the description of *why* things move. Of course, in our study of motion the *clues* of kinematics should precede the *motives* of dynamics!

Kinematics

The American pioneers often crossed bare stretches of desert on their westward journey. Sometimes a group of travelers

13-2 The wagon trains used landmarks to find their way across the vast plains to the West.

would lose the trail and wander through the desert until they ran out of water and died in the burning sand. A water hole might be just a few miles away, but without landmarks to guide them, people were often misled by the endless sameness of the desert sand.

Frame of reference

In science we need landmarks to find the trail. Without them, our studies are as futile as the lost pioneers' wanderings. Scientists call such a landmark a *point of reference.* A group of these landmarks form a **frame of reference.** Without these the study of physics would be pointless.

In the study of motion, the frame of reference determines what motion will be described. How fast are you moving right now? Suppose that you are in a classroom in New York City. A person in the room with you would claim that you are standing perfectly still, but if someone were observing you from a station-

13-3 If you were in space, your frame of reference would show you that the Earth is rotating very rapidly, even though it seems to us that our planet is standing still.

ary point above the North Pole, he would observe you moving approximately 310 meters per second! The person in the room with you does not "see" you move because he is moving at the same speed. The observer stationed over the North Pole sees that you are moving with the earth's rotation. If someone could observe you from outside our solar system, his frame of reference would allow him to perceive that you are really moving more than 29,000 meters per second as the earth whirls around the sun!

No single frame of reference is the *only* one for all motion. You must state which frame of reference you are using to describe a type of motion.

Speed

Speed is the rate at which an object changes position. The length covered in a change of position is called a *distance*. The equation for speed is $v = d/t$ (v is the speed and d is the distance an object covers in the time t). The unit for speed is meters per second (m/s). The distance that the object moves in a given amount of time is its speed. A car that covers 21 m in 1 s is moving at a speed of 21 m/s. A bicycle may cover 21 m in 3 s; its speed is 7 m/s. The car is moving three times faster than the bicycle.

If you know the speed of the car as well as the distance it will cover, you can calculate the amount of time that the trip will take. Suppose that a friend's house is 1.5 km away. How long would it take to cover that distance if you could maintain an

13-4 The route to your friend's house is marked on this map. Why would you use your average speed on the trip rather than your fastest speed to calculate the time it took to make the trip?

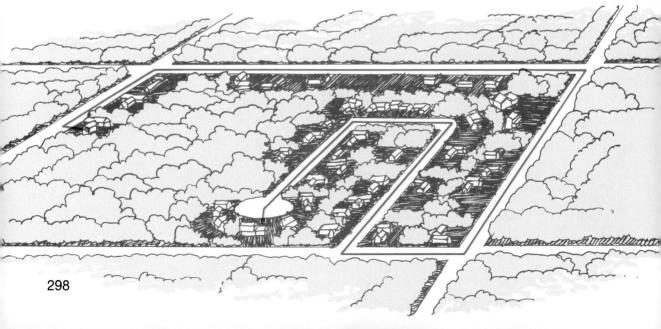

average speed of 15 m/s the entire trip? Divide the distance of 1.5 km (1500 m) by the speed of 15 m/s and you obtain the time for the whole trip: 100 seconds, or 1 minute and 40 seconds.

$$\frac{\text{distance}}{\text{speed}} = \text{time of trip}$$

If the average speed of a vehicle is known and the amount of time that the trip takes is also known, then the distance of the trip can be computed. We could use this equation: speed · time = distance. The distance the vehicle travels is the product of the speed and the time. It takes 2 hours for a Japanese bullet train to go from Tokyo to Nagoya. Bullet trains can attain speeds of 225 km per hour. Can you calculate the distance?

$$(225 \text{ km/hr}) (2 \text{ hr}) = 450 \text{ km}$$

13-5 Modern bullet trains speed Japanese commuters to their destinations. How long would it take a commuter to travel home if his house were 112.5 km from Tokyo?

Velocity

Velocity and speed are different quantities. The **velocity** (vuh LAHS uh tee) of an object involves both its speed and its direction. Therefore the velocity gives more information about its motion. Compare a velocity and a speed. A velocity of 6 m/s *north* is different from a speed of 6 m/s. The speed value does not depend on direction; it is the same whether it "points" east, west, north, or south.

Acceleration

Speed and velocity can change. When a sprinter hears the starting gun, he changes his speed from rest to a high speed in a short amount of time. This is called acceleration. **Acceleration** (ak SEL uh RAY shun) is the rate of the increase of velocity in a given interval of time. A similar term describes a decrease in velocity. **Deceleration** (dee SEL uh RAY shun) is the rate at which an object or person "slows down" in a given interval of time.

Acceleration and deceleration are both expressed by the same equation: $a = (\triangle v)/t$, where a is the acceleration (or deceleration), t is the time interval involved in the change in the

13-6 When does a runner accelerate and decelerate during a sprint? Is there a point during the race when he is not doing either?

speed, and ($\triangle$v) is the change in the speed. The delta (DEL tuh) symbol ($\triangle$) used in this equation stands for the words *change in.* Since acceleration and deceleration both involve changes in speed, this symbol makes it easier to write the equation. The change in the speed is found by subtracting the starting speed from the final speed for the time interval. For example, if a car moving at 5 m/s accelerates to 20 m/s, subtract 5 m/s from 20 m/s (20 m/s - 5 m/s = 15 m/s). If the change takes 5 s, the acceleration is

$$\frac{15 \text{ m/s}}{5 \text{ s}} = \frac{3 \text{ m/s}}{\text{s}} = 3 \text{ (m/s)/s}$$

Notice that the units of acceleration are those of speed divided by time. Instead of writing (m/s)/s (that is, meters per second, per second), physicists frequently write the units of acceleration as m/s^2 (meters per second squared). Deceleration is calculated the same way. For example, suppose that a car comes to a stop from a speed of 30 m/s in 10 s. The rate of change in the velocity is 0 m/s - 30 m/s = -30 m/s. (The negative sign indicates a deceleration.) The deceleration is

$$\frac{-30 \text{ m/s}}{10\text{s}} = -3 \text{ m/s}^2$$

Calculations like these tell us how things move, but they do not tell us why things move. Kinematics is only the description of motion. We must enter the domain of dynamics in order to find out why things move.

Dynamics

Medieval scientists believed that all things would slow down and eventually stop if left to themselves. This idea seems logical enough. If your engine quits, the car rolls to a stop. If you stop pedaling your bike, it will slow down and fall over. But logical as it appears, this assumption is definitely wrong! The natural tendency of all things is not to slow down and stop. Quite the contrary, when no outside forces work on an object, it will continue in its original state of motion. That is, it will stay at rest if it was at rest; if it was moving, it will keep moving in the same direction and at the same speed.

The Italian physicist Galileo was the first to investigate this principle. On the basis of his experiments, Galileo chose to believe that objects would continue moving indefinitely unless they were affected by some outside influence. The English physicist Isaac Newton later extended Galileo's studies. Their work forms the foundation for the area of dynamics—the study of *why* things move.

Newton's first law of motion

The push or pull of forces can affect the motion of an object only if they are unbalanced. Consider two boys pushing on a door, one on the inside and the other on the outside. As long as both boys push on the door with equal strength, the door will not move. But suppose that one of the boys slips. He can no longer push on the door with as much strength. Consequently, the door will move in his direction. These unequal forces on the door are examples of **unbalanced forces.** Only unbalanced forces can change the motion of an object.

Have you ever pushed a car to a gas station? If you have, you know how difficult it was to get the car moving. You were applying an unbalanced force to an object at rest, trying to overcome its tendency to remain at rest. Of course, once you get an object moving, it presents a different problem. Have you ever

13-7 What forces are resisting motion in the stalled car? Why would the car roll more easily downhill?

13-8 In the motion of these bumper cars, a transfer of momentum occurs. The first car hits a stopped car and transfers its momentum. It will come to rest while the second car jolts forward. Under ideal frictionless conditions, a complete transfer of momentum could occur. What prevents a complete transfer in the bumper cars?

tried to stop a baseball with your bare hands? If you have, you know from painful experience that an object in motion will continue in motion until an outside, unbalanced force acts on it. The property of matter which causes it to resist a change in the state of motion is called **inertia** (in UR shuh). The word *inertia* comes from a Latin word which means laziness, sluggishness, or unwillingness to change.

You will be impressed with the effects of inertia if you ride in a bumper car. When you slam into another car, you lunge forward in your seat. The bumper car stops, but you do not! Your inertia (your tendency to stay in motion) keeps you moving forward. On a runaway-mine-car ride, your body demonstrates inertia by knocking against the side of the car as you whirl around a curve. What has happened? Because of inertia, your body continues in a straight line as the car turns on the track. You continue to move in a straight line until the side of the car *changes* your motion—not very gently!

All of these observations can be summed up in one statement: objects at rest tend to remain at rest, and objects in motion tend to remain in motion (in the same direction and at the same speed) until acted on by some outside, unbalanced force. This is called **Newton's first law of motion.**

Before the sixteenth century, most people believed that the earth was stationary. If the earth moved, they reasoned, we should be able to detect some effects of that motion. For example, if a person jumped a foot off the ground, he should come down in a different place. While he was in the air, the earth would shift its position under him. You know from observation, however, that he will come down in the same place. Until they fully understood Newton's first law of motion, scientists could not solve this problem.

The earth is moving, but so is the person; and the person is moving in the same direction as the earth. The person also moves at the same speed as the earth. Because the inertia of his motion keeps him in the same place *in relation to the earth*, he does not appear to be moving at all.

Newton's second law of motion

One of the benefits of a small, lightweight car is that moving it takes very little force. Such cars have small engines that use very little fuel. Larger, heavier cars need bigger, more powerful engines. Why? Because they have more inertia. An object with a large mass resists change more than one with less mass. Therefore it takes a larger force to set a large mass in motion than it takes to set a small mass in motion. In fact, mass is the measure of the inertia of an object.

A small, four-cylinder engine can easily accelerate a lightweight economy car from 0 to 80 km/h in less than 10 s. But what would happen if a four-cylinder engine were placed in a full-sized pickup truck? The same acceleration would take much more time. If the same force is applied, a smaller mass will be accelerated at a greater rate than a larger mass.

13-9 Racing cars often have light fiberglass bodies. Why would a racer design his car this way?

This principle is applied in the design of lightweight racing bicycles. A standard bike may have a mass of 15 kg. Every pump of the pedals must accelerate the mass of the bike as well as the mass of the rider. If the mass of the bike is reduced, the same force on the pedals will cause a greater acceleration. This is why racing bikes are manufactured from very lightweight materials. Sometimes holes are drilled through various parts to reduce the mass of the racing bike even further. The mass of a fully equipped racing bicycle is usually under 10 kg!

Bicycle racers train for a race with a daily schedule of strenuous exercise. They develop strong leg muscles that are capable of applying much more force to the pedal than most of us could. If you tried to race one of these athletes, he would probably leave you in the dust even if you were riding a bicycle like his. The size of the force, as well as the mass of the object, affects the rate of the acceleration. The force applied by the muscled legs of a well-trained racer would give him an easy victory over an average bike rider.

These observations show direct relationship between force, mass, and acceleration for any given object. This relationship is

13-10 Many hard hours of training, as well as specially built, very light bikes, make the difference between winning and losing in a bicycle race. Do you remember which simple machine is used in bicycles?

stated in **Newton's second law of motion:** the value of an unbalanced force *(F)* is equal to its mass *(m)* multiplied by its acceleration *(a)*.

$$F = m \cdot a$$

We can use this equation to calculate the force needed to give an object a certain acceleration. An economy car has a mass of approximately 1000 kg. How much force would it take to accelerate such a car 10 m/s^2?

$$F = 1000 \text{ kg} \cdot 10 \text{ m/s}^2$$
$$= 10{,}000 \text{ kg m/s}^2, \text{ or } 10{,}000 \text{ N}$$

(Note: A kilogram-meter per second squared is the same as a newton.)

Now let us compare this value to the force needed to give a full-sized car the same acceleration. A full-sized car has a mass of at least 2000 kg.

$$F = 2000 \text{ kg} \cdot 10 \text{ m/s}^2$$
$$= 20{,}000 \text{ kg} \cdot \text{m/s}^2, \text{ or } 20{,}000 \text{ N}$$

A full-sized car requires *twice* the force to give it the *same* acceleration! Does this help you to understand why smaller cars are often called "economy cars"?

Newton's third law of motion

Have you ever jumped out of a small boat into the water? When you dive into the water, the boat moves *backward*. The action of the dive causes the reaction of the movement of the boat. This observation demonstrates the **action-reaction principle**, or **Newton's third law of motion.** The third law says that for every action, there is an equal (in strength) but opposite (in direction) reaction. The action force is always exerted on a different body than the reaction force. In this case, the action force was exerted on the boat, and the reaction force was exerted on your body.

Some action and reaction forces do not involve motion. For example, when you push on a wall, the wall pushes back on you! How do we know that the wall pushes back? What would happen if the wall were not there? (Warning: leaning against a block of atmosphere at the top of a cliff can be hazardous to your health!) If the wall were not there, you would fall over. The force that the wall exerts on your body is the reaction to the push of your body. What causes the push of the wall? As the molecules of your body try to invade the space already occupied by the wall molecules, the wall molecules push back. Otherwise you would fall through walls!

FACETS
OF BASIC SCIENCE

Getting a Lift out of Newton's Third Law

What makes a helicopter hover? Helicopters apply the action-reaction principle. The whirling blades are angled so that they push the air particles downward. This is the *action.* In turn, the air particles push the blades upward. This *reaction* force is called *lift.* When the lift is greater than the weight of the helicopter, the helicopter climbs upward. When the lift is the same as the weight, the helicopter hovers.

The action-reaction principle is also applied in modern airplanes and jets. The propellers of airplanes and the turbines of jets power an aircraft by pushing air particles and exhaust gases backward. The reaction force of these particles pushes the aircraft forward. Bell Aircraft and NASA are working together on a unique combination of helicopter and airplane for the United States Army. This special aircraft is capable of both vertical takeoff (like a helicopter) and horizontal flight (like a traditional aircraft). Its oversized propellers can be rotated on its wings. At takeoff the propellers are tilted upward to provide maximum lift. As the plane rises, the propellers can be leveled for horizontal flight.

307

FACETS
OF BASIC SCIENCE

Orbit 2N

"Four, three, ignition sequence, one, liftoff!" The crowd cheered as the huge booster lifted the special payload into space. America had launched her first permanent space station.

Several days later, the station reached an important rendezvous with two space shuttles. As the bays of the shuttles opened, a fantastic panorama greeted the construction crews. From their vantage point in the dark vastness of space, they viewed the blue earth on one side and the dimpled face of the moon on the other. This, the space station's final location, was called the 2N position. Why had this location been chosen?

NASA scientists had long studied the effect of the earth's gravitational pull on the orbits of satellites. From time to time stories appeared in newspapers about satellites that had reentered the earth's atmosphere. Apparently, the earth's

gravity caused satellite orbits to "decay" after a while, pulling the satellites back into the atmosphere. The results were sometimes fantastic. As a satellite sped through the upper layers of the atmosphere, tremendous friction transformed the hurtling metal into a ball of flame. At night, viewers were treated to a cometlike streak across the sky. But this entertainment could prove dangerous. Small satellites "burned up" quickly during their journey through the atmosphere, but larger objects, like a space station, would send huge chunks of molten metal crashing to the earth. If these satellite remnants fell in a populated area, the results could be tragic! To prevent such a catastrophe, NASA scientists needed a "gravity-free" location for America's first permanent space station.

Both the moon and the earth exert a gravitational force, but

because the moon has less mass than the earth, its gravity is much weaker. Scientists calculated that as a spaceship traveled from the earth to the moon, the earth's gravitational force would become weaker and the moon's gravitational force would become stronger. At a point 340,000 km from the earth (about five-sixths of the way to the moon), the gravitational pull of the moon would exactly equal the earth's pull. Since at this point the earth and moon would pull in opposite directions, the two forces would cancel each other. At this point, called the 2N position, any object would be practically free from gravity.

Although America has not yet launched a permanent space station, this story is not far from fact. The possibility exists that the United States will develop such a program in the near future.

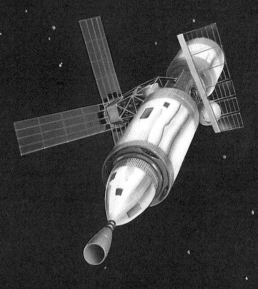

The benefits of a gravity-free space station would be enormous. Permanent telescopes, unhindered by clouds or smog, could map the far reaches of the universe. Huge solar collector cells, also unobstructed by the earth's atmosphere, could reap the sun's energy and beam it back to earth. Another exciting possibility that has yet to be developed is the construction of space factories. The earth's gravity hinders many manufacturing processes. For instance, when glass lenses are made, gravity causes the cooling glass to sag. This bending limits the precision and size of the lenses. New degrees of precision could stem from the availability of a gravity-free workshop.

Biological factories would also be possible in a permanent space station. Many disease-fighting drugs are made by bacteria that reproduce much faster in a zero-gravity environment. A zero-gravity laboratory could produce large amounts of these medicines in a very short time.

A permanent space station could also serve as an outer-space switchboard, relaying radio and television messages around the world. It is even possible that such a space station could be used as a supply depot or a way station for mining the minerals of the moon. Lastly, a permanent space station would be a valuable addition to our national defense. This important function could determine the outcome of a major military conflict.

Of course, some action and reaction forces do involve motion. Without them, rockets could not fly. The burning fuel coming out of the rocket engine is really just a continuous, directed explosion. The bell housing of the rocket engine directs the explosion backward. The *action* of redirecting the hot gases causes a *reaction* force on the rocket itself. This force pushes the rocket forward. Did you ever wonder how rockets travel through the vacuum of space? Because the reaction force to the action of the engines propels the rocket, the hot gases do not need air to push against.

Gravity

Have you ever wondered *why* what goes up must come down? Things fall toward the ground because the earth attracts objects towards itself. This attraction is called the earth's **gravity.** In fact, all the objects in the universe attract each other. These attractions are called **action-at-a-distance forces** because they act on objects without touching them. How can a force act on an object without touching it? That is a very good question! In fact, it is such a good question that it has stumped scientists for many

13-11 Many thousands of newtons of thrust must be developed to create the expected reaction from the rocket blast.

years. Although we know that gravity exists, we do not know how it works.

We do know that gravitational (GRAV uh TAY shun ul) forces are directly related to the mass of an object. In fact, only very massive objects such as planets and stars exert enough gravity to be felt. The gravity of the sun is very strong. The gravity of the earth is much less. Why? Because the gravitational pull depends on the mass of the object; the more massive the object, the greater its gravitational pull.

We also realize that gravity has a limited range of influence. For example, by the time the unmanned spacecrafts Voyager I and II traveled past Mars, the Earth's gravity no longer had any noticeable effect on them. As the distance from an object's center of gravity increases, the influence of its gravity becomes weaker. There are slight differences in gravity even on the earth's surface. Our planet is not a perfect sphere; it is slightly flattened at the poles. Would an Eskimo experience a slightly stronger pull from gravity than a person living near the equator?

Even though we cannot fully understand the force, we can measure it. You probably know the strength of gravity's pull on your body. It is your weight. In the metric system you would measure your weight in newtons. The average ninth-grader weighs 500 N.

13-12 This astronaut appears to be completely weightless, but in reality he is not. His aircraft is accelerating at the same rate he is, so his weight does not affect his motion in the aircraft. Where would you have to travel to be completely weightless?

13-13 Galileo may have performed his experiments with falling bodies from the top of the Leaning Tower of Pisa.

Falling bodies

Galileo began his experiments when he was a professor at the University of Pisa in Italy. A popular story says that Galileo dropped various weights from the famous leaning tower to investigate their rate of fall. Although there may be more fiction than fact in the details of the story, we do know that Galileo reached a surprising number of correct conclusions about the way objects fall.

The scientists of Galileo's day held firmly to the 2000-year-old ideas of the Greek philosopher Aristotle. Aristotle had proclaimed that a heavier object should fall faster than a lighter object. Galileo challenged this faulty conclusion in two ways—by a "thought experiment" and by an actual physical experiment.

Galileo's "thought experiment" showed clear thinking and originality. He imagined two small, equal weights falling side by side. If the weights were released from the same height at the same time, they obviously would strike the ground at the same instant. If the experiment were repeated again with a light but loose chain connecting the weights, the same thing would happen. He imagined that the weights were dropped repeatedly and the chain was shortened each time. Eventually, the two weights would be closely bound together, forming a single weight. This doubled weight would fall in the same amount of time as each of the smaller weights. Aristotle had said that the doubled weight should hit the ground in half the time the single weights took to fall. Galileo's scientific insight told him that there should be no difference between them.

Galileo later tried dropping many different objects. He found that if the masses of the two objects were great enough compared to their surface areas, then size, shape, and weight made little difference in how fast they fell. You can prove this for yourself. Try dropping a heavy book and a pencil from the same height. They will fall side by side and land at the same time. Remember that the book has more mass than the pencil. Because of this greater mass, the earth attracts the book with a greater force than it attracts the pencil. But the book also has more *inertia* than the pencil, which keeps it from accelerating faster. The force and the inertia exactly offset each other.

Now try dropping a pencil and a piece of paper at the same time. The pencil hits the floor first. In this case, another force enters the picture—*air resistance*. The air greatly slows down the paper because of the paper's small inertia and large surface area.

13-14 What did Galileo conclude from his thought experiment in which two chained weights hit the ground at the same time?

Now wad the paper into a ball and drop the paper and the pencil again. What happens now that the surface area of the paper is decreased? A smaller surface area will cause a lower air resistance.

What would happen if no air were present when the uncrumpled paper and the pencil were dropped? Galileo predicted that they would fall at exactly the same rate, but to test his theory you would need to drop the paper and pencil in a sealed room with all the air removed by a vacuum pump. Or you could

take your experiment to the surface of the moon where there is practically no atmosphere at all.

Astronaut David Scott did just that! On the *Apollo 15* mission, he took a hammer and a falcon feather (from the Air Force mascot) with him in the lunar landing module. Once on the surface of the moon, he dropped the hammer and the feather before the watchful eye of a television camera. In exactly 1.33 seconds the feather and hammer simultaneously hit the surface of the moon!

13-15 *Apollo 15* astronaut David R. Scott tried an elementary physics experiment on the moon's surface. In this unusual laboratory, he dropped a hammer and a feather from waist level to find out if both objects would indeed fall at the same rate. They did!

Gravitational acceleration

How much will the pull of gravity accelerate an object? Suppose that a steel ball 1 cm in diameter is dropped from the top of a ten-story building. A velocity-measuring device is set up to record the velocities at given intervals of time. At the end of 1 s, the ball is falling at a rate of 9.8 m/s. At the end of 2 s, the ball has a velocity of 19.6 m/s downward. At the end of 3 s, the ball has reached a velocity of 29.4 m/s downward. The velocity increases by 9.8 m/s for every second the ball falls. Therefore, the acceleration of the ball due to gravity is 9.8 m/s per second, or 9.8 m/s^2. Near the surface of the earth, all objects are accelerated at an average rate of 9.8 m/s. How fast would the steel ball be traveling after 4 s?

Scientists have discovered that the distance that an object falls can be calculated from its acceleration due to gravity and the length of time it falls. Suppose that you wanted to measure the height of a building near your school. If you dropped a small steel ball from the top of that building and carefully timed its descent, you could solve this equation to find the height of that building:

$$\text{distance} = \tfrac{1}{2}\,(9.8 \text{ m/s}^2) \cdot (t)^2$$

If the steel ball took 2.00 s to fall (of course, you would need a very accurate timepiece!), the equation would read:

$$\text{distance} = \tfrac{1}{2}\,(9.8 \text{ m/s}^2) \cdot (2.00 \text{ s})^2$$

$$d = (4.9 \text{ m/s}^2) \cdot (4.00 \text{ s}^2)$$

$$d = \frac{4.9\text{m} \cdot 4.00 \text{ s}^2}{\text{s}^2}$$

$$d = 19.6 \text{ m}$$

Therefore the building is 19.6 m tall.

FACETS
OF BASIC SCIENCE

Pendulum Motion

Pendulums (PEN joo lumz) first caught Galileo's attention as he watched a chandelier swing back and forth in a cathedral in Italy. He observed that the **period** of the pendulum (how long it takes to swing back and forth to make one complete cycle) was the same whether the chandelier made large swings or small swings. Later, Galileo made experimental pendulums of different weights; these may have been no more than weights hanging on pieces of string. He found that the weight of the pendulum does not affect its period. The only variable that seemed to matter was the *length* of the pendulum.

One other factor, however, can change the period of the pendulum. If its location is changed, its acceleration may change because of a difference in gravity. Where the acceleration due to gravity *(g)* is greater, the pendulum will swing faster. Where *g* is less, the pendulum will swing more slowly. At the surface of Jupiter, a pendulum would swing considerably faster than it swings on the earth; its period would be much shorter. At the surface of a very small astronomical body that has a low mass, such as the moon, a pendulum would swing very slowly; it would have an extremely long period. If you *could* put a pendulum on the "surface" of the sun, it would swing 12.8 times faster there than it would on the surface of the moon!

Acceleration Due to Gravity at Different Places in the Solar System

Body	g at surface in m/s^2
Sun	274.4
Earth	9.80
Moon	1.67
Mars	3.92
Jupiter	26.46
Saturn	11.76
Neptune	9.80

When an object falls through the atmosphere, it eventually reaches a **terminal** (TUR muh nul) **velocity**, the highest velocity at which that object can fall. What limits the velocity of any falling object? As the object falls through the air, the air pushes against it. This push, the air resistance, increases as the object accelerates. Eventually, the push of the air resistance will become as great as the pull of the object's weight. The object stops accelerating. Why? When the force of the air resistance equals the force due to the pull of gravity on the object (its weight), the forces are balanced. Since there is no unbalanced force on the object, there is no force to accelerate the object.

Different objects have different terminal velocities. Objects with very little surface area can reach very high speeds as they fall, but light objects with large surface areas fall at much slower speeds. How does this principle apply to a parachute?

13-16 The terminal velocity of a parachute allows parachutists like these to land safely. What role does the large surface area of a parachute play in determining its terminal velocity?

Scientifically Speaking

mechanics

kinematics

dynamics

frame of reference

speed

velocity

acceleration

deceleration

unbalanced forces

inertia

Newton's first law of motion

Newton's second law of motion

action-reaction principle

Newton's third law of motion

gravity

action-at-a-distance forces

period

terminal velocity

Questions to Talk Over

1. John and Bill left their houses at the same time to go to the grocery store. If Bill's house is twice as far from the store as John's house and Bill and John arrived at the store at the same time, what does that indicate about their relative speeds?
2. Describe the famous race between the tortoise and the hare in terms of acceleration, velocity, and deceleration.
3. What might happen if the earth suddenly stopped spinning?
4. Newton's third law states that for every action there is an equal and opposite reaction. Pretend you are accidentally locked out of your space vessel. All you have is forty rubber bands in the pocket of your space suit. Could you reach the deep-space station that is four hundred yards away?
5. You realized that you forgot to strap on your parachute seconds after you ejected from your F-16 jet fighter. Your last recorded altitude over Lake Michigan was 3000 m. If you are to have a chance at surviving the fall, what is the best way to position your body? Why?

JOHANNES KEPLER
GERMAN ASTRONOMER (1571-1630)

"Knowest thou the ordinances of heaven? canst thou set the dominion thereof in the earth?" (Job 38:33)

Sir Isaac Newton once commented, "If I have seen further, it is by standing on the shoulders of giants." Johannes Kepler (yo HAHN us KEP lur) was one of those giants. Kepler was the first man to demonstrate that the motions of the planets are precise, predictable, and obedient to definite rules. The German astronomer's three laws of planetary motion are used extensively today in calculating the orbits of satellites and in mapping routes for space travel. Kepler is also

called "the father of modern optics" because of his masterful mathematical analysis of lenses and mirrors.

Kepler, a devout Lutheran, trusted Christ as his Saviour at an early age. Although he was persecuted for his Protestant beliefs, he remained true to the Lord through his entire life. Kepler saw himself as God's instrument for revealing the details of His handiwork to men. "Since we astronomers are priests of the highest God in regard to the book of nature," he once wrote, "it befits us to be thoughtful not of the glory of our minds, but rather, above all else,

of the glory of God." Seeking to give his children a thoroughly Christian upbringing, Kepler wrote Bible study guides to aid their understanding. One of these guides, "The Body and Blood of Jesus Christ Our Saviour," is still preserved in the University of Tübingen (TOO bing un) library.

Michael Maestlin, whom Kepler met at the University of Tübingen, inspired Kepler for his life's work. Though he taught his students the old geocentric (earth-centered) theory of the solar system, Maestlin exposed them to the newer ideas of Copernicus in a way that kindled

320

Kepler's imagination. His consuming curiosity compelled Kepler to study the subject on his own. After-class discussions with Maestlin, who was a fellow Christian, sparked new ideas that would lead to the publication of his first book.

In 1591 Kepler graduated from the Faculty of Arts at Tübingen, receiving the equivalent of today's master of arts degree. At that time he felt certain that he was destined for the Lutheran ministry. Accordingly, he enrolled at the Theological Faculty and continued his studies. Before he completed his theological examinations, however, an unexpected opportunity arose. The death of the mathematics and astronomy teacher at the Protestant seminary in Graz, Austria, had created a vacancy. When the senate of the University of Tübingen was asked to recommend a candidate, they chose Kepler. His extraordinary ability had not gone unnoticed.

Kepler's years at Graz were both challenging and rewarding. Here he produced his first serious scientific treatise, *The Mystery of the Universe*, an ambitious geometric description of the solar system. The work closed with a magnificent hymn of praise to the Creator. The treatise was well received, and, because he shrewdly placed it in the hands of several leading astronomers (including Galileo and Tycho Brahe [TEE ko BRAH]), Kepler's name became known in several of the scientific centers of Europe.

As the sixteenth century drew to a close, the political and religious conditions in Graz grew increasingly turbulent. Faced with severe religious persecution, Kepler and his family fled from Graz in 1600. Earlier the same year he had accepted an invitation to visit Prague to see Tycho Brahe, imperial mathematician to Rudolph II, Emperor of Bohemia. Recognized as the world's leading astronomer, Tycho had been making remarkably accurate observations of the planets for twenty years. It now remained for someone to "make sense" out of the massive columns of data he had assembled. Kepler wanted access to these observations, and Tycho was eager to add a theoretician of Kepler's caliber to his staff of assistants. It was indeed Providence that brought together these two giants whose abilities complemented each other so well. Kepler was aware of the unique opportunity that had been afforded him and thankful for the strange turn of events that brought it to pass. He later said, "I see how God let me be bound with Tycho through an unalterable fate and did not let me be separated from him by the most oppressive hardships."

When Kepler arrived in Prague, Tycho assigned him the task of interpreting observations of the planet Mars. These calculations occupied the German astronomer for many years. Kepler explored numerous blind alleys and was often forced to start over again. However, his perseverance bore fruit. One by one he formulated the three laws of planetary motion familiar to every student of astronomy:

1. Planets move in ellipses with the sun at one focus.
2. An imaginary line from the center of the sun to the center of a planet always sweeps over an equal area in equal time.
3. The squares of the periods of revolution are to each other as the cubes of the mean distances from the sun.

Kepler's third law provided a foundation for Newton's law of gravitation just half a century later. Kepler was well ahead of his time; no one claimed to have anticipated his discoveries. In fact, to other astronomers of his day, the area and ellipse laws were new, unorthodox, and difficult to understand.

Kepler's later life was one of hardships—sickness and death in his family, religious persecution, war, a fire, and a trial in which his mother was falsely accused of witchcraft. But his faith in Christ brought him triumphantly through these tribulations, and he gave God the glory for His sustaining grace.

Kepler's name has been immortalized by his three laws of planetary motion. A prominent crater on the moon has been named in his honor. His native Germany has paid him homage by erecting elaborate monuments to him in Regensburg and Weil der Stadt. His birthplace in Weil der Stadt has been converted into an attractive museum. Any fame he achieved, however, was simply a by-product of his lifelong endeavor to glorify the name of the heavenly Father. "Let also my name perish," Kepler stated, "if only the name of God the Father . . . is thereby elevated."

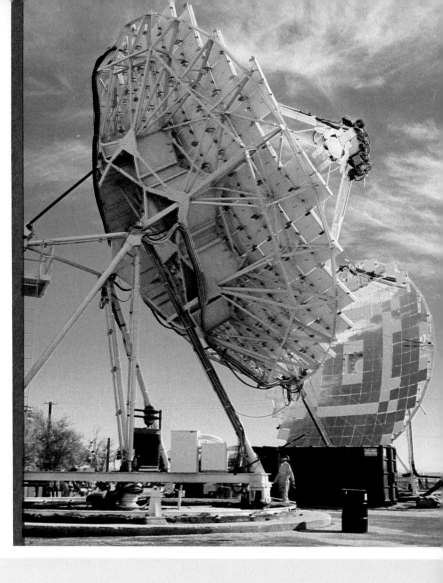

ENERGY

CHAPTER
14

Everyone seems to be talking about energy these days.
"I just don't have the energy I used to have."
"Our appliances are energy efficient."
"This new car is rated best for fuel efficiency."
"These granola bars are high in energy value."
With all this emphasis on energy, you would think that everyone understands exactly what energy is. Do we? What is **energy**?

Matter and energy are two related facets of our physical universe. Matter is the substance of the universe, while energy is the mover of matter. This simple statement represents a very sophisticated idea. It is easy to understand what matter is.

Matter makes up all the things around you. It is everything that has mass and occupies space. You can examine matter. You can see it or touch it or taste it or smell it.

But can you pick up energy and examine it? No—we recognize the presence of energy in other ways. When you see a red-hot bar of iron, a moving car, a coiled spring, a can of gasoline, or a rock balanced on the edge of a cliff, you know that each of these has energy. Do these examples have something in common that might help us to understand what energy is?

In all these examples, energy is the capacity to perform work. Every time something does work or has the potential to do work, energy is transferred or stored. We can observe energy as it works. We see the thermal energy of a blast furnace do work as it melts steel by increasing its molecular motion. The mechanical energy of a thresher does work as it harvests corn. The sound energy of a sonic boom does work when it smashes glass. The light energy of the sun can actually work by pushing a solar sail through space.

14-1 If all the earth's fuels were gathered together and burned at the same rate as the sun "burns," they would be consumed in only four days.

Forms of Energy

Scientists theorize that the sun converts 657 million tons of hydrogen into 653 million tons of helium every second. What happens to the missing 4 million tons of matter? They are converted into energy and discharged into space. The sun releases its energy in many different forms: light and heat from its solar flame, nuclear energy from its plasma furnace, and electrical and magnetic energy from its sunspots.

Today scientists recognize at least eight forms of energy: **thermal energy, light energy, sound energy, chemical energy, electrical energy, magnetic energy, mechanical energy,** and **nuclear energy.** Each form of energy is the capacity to do work.

Thermal energy

Thermal energy is related to the motion of molecules or ions in matter. The more vigorous the motion of these particles, the more thermal energy a substance possesses.

Thermal energy from our sun directly or indirectly powers much of nature. For example, the earth's atmosphere (powered by thermal energy) acts as a giant wind engine. The sun's rays are stronger near the equator than they are in the polar regions. Since the sun's rays quickly heat the tropical air, the cooler, denser polar air flows in to displace it. This air flow is twisted by

the rotation of the earth and disturbed by local atmospheric conditions. The result is the pattern of winds that wrap around the earth.

Thermal energy from the sun also causes the earth's water cycle. Every day the sun's warmth evaporates over 700 cubic kilometers of water from the earth's oceans, streams, rivers, and lakes. This moisture is carried inland in great billowy clouds and released as rain, mainly over the mountains. The rainwater rushes down slopes to form streams, rivers, and lakes. When man uses dams to tap the energy of this moving water, he indirectly taps the thermal energy of the sun.

Light energy

"Let there be light." When God spoke those words, He instantly lit the universe. On the fourth day, when He created the sun to rule the day and the moon to rule the night, He established the pattern for illuminating the earth. We *see* only a small percentage of the *light energy* that comes from our sun. What scientists call "light" actually includes a wide family of energy forms. These forms include radio waves, infrared waves, visible light waves, ultraviolet waves, x-rays, and gamma rays. Light energy travels as waves at speeds in excess of 300 million m/s!

Sound energy

Sound energy is another form of energy that travels in waves. Unlike light waves, which can travel through the vacuum of space, sound energy can travel only through matter: solids, liquids, or gases. The speed of sound depends on the nature of the matter it travels through. The sound's rate of vibration determines whether or not our ears can detect it. If the rate of vibration is between approximately 20 and 20,000 vibrations per second, the human ear can detect the energy as sound. God has equipped many animals to detect vibrations of sound energy in ranges that we cannot sense.

Chemical energy

Plants change the energy of the sun into *chemical energy* by a process known as *photosynthesis* (FO to SIN thih sis). In photosynthesis, plants use light energy to produce the chemicals that "fuel" their growth. Man also needs chemical energy to grow. You fuel your body with the chemical energy in food. We also tap the chemical energy of fuels to power our cars and heat our homes.

Chemical energy is associated with the outer electrons of atoms. When electrons jump to positions farther from their nuclei, they store chemical energy. When they return to their normal positions, chemical energy is released.

Electrical energy

Scientists have developed special photovoltaic cells that can convert the energy of sunlight directly into electrical current. Many of our space probes tap the power of the sun with panels of photovoltaic cells. They use the resulting *electrical energy* to run their instruments.

Electrical energy is associated with the flow of charged particles through a conductor. It is an amazing form of energy. You may not realize it, but all the electrical energy that is used in your home is delivered through a copper wire as thin as a strand of spaghetti!

Magnetic energy

Magnetic energy is closely related to electrical energy. It is stored in magnets and in their surrounding magnetic fields. Magnetic energy accomplishes work by producing attractive and repulsive forces that cause certain objects to move.

Mechanical energy

Mechanical energy is the energy possessed by *objects* that are in motion or that have the potential to move. Wind possesses mechanical energy. You have probably seen pictures of the terrible destructive power of wind. The 800 km/hr winds of a tornado can lift an entire house and hurl it hundreds of feet through the air!

Nuclear energy

Nuclear energy is man's most recent energy discovery. It is also the most dangerous form of energy. Its name tells its source: the nucleus of the atom. Nuclear energy is produced by the forces that God has established to hold the smallest particles of matter together. The energy is released by splitting a nucleus or by fusing several small nuclei together. In either case, tremendous amounts of energy are released. If the nuclear energy stored in a pencil eraser could be tapped completely, it could power a major city for an entire year.

FACETS
OF BASIC SCIENCE

The Changing Forms of Energy

Under the proper conditions energy can be transformed from one type to another. We use energy transformations every day to light our homes, cook our food, and travel to school.

A lamp transforms electrical energy into light energy. An oven transforms electrical energy into thermal energy. A car transforms chemical energy (from gasoline) into mechanical energy (motion). Our bodies transform chemical energy (from food) into thermal energy in our cells, electrical energy in our nerves, and mechanical energy in our muscles.

The following table lists the primary energy transformations that take place in a variety of common devices. Some devices produce more than one form of energy. When an incandescent bulb changes electricity to light, heat is also generated. When an engine converts chemical energy in fuel to mechanical energy, heat and sound are also produced. A device is *efficient* if most of the energy that goes into the device comes out in the desired form.

Some devices produce the same general form of energy as they take in. A hand-operated egg beater receives mechanical energy as you turn the crank, and it delivers mechanical energy to the eggs. Is this an energy transformation? No, you are simply altering a single form of energy to make it more useful. The beaters move faster than you could move your hand.

How many types of energy transformation are there? Look at the diagram; it shows every possible energy transformation. There are twenty-eight lines connecting the different forms of energy. *Each* of those lines represents *two* directions of change. Therefore, fifty-six energy transformations are possible!

Energy Transformations

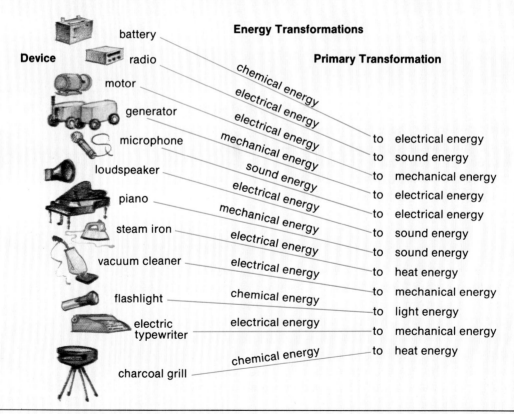

Device	Primary Transformation
battery	chemical energy to electrical energy
radio	electrical energy to sound energy
motor	electrical energy to mechanical energy
generator	mechanical energy to electrical energy
microphone	sound energy to electrical energy
loudspeaker	electrical energy to sound energy
piano	mechanical energy to sound energy
steam iron	electrical energy to heat energy
vacuum cleaner	electrical energy to mechanical energy
flashlight	chemical energy to light energy
electric typewriter	electrical energy to mechanical energy
charcoal grill	chemical energy to heat energy

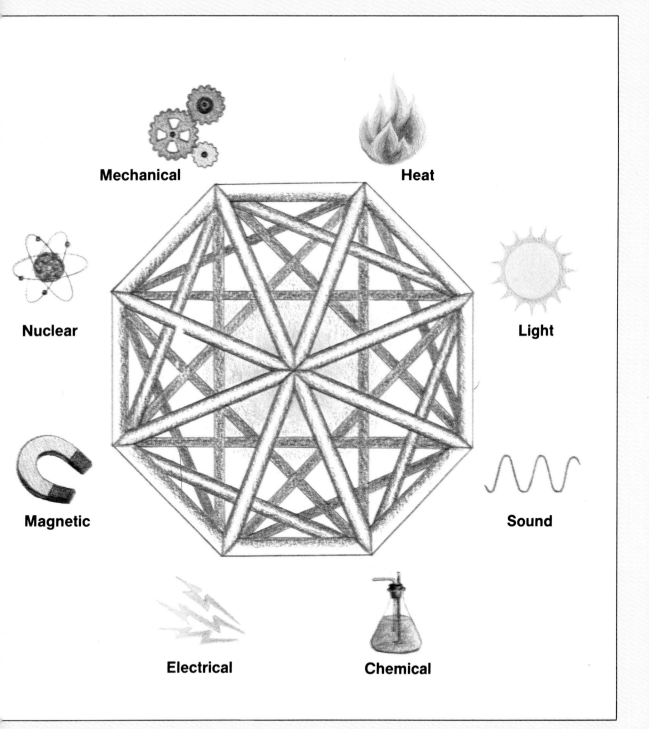

Mechanical

Heat

Nuclear

Light

Magnetic

Sound

Electrical

Chemical

Categories of Energy

Any form of energy can be either used or stored. For instance, a form of energy such as heat can be stored in a hot object for later use or released to a nearby cooler object. Scientists classify energy into two broad categories—potential or kinetic—based on whether it is used or stored.

Defining potential and kinetic energy

Energy that is being used, or the energy of motion, is called *kinetic energy*. Energy that is stored by the position or condition of an object or substance is called **potential energy.** A skier at the top of a hill has the capacity to do work because of his *position*. He has potential energy. His potential energy is converted into kinetic energy as he skis down the hill.

14-2 As a skier skis downhill, he is converting potential energy to kinetic energy. How did he get the potential energy in the first place?

Winding an alarm clock gives potential energy to its mainspring. The potential energy is converted back into kinetic energy as the mainspring unwinds to drive the gears, the hairspring, and the hands of the clock. A wound mainspring has potential energy because of its *condition*—the state of strain on the spring. Flexible materials, such as spring steel and rubber, can be deformed in ways that cause them to store energy. The energy will be released as they are allowed to return to their original conditions.

Kinetic and potential energy can be readily converted back and forth. The pendulum of a grandfather clock is constantly interchanging kinetic and potential energy. At the top of its swing, the pendulum's energy is all potential. At the lowest point of its swing, the pendulum's energy is all kinetic. At points in between, part of the energy is kinetic and part is potential.

14-3 How do kinetic and potential energy constantly interchange in a roller coaster?

Calculating potential and kinetic energy

The potential energy (P.E.) of an object is calculated by multiplying the mass of the object (m) by the acceleration due to the earth's gravity (g) and the height of the object (h):

$$P.E. = mgh$$

If m is in kilograms and h is in meters, the correct value to use for g is $9.8/s^2$. Your answer will be in kilogram-meters squared per second squared *(joules)*.

If you lift a 1-kg book a distance of 1 m and place it on a shelf, how much potential energy have you given to the book?

$$P.E. = mgh$$
$$P.E. = (1 \text{ kg}) (9.8 \text{ m}/s^2) (1 \text{ m})$$
$$P.E. = 9.8 \text{ J}$$

14-4 The girl has added 9.8 J of potential energy to the book.

14-5 In medieval times, defenders of castles used the properties of kinetic energy to ward off attackers.

The kinetic energy (K.E.) of a moving object is calculated by multiplying one-half of its mass by its velocity (v) squared:

$$K.E. = \tfrac{1}{2}mv^2$$

The kinetic energy of a 5-kg rock thrown through the air with a velocity of 10 m/s would be:

$$K.E. = (\tfrac{1}{2})(5 \text{ kg})(10 \text{ m/s})^2$$
$$K.E. = 250 \text{ J}$$

Suppose that in the above problem the same stone had been thrown with *twice* the velocity, 20 m/s. The kinetic energy would then be four times as much!

$$K.E. = \tfrac{1}{2}mv^2$$
$$K.E. = (\tfrac{1}{2})(5 \text{ kg})(20 \text{ m/s})^2$$
$$K.E. = 1000 \text{ J}$$

Because the velocity is squared in the kinetic energy equation, doubling the velocity *quadruples* the kinetic energy. This relationship between velocity and kinetic energy explains why a car traveling at 88 km/h takes so much longer to stop than a car moving at 44 km/h.

FACETS
OF BASIC SCIENCE

STOP!

The kinetic energy of a car must "go somewhere" when the car stops. This energy is normally converted to heat in the brakes. If a car comes to a skidding halt, some of the energy is also converted to heat in the tires and on the road.

The U.S. Department of Transportation has conducted extensive tests to determine the distance standard passenger cars need in order to stop on dry, clean, level pavement. The results of these tests are given in the table.

The driver reaction distance is based on a reaction time of 0.75 seconds. Though the reaction *time* stays the same at all speeds, the driver reaction *distance* increases in direct proportion to the speed. The braking distance is the distance needed to stop once the brakes are applied. Researchers found that when the speed is doubled, the braking distance is *more than quadrupled*. This dramatic increase is caused by the fact

that doubling the speed quadruples the kinetic energy, coupled with the fact that automobile brakes work less efficiently at higher speeds. Adding the driver reaction distance to the braking distance gives the total stopping distance. Stopping a car requires more distance than you might think. The figures given here are for *ideal* conditions. The stopping distance can be much greater when the car is going downhill, when the weather is bad, or when the road is dusty, wet, or gravel-covered.

Speed mph	Driver Reaction Distance in feet	Braking Distance Range in feet	Total Stopping Distance Range in feet
20	22	18-22	40-44
25	28	25-31	53-59
30	33	36-45	69-78
35	39	47-58	86-97
40	44	64-80	108-124
45	50	82-103	132-153
50	55	105-131	160-186
55	61	132-165	193-226
60	66	162-202	228-268
65	72	196-245	268-317
70	77	237-295	314-372
75	83	283-353	366-436
80	88	334-418	422-506

Laws of Conservation

God sustains His creation. Hebrews 1:3 tells us that God is "upholding all things by the word of his power." II Peter 3:7 declares that "the heavens and the earth . . . by the same word, are kept in store."

How does God preserve His handiwork so that it holds together and continues to endure, year after year, century after century? We do not completely understand His methods. At least a part of the answer, however, has to do with what scientists call **conservation principles.**

Conservation of energy

James Prescott Joule (JOOL) (1818-1889), the English physicist for whom the SI unit of energy is named, was one of the first to recognize the importance of conservation principles in nature. Joule and other scientists of his day—most notably German physicist Hermann von Helmholtz (HELM HOLTS) (1821-1894)—performed extensive experiments establishing the fact that when energy is converted from one form to another, no energy is lost. From their experiments came the remarkably broad generalization known today as the **law of conservation of energy:** *Energy can be changed from one form to another but can never be created or destroyed.* This principle is also called the *first law of thermodynamics.* No exceptions to the law of conservation of energy have ever been found. Nuclear power plants, for instance, use small uranium pellets to power their reactors. When the fuel

14-6 The pellets that power a nuclear plant are very small compared to the energy they produce.

is "spent," the pellets are removed. Although it may appear that the pellets have not been altered in any way, a small amount of their mass has disappeared. That mass must have been transformed into heat, light, and other forms of energy in the reactor. Therefore scientists now believe that matter is actually a form of energy that can be transformed into other forms of energy.

The conservation of momentum

Newton described momentum (MO MEN tum) as a "quantity of motion." Today scientists define **momentum** (p) as *mass* (m) *times velocity* (v).

$$p = mv$$

The greater the mass of a moving object, the greater its momentum; and the greater its velocity, the greater its momentum.

Because of the effect of mass on momentum, a slowly moving truck can easily have more momentum than a speeding motorcycle. To illustrate the importance of mass, let us compare the action of a bowling ball knocking down pins to the action of a volleyball traveling at an equal speed and aimed at the same pins. The volleyball will bounce away after knocking down only

14-7 The faster a bowling ball is rolled, the more momentum it will have to knock down pins.

one or two pins; it is simply too light to produce a strike. Because of its small mass, the volleyball has little momentum.

What is the momentum of a bullet traveling at 350 m/s if its mass is 0.002 kg?

$$p = mv$$
$$p = (0.002 \text{ kg}) (350 \text{ m/s})$$
$$p = 0.7 \text{ kg-m/s}$$

Note the units of the answer. There are no special units for momentum as there are for energy. Therefore we must retain a combination of the units that go into the calculation. Multiplying kilograms by meters per second gives kilogram-meters per second (kg-m/s) for the units of momentum.

Newton's third law of motion predicts that every action will produce an equal and opposite reaction. Therefore a rifle should recoil as a bullet is fired from it. The "action" (firing the rifle) changes the momentum of the bullet, and the "reaction" (the recoil) changes the momentum of the rifle. According to the **law of the conservation of momentum,** the changes in momentum must be equal. This principle states that without outside influ-

FACETS
OF BASIC SCIENCE

Is Perpetual Motion Possible?

For many centuries men dreamed of building a machine that, once set in motion, would continue to operate indefinitely without the addition of fuel or energy. The most desirable type of perpetual (pur PECH oo ul) motion machine, of course, would be one that could not only keep itself running, but also produce additional energy to do useful work. Such a machine would save time and energy. But as soon as the principle of the conservation of energy became established in the mid-1800s, scientists realized that the idea of a machine that would keep itself going was an impossible dream. The moving parts of all man-made machines produce energy-eating friction. Thus, no machine can keep up with its own continuing energy needs, much less develop energy to spare. No one has ever succeeded in building a true perpetual-motion machine.

Even though none of the machines actually worked, some very ingenious ideas were tried. One consisted of an endless chain running over a series of pulleys (Figure 1). Because the right-hand side of the chain is longer, the inventor of this machine expected the added weight to pull the chain around in a clockwise direction. Though this idea may appear feasible, it turns out that the pulleys on the right take up the additional weight, and the chain fails to move.

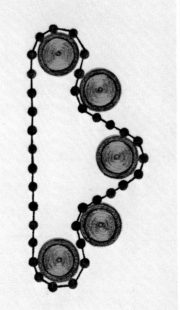

Another effort consisted of eight sledgehammers attached to a large wooden wheel (Figure 2). At the end of the handle of each hammer are two spikes—one a fulcrum about which the hammer turns, and one that acts as a stop to hold the hammer in an extended position as it falls to the right. Because of this positioning, the weights on the right act through longer lever arms than those on the left and hence should turn the wheel in a clockwise direction. The flaw in this machine, however, is that there are always more hammers on the left than on the right; hence there is too much weight to be overcome, and the machine quickly comes to a halt.

Both of these machines were supposed to operate by gravity. Christian Huygens, the noted seventeenth-century physicist, pointed out that in order for a gravity-operated perpetual-motion machine to work, its overall mass must keep moving to a lower level. But when that mass moves to the lower level, it has no way to return to its original position. When it cannot move any lower, motion stops. Thus, gravity-operated perpetual-motion machines are doomed to failure.

Perpetual-motion buffs also experimented extensively with magnetism. A magnet can produce motion by repelling a second magnet. Suppose we put wheels on a large number of bar magnets and arrange them on a circular track so that each magnet is repelling the one in front of it, and in turn being repelled by the one behind it. Will not the entire circle of magnets now move around the track by mutual repulsion? Again nature fails to cooperate. Since each magnet receives an equal amount of repulsion from in front and behind, there is no unbalanced force on it, hence no motion. What is true for the individual magnets is true for the entire circle of magnets. The circle simply locks itself into place and refuses to move in either direction.

Perhaps you have seen devices that appear to be perpetual motion machines. One type of clock is especially baffling. This clock is fully glass-enclosed. Inside, brass spheres continually rotate back and forth. No wires or tubing connect the clock to any power source. The clock contains no batteries and never needs to be wound. But it *does* receive energy from its surroundings. This type of clock operates by responding to changes in atmospheric pressure. It uses this energy to drive a train of gears, which in turn moves the hands of the clock. Although, if its parts never wore out, this device could continue to run indefinitely, it is not a perpetual-motion machine because it derives its energy from its surroundings.

The law of conservation of energy combined with several centuries of experimental failure has convinced us that perpetual motion in a man-made machine is impossible.

337

ence the total momentum of objects before a change in momentum must equal their total momentum after the change.

Not only does the law of conservation of momentum apply to objects moving away from each other, such as the rifle and the bullet, but it also applies to *colliding* objects. The total momentum of all the objects taking part in a collision must be the same before and after the impact.

When two objects of unequal mass collide, the lighter object is accelerated after the collision to a much faster speed than is the heavier object. Suppose that a 1200-N football player collides with a 400-N player running in the opposite direction. If they are moving at the same speed before the collision, the lighter man's speed after the collision is considerably greater than that of the heavier player.

Now consider an example that illustrates the conservation of both momentum and energy. Picture six balls in a row on a metal track. If a single ball is rolled from the left toward the group, the rolled ball hits the first ball of the group and stops dead. At the same instant, the ball at the right-hand end leaves the group at the same speed as the ball that hit the group. The other five balls do not move! They *transmit* the motion to the ball that rolls away.

If two balls are rolled in from the left, two balls leave from the right.

What happens when seven moving balls hit the six stationary ones?

In this case, one of the seven moving balls keeps moving. This ball, together with the six balls that started from the rest, makes seven balls in motion after the impact, giving the same momentum as was present before the impact.

Scientifically Speaking

energy	electrical energy	conservation principles
thermal energy	magnetic energy	law of conservation of energy
light energy	mechanical energy	momentum
sound energy	nuclear energy	law of the conservation of momentum
chemical energy	potential energy	

Questions to Talk Over

1. One early automobile was called the Stanley Steamer. Can you guess what energy transformations took place when one of these automobiles was driven?

2. A carpenter experimented with several hammers of different sizes and finally selected one that was just right for his work. The heaviest hammer he tried had a mass of 1 kg but was very hard to swing. The carpenter found that he was able to swing a 0.5-kg hammer twice as fast as the 1-kg hammer. With which hammer could the carpenter generate more kinetic energy in a given amount of time? Was he smart to select the lighter hammer, which he could swing faster?

3. Jane enjoys bouncing on a trampoline. Sometimes she simply bounces up and down with her legs straight. Sometimes she sits down on a bounce and then bounces to her feet. While she bounces on the trampoline, Jane is continuously converting kinetic energy into potential energy and potential energy back into kinetic energy. Discuss Jane's kinetic and potential energy with respect to her position on the trampoline. At what point in each bounce does Jane have the most potential energy? At what point does she have the most kinetic energy? Does Jane convert more potential energy into kinetic energy when she lands sitting or when she lands standing? Why?

4. As a bullet is shot from the muzzle of a gun, the gun kicks backward and momentum is conserved. What actually forces the gun backward? The bullet? The exploding gases? Some other force?

5. An engineer designed and built a roller coaster for an amusement park. He made the second hill higher than the first hill. Why was he fired from his job?

SIX

THE ENERGY OF MATTER

15 Heat
16 Electricity
17 Magnetism

HEAT

CHAPTER
15

The cold drizzle continues to fall. You rush up the steps and burst into the warm hallway. Calling from the living room, your mom reminds you to wipe your feet. "Oh, by the way," she adds, "I poured something for you to drink." As you head toward the kitchen, which do you expect to see: a mug of hot chocolate or a glass of ice-cold lemonade? On a cold, damp day you need the *thermal energy* of hot chocolate to make up for your body's lack of warmth.

Warming you is not the only function of thermal energy. In the past, thermal energy produced steam that propelled locomotives across continents and ocean liners across the seas. Today steam produced by thermal energy drives huge turbines that generate electricity for cities and industry. In the near future, thermal energy from within the earth (geothermal energy) and thermal energy from the sun (solar energy) may increasingly help to meet the demands of our energy-hungry society. The benefits of thermal energy—both for now and for the future—make it an important influence in our lives.

Defining Thermal Energy

Many years ago, scientists thought that thermal energy was a weightless, invisible fluid. They named this fluid *caloric* (kuh LAW rik). All matter supposedly contained a measurable amount of this fluid; hot objects contained more than cold objects. When a hot object touched a cold object, caloric flowed from the hot object to the cold object until equal quantities of each material contained equal amounts of this mysterious fluid.

The **caloric theory** remained popular because it seemed to explain many everyday occurrences. Have you ever bought an ice-cream cone on a hot summer day, then raced to eat it before it melted and dripped all over you? The caloric theory would have explained this phenomenon by stating that the caloric in the warm surrounding air flowed into the cold ice cream and made it melt. This description of melting appeared to be correct, but could the caloric theory describe other observations of thermal energy?

The kinetic theory of thermal energy

The observations of an American-born scientist eventually toppled the caloric theory. Benjamin Thompson left America and later arranged for a royal title in the court of Bavaria. The new count changed his name to Rumford (RUM furd), after his hometown in New Hampshire. He rose quickly in the Bavarian government and was soon appointed minister of war. One of his duties was to supervise the manufacture of weapons. This duty gave Count Rumford an opportunity to observe cannon-boring operations.

The cannon-boring procedure was relatively simple. A solid brass cylinder mounted on a rotating shaft was pushed against a stationary drill bit. As the cylinder was hollowed out, great quantities of thermal energy were released—enough, in fact, to boil the water that was poured into the cylinder to cool the bit. How was this thermal energy produced?

According to the caloric theory, the metal that was drilled from within the barrel released its caloric. As more metal was

15-1 Count Rumford.

removed, more caloric should have been set free. Count Rumford devised an experiment to test whether or not the metal itself released the caloric. He pressed a dull drill bit against a rotating cannon barrel for half an hour and found that only a tiny amount of metal, but a large amount of caloric (actually thermal energy) was released. He then compared this amount of caloric to the caloric released when a much larger amount of metal was removed in a much shorter time with a sharp bit. The two amounts of caloric were just about the same. This was astounding! How could two different amounts of the same metal release the same amount of caloric? Count Rumford realized that the caloric theory was incorrect.

15-2 Rumford compared the amount of thermal energy produced when a cannon was bored with a dull bit to the amount of thermal energy produced when a sharp bit was used. What did he discover?

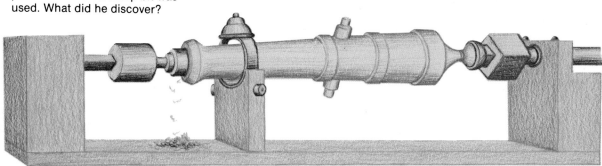

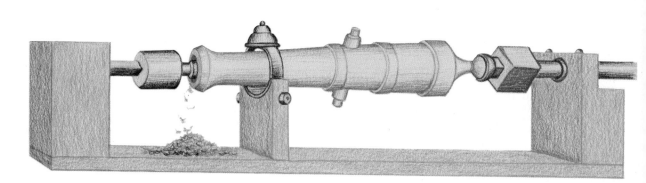

If the release of caloric did not account for the thermal energy produced by the cannon-boring, what did? Count Rumford observed that the energy release stopped when the drilling stopped. He reasoned that the motion of the barrel against the bit, and not caloric, produced the thermal energy. Count Rumford did not know *how* motion produces thermal energy, but his experiments sparked the research that led to the answer—the kinetic theory of thermal energy.

The *kinetic theory of thermal energy* identifies the thermal energy of an object with the motion of its particles (which may be atoms, ions, or molecules). Rub your hands briskly together and see what happens. The faster you rub your hands, the warmer they become. The American Indians found that by rubbing two sticks together they could produce enough thermal energy to start a flame. According to the kinetic theory, rubbing two objects—two sticks, for instance—together causes the molecules in the objects to move faster. As the motion of the molecules increases, the energy in the sticks increases. The more "stirred up" the molecules become, the warmer the sticks become. The total energy of the particles in an object is called the object's *thermal energy*. Which would contain more thermal energy: a "hot" stick or a "cold" stick of the same size?

15-3 (above) By rubbing sticks together, American Indians produced enough thermal energy to start fires. **(left)** According to the kinetic theory, what happens to the molecules involved when an electric sander is used to smooth a board?

Measuring particle motion

We describe particle motion with the everyday words *hot* and *cold*. These terms are very subjective. You may feel "too hot" while a friend may feel "just right." Unless we can *measure* the hotness or coldness of objects, these concepts are scientifically useless.

FACETS
OF BASIC SCIENCE

A Short History of Thermometers and Temperature Scales

One of the first thermometers was built around 1600 by Galileo. The "thermoscope" (THUR muh skoap), as Galileo called it, consisted of a long, slender glass tube sealed at one end and inverted with its open end in a pan of water. The level of water in the tube rose and fell as the volume of the air trapped inside fluctuated with the temperature. Galileo's thermoscope proved to be fairly accurate; it could clearly indicate the temperature of the hands of the person who held it. Unfortunately, the thermoscope also responded to small changes in atmospheric pressure.

Later scientists revised Galileo's thermoscope by replacing the air with a combination of water and alcohol and completely sealing it in a tube. Using expandable liquids instead of gases made these thermometers less sensitive to atmospheric pressure changes. Today, many thermometers contain mercury. Mercury's volume changes predictably over a greater range of temperatures than the volume of either water or alcohol.

In time, scientists added *calibrations* (KAL uh BRAY shunz) to their thermometers so that they could measure specific temperatures. For instance, many scientists marked the level of the liquid in their thermometers as they were measuring the boiling point of water. Then, each time the liquid's level returned to that

Galileo's thermoscope

The measurement of an object's hotness or coldness is called its *temperature*. Temperature is expressed in units called **degrees** (°, or *kelvins* on the absolute scale). As an object becomes hotter, the number of degrees in its temperature increases. Temperature actually indicates the *average* kinetic energy of an object's particles. As the particles gain kinetic energy, they move faster and the object's temperature rises.

mark, the scientists knew that the temperature the thermometers were measuring was the same as the temperature at which water boiled.

Gabriel Fahrenheit (FEHR un HITE), a German-Polish instrument maker, used three temperatures to calibrate his thermometer: the freezing point of a water, salt, and ice mixture; the freezing point of pure water; and the average temperature of a normal human body. He divided his scale into equal units, or degrees Fahrenheit (°F) between these three key calibrations. The Fahrenheit scale is still used in much of the United States.

In 1742 a Swedish astronomer named Anders Celsius devised a simpler temperature scale. He divided the temperature range between the freezing and boiling points of pure water into one hundred equal temperature intervals. He used the same size intervals to measure temperatures above and below this temperature range as well. The French commission that designed the metric system later named the freezing point of water 0 degrees Celsius (0°C) and the boiling point 100 degrees Celsius (100°C). The fact that each interval, or degree Celsius, is equal to one-hundredth of the temperature range between these two easily

reproducible points makes the **Celsius scale** easy to calibrate and use. Most countries and almost all scientific laboratories use the Celsius scale to measure temperature.

In 1848 Lord Kelvin, a famous English physicist, developed a temperature scale called the **Kelvin scale**, which has only positive temperature values. The calibration of the Kelvin scale reflects the fact that negative kinetic energy does not exist. Using the Kelvin scale, we can directly compare the average kinetic energy of the particles in any two objects. For this reason, the temperatures on the Kelvin scale are also known as *absolute temperatures*. The lowest temperature on the Kelvin scale, 0 kelvins, represents the temperature at which an object possesses an absolute minimum of kinetic energy. This temperature is also known as **absolute zero.**

Once you know the Celsius temperature of an object, its absolute temperature is simple to calculate. The sizes of the temperature intervals, or degrees, in the Celsius and Kelvin scales are the same. Absolute zero (0 K) on the Kelvin scale corresponds to -273°C on the Celsius scale. Therefore, to convert a temperature from the Celsius scale to the Kelvin scale, one simply adds 273 degrees. To convert a Kelvin

temperature to the corresponding Celsius temperature, one simply subtracts 273 degrees. The following equations express the relationship between these two scales:

$$C + 273 = K$$
$$K - 273 = C$$

In these equations, C stands for the Celsius temperature and K stands for the Kelvin temperature. Note also that in the modern metric system, temperatures on the Kelvin scale are expressed as kelvins (K), not as degrees Kelvin (°K).

Sample problem 1:
A hummingbird has a body temperature of 43°C. Find the corresponding Kelvin temperature.
Solution: K = C + 273
K = 43 + 273
K = 316 kelvins

Sample problem 2:
Dry ice sublimates at -78.5°C. What is the corresponding absolute temperature?
Solution: K = C + 273
K = -78.5 + 273
K = 194.5 kelvins

Sample problem 3:
Liquid nitrogen boils at 77 kelvins. Convert this temperature to degrees Celsius.
Solution: C = K - 273
C = 77 - 273
C = -196°C

15-4 Huge chunks break off glaciers and form icebergs in the waters of Glacier Bay in Alaska. Many glaciers are over a kilometer wide and more than 150 m thick.

Distinguishing between temperature and thermal energy

Which is hotter—a ton of molten copper or a glacier in Alaska? Obviously, the molten copper is the hotter of the two. Now for a harder question: Does the copper or the glacier contain more thermal energy? The answer to this question may surprise you. The glacier, though much colder, contains more thermal energy than the molten copper! How can this be?

To understand this seeming contradiction, we need to distinguish between temperature and thermal energy. Temperature measures the *average* kinetic energy of an object's particles. In other words, temperature measures the energy of motion possessed by an average particle in the object. Thermal energy measures the *total* energy of *all* the particles in an object. Thus, thermal energy includes the energy of motion of all the object's particles.

15-5 The metal copper melts at 1080° C. This huge crucible is pouring molten copper into a smelting furnace, where it will be purified.

If two cubes of iron—one large and one small—were heated to the same temperature, their individual atoms would possess the same average kinetic energy. However, the large cube would contain *more* atoms with that average kinetic energy. The total energy of the atoms in the large cube would be greater than the total energy of the atoms in the small cube. Thus the large cube would possess more thermal energy. If these cubes with identical temperatures were thrown into identical buckets of ice, the large cube would release much more thermal energy and melt much more ice than the small cube.

By the same principle, the glacier has more thermal energy than a ton of molten copper. The fact that the temperature of the glacier is lower than the temperature of the copper shows that the glacier's particles have less average kinetic energy than the copper particles have. However, the glacier has many more particles than the ton of copper has. Therefore, the *total* energy of the glacier's particles adds up to more than the *total* energy of the copper particles. Since thermal energy measures an object's total energy, the glacier has more thermal energy than the molten copper.

Measuring thermal energy

Since temperature and thermal energy measure different physical properties, they must be expressed in different units. Temperature, as you know, is measured in degrees; thermal energy is measured in units called **calories** (KAL uh reez) (**cal**).

Originally, a calorie was defined as a certain quantity of caloric fluid. The downfall of the caloric theory made this use of the word obsolete, but the term itself has survived, and today it represents a certain quantity of thermal energy. The *calorie* is that amount of thermal energy which, when transferred to 1 g of water, causes an increase of 1°C in the water's temperature.

The calorie may measure the amount of thermal energy that is transferred from one object to another. It may also measure the amount of thermal energy that a substance could potentially release. One of the most common uses of the calorie is to measure the thermal energy stored in foods. The **Calorie (Cal)** used to measure the energy stored in foods is actually one thousand times as large as the calorie used to measure the energy stored in other substances. To distinguish between the two "sizes" of calories, the *c* of the large Calorie is often capitalized. Therefore, 1 Cal = 1000 cal. You can see from the values on Table 15-7 why food Calories have been made larger than regular calories. In terms of regular calories, an 8-oz steak contains 1,078,000 cal. The figure we normally use, 1078 Cal, is much easier to comprehend and work with.

15-6 Is a calorie the same as a Calorie?

**Table 15-7
Approximate
Caloric Contents**

Food	Amount	Calories	Food	Amount	Calories
apple	1	66	jam	1 tbsp.	54
bacon	1 slice	49	chocolate ice cream	1/3 pt.	191
banana	1	87	macaroni	1 cup	168
green beans	1/2 cup	16	mayonnaise	1 tbsp.	100
chocolate cake with chocolate icing	2-in. slice	445	milk	8 oz.	151
fudge	1 oz.	112	pancake	4-in. diameter	61
T-bone steak	8 oz.	1078	peanut butter	1 tbsp.	72
hamburger sandwich	1	576	popcorn, plain	1 cup	42
white bread	1 slice	62	potato chips	2 oz.	312
brownie	1	140	French fries	10 2-in. pieces	156
butter	1 tbsp.	100	orange	1	75
Life Saver, fruit flavored	1 piece	9	rice	1 cup	187
catsup	1 tbsp.	21	sausage	4 oz.	538
celery	1 stalk	6	soft drink, cola flavored	8 oz.	96
cornflake cereal	1-1/3 cups	105	tea	1 cup	1
chocolate chip cookie	1	51	tomato soup	1 cup	83
egg	1 large	81	spaghetti	1 cup	159
fried chicken	1 drumstick	89	strawberries	1/2 cup	28
			walnuts, shelled	1/2 cup	654

Starches, sugars, and fats are the main sources of energy for our bodies. One kilogram (about 2½ cups) of sucrose (table sugar) has the potential of releasing over 2000 Cal. The same amount of fat can release three times as many Calories. Your body uses the thermal energy of food to provide itself with energy. If your body did not receive enough thermal energy— enough Calories—you would become underweight and ill. On the other hand, if you consumed more Calories than your body needs, you would gain weight.

How much energy do you need? The answer depends on your age, your size, and your level of activity. Nutritionists have determined the average caloric intakes needed by individuals of different ages (see Table 15-8). Since different foods contain different amounts of Calories, nutritionists have also prepared tables showing the caloric content of most foods. You can determine your intake of Calories by measuring the amount of each food you eat and comparing it to the value given for that food in a caloric content chart.

Table 15-8

Average Caloric Requirements		
Age	Males	Females
1-3	1300	1300
3-6	1600	1600
6-9	2100	2100
9-12	2400	2200
12-15	3000	2500
15-18	3400	2300
18-35	2900	2100
35-55	2600	1900
55-75	2200	1600

Transferring Thermal Energy

Remember the last time you opened a car door on a broiling summer afternoon and were met by a blistering blast of hot air? After gingerly seating yourself on the scorching car seat, you quickly became aware of its energy-storing capabilities. The longer you sat there, the more you felt the sun pouring additional energy into you and the car. All these sensations are evidences of **heat**—the *flow* of thermal energy from one object to another. Thermal energy can flow by three different processes: conduction, convection, and radiation.

15-9 For centuries glassblowers have used thermal energy to shape practical and beautiful items. The glow of the glass is caused by conduction of thermal energy.

Conduction

When two objects at different temperatures touch each other, heat flows from the hotter object to the cooler object. This process is called **conduction** (kun DUK shun). Remember the steaming mug of hot chocolate we described at the beginning of this chapter? The hot chocolate became "hot" because of conduction. A pan containing milk and chocolate was placed on a hot burner. First the pan was heated by contact with the burner. Then the chocolate mixture was heated by contact with the pan. Later, you were warmed by contact with the hot chocolate! Conduction took place as thermal energy flowed from the burner to the pan, from the pan to the chocolate mixture, and finally from the hot chocolate to you.

How does conduction transfer thermal energy? According to the kinetic theory, when a warm object contacts a relatively cool object, kinetic energy is conducted from the warmer object to the cooler object. This happens as the slower-vibrating particles of the cooler object are agitated by the faster-vibrating particles of the hotter object. Gradually, the hotter particles lose some of their kinetic energy to the cooler particles. When the average kinetic energy of the particles of both objects has become equal, the two objects are at the same temperature and conduction stops. This condition is called **equilibrium** (EE kwuh LIB ree um).

The process of conduction is obvious when a piece of red-hot iron is plunged into a bucket of cool water. The popping, fizzing, and bubbling of the water testifies that energy from the iron atoms is being transferred to the water molecules. When the popping, fizzing, and bubbling stop, the iron and water have reached equilibrium, and the conduction of thermal energy has ceased.

Conduction is the chief method of heat flow in solids. Because the atoms of solids are held firmly in place, energy is conducted through them by vibrations of the atomic bonds and by the movement of valence electrons from one atom to the next.

Some solids conduct thermal energy better than others. Since metals easily give up their valence electrons, they are generally excellent **conductors** (kun DUK turz) of thermal energy. Silver is the best heat conductor, but it is also very expensive. In most situations, less expensive conductors such as copper and aluminum are more practical. In homes that have hot-water heating systems, copper pipes transport heated water throughout the house. At various points along the pipes, aluminum fins attached to the copper tubes conduct thermal energy from the water into the surrounding air.

Table 15-10

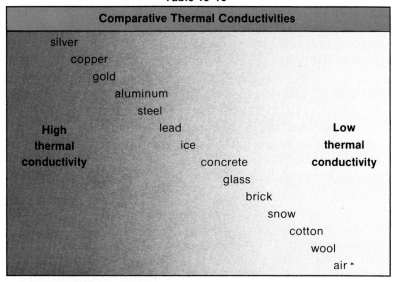

Comparative Thermal Conductivities
silver
copper
gold
aluminum
steel
High lead **Low**
thermal ice **thermal**
conductivity concrete **conductivity**
glass
brick
snow
cotton
wool
air

At the opposite end of the scale are substances such as wool, brick, and glass. These materials resist heat flow and are called **insulators** (IN suh LAY turz) (from the Latin word *insula*, meaning "island"). An object surrounded by insulating materials forms an "island" of one temperature in the midst of a surrounding "sea" of other temperatures. The ceramic materials used to make the exterior tiles of NASA's space shuttle are excellent insulators. They resist heat flow so effectively that the tiles may be handled without risk of burns even while they are glowing with thermal energy. The tiles protect the space shuttle's occupants from the searing temperatures generated when they reenter the earth's atmosphere.

Gases can be extremely good insulators. Gases that are confined so that they cannot circulate prevent almost all heat flow by conduction. Storm windows use air—a mixture of gases—for insulation. The trapped air between the double panes of a storm window greatly reduces the conduction of thermal energy through the window. A wool sweater is warm on a chilly day because the air trapped between the wool fibers insulates the wearer. The fiberglass insulation used in homes also uses trapped air to reduce conduction.

15-11 You should not try to cook hot dogs this way! How does this scientist keep from burning his hand?

Convection

That blast of hot air that greets you when you open a car door on a warm day illustrates the existence of another method of heat flow—**convection** (kun VEK shun). In convection, moving particles transfer thermal energy from one place (such as the car) to another (such as your face).

Convection and conduction both depend on the movement of matter to transfer thermal energy. What, then, distinguishes convection from conduction? In conduction, the particles are confined and remain relatively stationary. Energy is passed along as vibrating particles flow from high temperature regions to low temperature regions.

Did you know that there is a connection between convection and gravity? Cooler, denser liquids and gases are more affected by gravity than warmer, less dense liquids and gases. When gravity pulls the cooler, denser substances downward, they in turn push the warmer substances upward. As these substances move, they produce currents that mix heated, faster-moving particles with cooler, more sluggish particles. Each time a warmer particle collides with a cooler particle, some of the energy from the warmer particle is transferred to the cooler particle. Gradually, convection can produce a uniform temperature throughout an entire group of particles. Once equilibrium has been reached, the convection process halts.

15-12 The convection currents in a pot help to transfer thermal energy throughout the water.

15-13 Convection currents also help to heat this room.

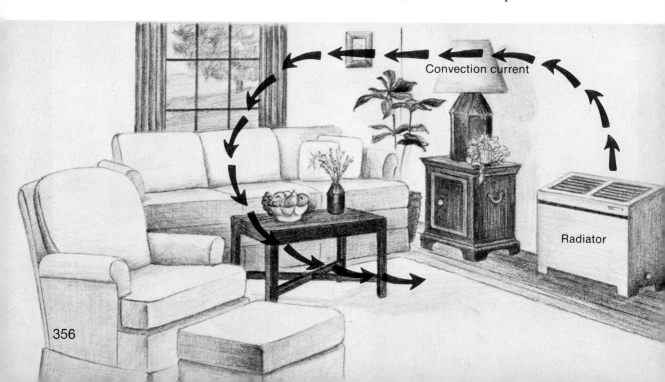

Convection current

Radiator

Convection operates in houses with radiators or hot-water pipes as heating elements. The air next to these heating elements is heated by conduction of thermal energy from the particles of the pipe or radiator to the particles of air. Once the air is heated, it is pushed up by the cooler air. The cooler air moves in to take the place of the warm air next to the heating element. This continuous cycle of warm air moving upward and cool air moving downward is called a **convection current.**

Homes with hot-air heating systems are also heated by convection. Warm air enters each room through vents or registers. As the cool air in the room falls and the warm air rises, it creates convection currents that help transfer the thermal energy throughout the room.

Convection currents also form in liquids. We depend on convection currents to heat a pan of water rapidly. The water at the bottom of the pan is heated by conduction from the pan's metal (which is heated by conduction from the stove's burner). As this heated water rises, it heats other water molecules by convection and also makes room for cooler molecules to move next to the hot metal at the bottom of the pan. If heated water did not rise in a convection current, all the water would have to be heated by the much slower process of conduction.

Convection currents in the atmosphere influence the weather near large bodies of water. The temperature of land changes

15-14 Convection currents over land and sea cause the constant winds which blow on the coast.

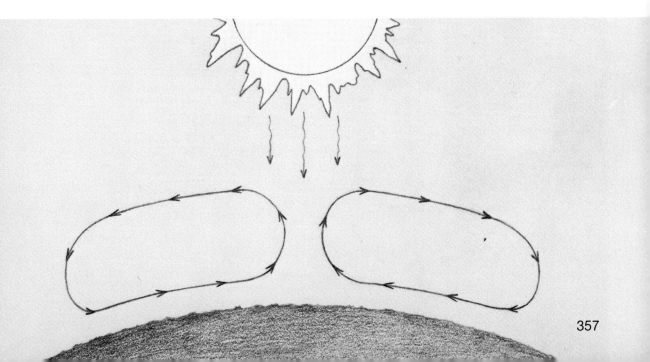

much more quickly than the temperature of water. In the morning sunlight, the land's temperature rises more quickly than the water's temperature. Consequently, the air over the land becomes warmer than the air over the water. Cooler air from over the water flows inland and forces the warmer air over the land to rise. This air movement is known as a *sea breeze* (or lake breeze). At midday, when the temperatures of the land and water are nearly the same, the air moves very little. During the early evening, the land cools more quickly than the water. As a result, the air over the water stays warm longer than the air over the land. The cooler, denser land air flows out onto the water, causing the warmer air to rise and creating a *land breeze*. Local sea and land breezes moderate the climates of coastal towns.

Radiation

Matter is very thinly distributed in the space between the sun and the earth—so thinly, in fact, that this space is almost a vacuum. Since convection and conduction both depend on matter to transport thermal energy, they cannot explain the heat flow from the sun to the earth. Thermal energy reaches the earth by **radiation** (RAY dee AY shun)—the transportation of thermal energy without the use of matter.

Scientists believe that radiation involves the transportation of thermal energy by light. Light itself is a form of energy. Light energy does not require the presence of matter to be able to travel from place to place. In fact, light travels faster through a vacuum than through matter. Whenever light strikes matter, some of the light's energy is transformed to thermal energy in the matter. The interaction between *infrared light* and matter produces especially large quantities of thermal energy. Therefore, scientists believe that infrared light is the main transporter of thermal energy from the sun to the earth.

Exactly how much thermal energy is transferred to matter by infrared light depends on how easily the matter absorbs the infrared light. Dark-colored materials readily absorb infrared light; light-colored materials reflect most infrared light. These properties explain why, on a sunny day, you may feel just as warm wearing a dark-colored shirt as you do wearing a light-colored sweater. They also explain why black automobile seats are much hotter than light-colored seats on a bright summer day.

15-15 Special thermal windows now help to regulate the temperature in many buildings. Each window is really two panes of glass separated by an air space which serves as an insulator; it cuts down the conduction of heat and reduces heating bills as well. The special glass used to make the windows reflects much of the sun's radiation and helps reduce cooling costs.

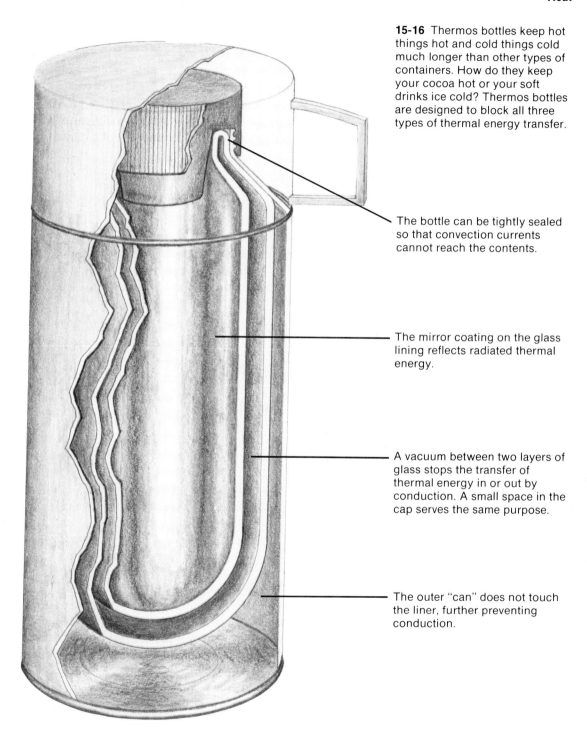

15-16 Thermos bottles keep hot things hot and cold things cold much longer than other types of containers. How do they keep your cocoa hot or your soft drinks ice cold? Thermos bottles are designed to block all three types of thermal energy transfer.

The bottle can be tightly sealed so that convection currents cannot reach the contents.

The mirror coating on the glass lining reflects radiated thermal energy.

A vacuum between two layers of glass stops the transfer of thermal energy in or out by conduction. A small space in the cap serves the same purpose.

The outer "can" does not touch the liner, further preventing conduction.

15-17 The steam rising over hot apple pie gives us an important clue as to why the filling stays hot longer than the crust.

Applying Thermal Energy

Have you ever burned your mouth on a piping-hot piece of apple pie? When you examined the pie, the crust seemed cool, but when the filling touched your mouth—ouch! The pie crust and the pie filling obviously cool at different rates. One reason for this difference is that pie fillings are mostly water. It takes a large amount of thermal energy to heat water, but once water is hot, it retains thermal energy better than most substances. The dry crust cooled quickly while the watery filling stayed hot.

The way a material gains and retains thermal energy is due largely to the composition of the material. Some materials, such as water, gain thermal energy slowly and retain it for a long time. Other materials, such as pie crust, gain and lose thermal energy very quickly. We can tell whether a material has lost or gained thermal energy by measuring changes in its temperature. If you had used a thermometer to check the temperature of the pie filling, you would have seen that it was still too hot to eat.

Specific heat

How do scientists measure the *amount* of thermal energy needed to change the temperature of specific materials? Scientists use calories to measure thermal energy. One calorie of thermal energy raises the temperature of 1 g of water 1°C. But does this amount of thermal energy raise the temperature of all substances 1°C? No; each substance reacts differently to thermal energy. Scientists call the amount of energy needed to raise the temperature of 1 g of a substance 1°C the **specific heat** of that substance. Some substances have small specific heats. It takes only 0.22 calories to raise the temperature of 1 g of aluminum 1°C. Lead requires still less energy—a mere 0.031 calories—to raise the temperature of each gram 1°C. Other substances, such as hydrogen and helium, have high specific heats. They must absorb large quantities of thermal energy before their temperatures change. Every substance has its own specific heat. Scientists use tables of specific heats to help identify and better use materials. Specific heat is expressed in calories per gram per degree Celsius (cal/g°C) (the number of calories needed to raise the temperature of 1 g of a material 1°C). Look at the specific heats shown in Table 15-18.

Compared to other substances, water has a very high specific heat. This property makes water useful for absorbing excess thermal energy. Because a small amount of water can absorb a

Table 15-18

Specific Heats	
Substance	**Specific Heat (cal/g°C)**
alcohol (ethyl)	.46
aluminum	.21
copper	.09
glass	.20
gold	.03
iron	.11
lead	.03
silver	.05
salt (sodium chloride)	.02
water	1.00

large amount of thermal energy from a hot engine, water is used as an engine coolant. Water's high specific heat also enables the Gulf Stream, the Japan Current, and similar currents to carry large amounts of thermal energy over great distances. England has a moderate climate because of the warming of the Gulf Stream.

Thermal energy transfers

Have you ever put ice into a cup of hot chocolate to keep it from burning your tongue? How does the ice cool the hot chocolate? When the ice is placed in the hot chocolate, thermal energy from the hot drink flows into the cold ice and causes it to melt. The water produced as the ice melts continues to absorb thermal energy and becomes warmer until the chocolate and the water have the same temperature. The end result: the hot chocolate is no longer as hot (it has lost thermal energy), and the ice is no longer cold (it has gained thermal energy). Now the hot chocolate is less likely to burn your tongue.

Not all the thermal energy transferred from the hot chocolate was used to raise the temperature of the ice and then of the water as the ice melted. Some of that energy was used to change the ice from a solid to a liquid. At 0°C water can exist as either a solid or a liquid. It takes 80 cal *more* per gram of water to change the solid structure of ice into a liquid. This extra energy does not

15-19 Engineers have found a way to tap the energy of the earth's interior: they have harnessed the natural steam power of geysers. Since this power comes from the earth's thermal energy, it is called geothermal power. This plant on the west coast of the United States produces 27,000 kW of electricity by routing the steam through turbines.

change the temperature of the ice; it simply helps the water molecules overcome the attractive forces that hold them in the solid state. Scientists call this extra energy the **heat of fusion.** Since water needs 80 cal to change each gram of solid to the liquid phase, its heat of fusion would be 80 cal/g.

Changing a substance from the liquid state to the gaseous state also requires some extra energy. The extra energy for a substance's liquid-to-gas phase change is called the **heat of vaporization** (VAY pur ih ZAY shun). Water needs 540 cal to change each gram of liquid to steam at 100°C. Therefore, water's heat of vaporization is 540 cal/g. There is no temperature change during the water-to-steam transition. All 540 cal used to evaporate a gram of water go toward separating the water molecules from one another to form steam. After water has become steam, its temperature remains 100°C until additional energy is added to it. To calculate the energy needed to change 10 g of water at 100°C into steam at 100°C you would multiply the number of grams that are evaporating by the calories per gram needed to cause the evaporation.

$$(10 \text{ g}) \times (540 \; \frac{\text{cal}}{\text{g}}) = 5400 \text{ cal}$$

Every substance possesses its own heat of fusion and heat of vaporization. Table 15-20 shows the heats of fusion and vaporization for several common substances.

Table 15-20

	Heats of Fusion and Vaporization			
Substance	Melting point	Heat of fusion	Boiling point	Heat of vaporization
alcohol (ethyl)	-117°C	24.9 cal/g	79.0°C	204 cal/g
aluminum	660°C	94.0 cal/g	1800°C	2520 cal/g
copper	1080°C	49.0 cal/g	2300°C	1150 cal/g
gold	1060°C	15.9 cal/g	2600°C	
iron	1540°C	7.89 cal/g	3000°C	1600 cal/g
lead	327°C	5.47 cal/g	1620°C	207 cal/g
silver	960°C	26.0 cal/g	1950°C	565 cal/g
salt (sodium chloride)	801°C	124 cal/g	1450°C	
tin	232°C	13.8 cal/g	2260°C	
water	0°C	80.0 cal/g	100°C	540 cal/g

Thermal Expansion

The concrete and steel of the Verrazano-Narrows Bridge in New York City span 1298 m from Brooklyn to Staten Island. That is, on a cold winter day they do. On a hot summer day, the concrete and steel stretch to 1299 m! An increase in thermal energy causes most materials to expand. Bridge designers must leave gaps, called finger joints, between the sections of the road-bed so that the bridge can expand without buckling. Roads and

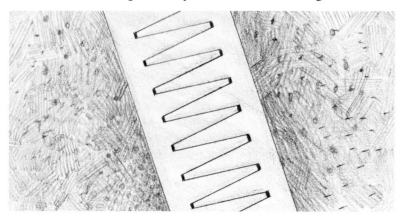

15-21 Finger joints allow a bridge to expand without buckling.

sidewalks are also built with compressible strips between the concrete slabs to allow the concrete to expand and contract as the temperature changes. The picture below compares power lines in the summer and winter. Can you guess what happened?

15-22 The heavy brown lines show the position of these power lines during the summer months. Can you explain why they sag?

The kinetic theory of matter describes how **thermal expansion** takes place. As particles are heated, they become more energetic and vibrate more vigorously; therefore, they take up more room. This increased volume of the particles increases the length, width, and height of a heated material. Solids, liquids, and gases all exhibit thermal expansion—some more than others. For instance, during the same temperature increase, brass expands almost seven times as much as porcelain.

Thermostats use the different expansion rates of different metals to control the temperatures of ovens and houses. Brass, for example, expands more than steel. If strips of these two metals are placed back to back and bonded together, they form a *bimetallic* (BY muh TAL ik) *strip.* When a bimetallic strip is heated, one side expands more than the other, causing the strip to bend. In a thermostat, a bimetallic strip is coiled like a watch spring. As the temperature drops, the bimetallic strip uncoils a tiny bit, pressing a movable arm against an electrical contact. This allows electricity to flow through the movable arm to the heating element. As the temperature rises to the proper level, the coiled bimetallic strip contracts and coils more tightly, pulling away from the movable arm. When the movable arm is no longer pressed against the electrical contact, electricity can no longer flow to the heating element.

Pyrex glassware (test tubes, flasks, and other utensils) is used in many laboratories because it can withstand sudden changes in temperature. This useful characteristic results from Pyrex's low expansion rate. Ordinary glass, because of its larger expansion rate, shatters or cracks if it is subjected to a quick change in temperature. When one part of an ordinary glass utensil is rapidly heated, it expands. Since glass conducts heat poorly, the rest of the utensil remains cool and does not expand. The stress produced by the size difference within the same piece of glass cracks or shatters the utensil. In the same type of situation, Pyrex glass resists breaking because it hardly expands at all when heated.

15-23 When the bimetallic strip in a thermostat contracts, it switches on the heat. You can adjust the temperature at which the heat will turn on by moving the coil.

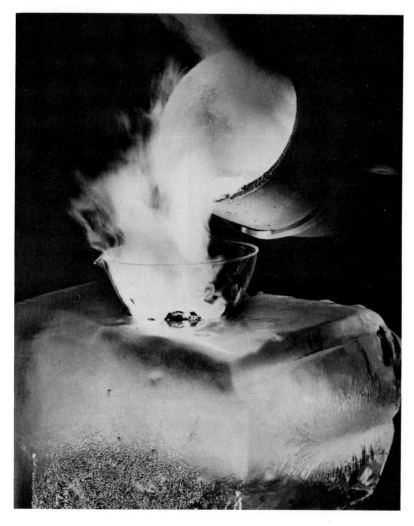

15-24 This special glass has an expansion rate so low that it can withstand the cold of ice and the extreme heat of molten bronze—at the same time!

FACETS
OF BASIC SCIENCE

Thermodynamics

Thermal energy, like all forms of energy, has the ability to do work. The English physicist James Joule performed many experiments to establish the relationship between thermal energy and work. He found that 1 cal of thermal energy is capable of performing 4.184 J of work. This relationship (4.184 J/cal) is known as the *mechanical equivalent of heat.*

Devices that transform thermal energy into work are called *heat engines.* One common type of heat engine is the steam engine. Hero, a scientist who lived in Alexandria, Egypt, built one of the first steam engines in 120 B.C. He connected two L-shaped pipes to a hollow ball. As heat was applied to water in the ball, steam escaped from the two pipes and twirled the globe. Unfortunately, the engine could not do much more than spin itself. In 1769 James Watt, a Scottish engineer, developed a steam engine that was useful for doing work. Soon steam engines were powering boats, trains, and factories around the world.

While inventors developed increasingly useful heat engines, scientists wondered what principles governed the transformation of energy from one form to another. It was at this time that the branch of physics called thermodynamics was born. **Thermodynamics** (THUR mo dye NAM iks: from the Greek words

Hero's steam engine

therme, meaning "heat"; and *dynamikos*, meaning "powerful") deals specifically with the conversion of thermal energy into other energy forms and into work. However, the principles, or laws, of thermodynamics influence many other aspects of modern science.

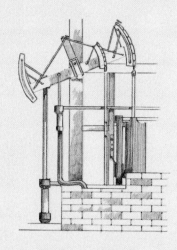

Watt's steam engine

The **first law of thermodynamics** is the law of energy conservation. We mentioned this law in Chapter 14. The first law states that while energy can be converted from one form to another, it cannot be created or destroyed. It tells us that the total amount of energy in the universe stays the same. This conclusion agrees with the biblical statement: "Thus the heavens and the earth were finished, and all the host of them" (Gen. 2:1). Since that time God has kept the amount of energy in the universe constant by preserving His creation. God is "upholding all things by the word of his power" (Heb. 1:3).

The **second law of thermodynamics** was formulated by several men, one of whom was Lord Kelvin. Lord Kelvin found that the energy in the universe, although it is conserved, becomes less available for performing useful work. One example of the second law is the transformation of energy in a gasoline engine. In a gasoline engine, the chemical energy in the bonds of the gasoline molecules is released as thermal

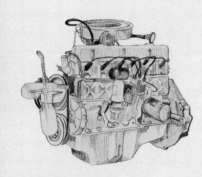

energy and light energy. Some of the thermal energy is used to produce pressure that moves the engine's pistons. However, much of the thermal energy and all the light energy is absorbed into the metal of the engine. This energy must be removed from the engine to prevent it from overheating. Some of the thermal energy is removed through a heat exchanger called a radiator. This thermal energy does not perform useful work. It has not been destroyed, but it can no longer be used.

The scientific measurement of the amount of unusable energy in a system is called that system's **entropy** (EN truh pee). Entropy measures the randomness, or disorder, in a system. (As energy becomes less orderly, it has less ability to do work.) According to the second law of thermodynamics, the entropy of the universe is always increasing. In other words, everything in the universe runs down!

Think of all the processes that show an increase of entropy.

Cold water mixed with hot water forms lukewarm water, but lukewarm water never separates into layers of hot and cold water. The molecules that escape from an open bottle of perfume spread throughout the room in a random pattern. The scattered perfume molecules never regather themselves into the bottle. Watches, batteries, and even people run down. Can their used-up energy be recovered? You may rewind a watch, recharge a battery, and rest and eat to "recharge" yourself, but none of these processes recover the original energy. If we consider all the natural processes that we can observe in the universe, we can see that all of nature is running down.

The second law of thermodynamics is a biblical principle. Both Hebrews 1:11 and Psalm 102:26 describe the earth and the heavens as waxing old like a garment. In the same way that clothing gradually wears out, the universe is gradually using up its supply of available energy. The second law also supports the biblical account of Creation. The fact that the universe is running down implies that it must have been "wound up" sometime in the past. The universe must have had a definite beginning. If it

were infinitely old, it would have run out of useful energy long ago.

No one has ever found a single exception to the first and second laws of thermodynamics. Both laws fully agree with Scripture and with every scientific observation that man has recorded. Some men have made "observations" of the past that they claim are scientific, but which violate the laws of thermodynamics. To evaluate these claims, we must ask two questions. First, are these really observations? Can anyone "observe" what happened before recorded history? Second, can these observations *prove* that the earth has gradually evolved over billions of years?

The first and second laws of thermodynamics contradict the theory of evolution. The first law refutes the evolutionary claim that the universe gradually evolved from a condition of having no energy to its present condition of having abundant energy. The second law refutes the evolutionary idea that matter organized itself from disorder and chaos into order and complexity. According to the laws of thermodynamics, evolution is false.

15-25 Why does the water on the surface of a lake, stream, or river freeze first?

Modern thermometers use the expansion and contraction of mercury or alcohol to measure changes in the surrounding temperature. As the temperature rises, the liquid expands and pushes up through a narrow, cylindrical hollow in the glass tube of the thermometer. When the temperature drops, the liquid contracts, and its level in the glass tube drops.

Water behaves uniquely as its temperature changes. Most substances contract steadily as their temperatures drop. Water also contracts as it is cooled—at least, until its temperature drops to 4° C. As its temperature falls below 4° C, water begins to expand. At 0° C water turns to ice, and still it expands. In fact, as it freezes, water expands about 11 percent! This expansion makes ice less dense than water and allows ice to float. If God had not designed water to expand as it freezes, rivers and lakes could freeze from the bottom to the top, killing all the life in them. However, since ice floats, it forms an insulating layer that helps to shield the underlying water (and the plants and animals in it) against freezing. God made water with this unusual property to preserve the life He created.

Table 15-26 lists various substances and tells how much a 1-m rod of each substance would expand if its temperature rose from 30° C to 40° C.

Table 15-26

Thermal Expansion Rates	
Substance	**Thermal expansion from 30° C to 40° C**
aluminum	0.238 mm/m
brass	0.169 mm/m
lead	0.292 mm/m
nickel	0.131 mm/m
silver	0.194 mm/m
stainless steel	0.164 mm/m
concrete	up to 0.127 mm/m
ordinary glass	up to 0.128 mm/m
Pyrex glass	up to 0.035 mm/m
wood (across grain)	up to 0.730 mm/m
wood (along grain)	up to 0.110 mm/m

Scientifically Speaking

caloric theory	radiation
degrees (°)	specific heat
Celsius scale	heat of fusion
Kelvin scale	heat of vaporization
absolute zero	thermal expansion
calories (cal)	thermodynamics
Calorie (Cal)	first law of thermodynamics
heat	second law of thermodynamics
conduction	entropy
equilibrium	
conductors	
insulators	
convection	
convection current	

Questions to Talk Over

1. The island of Bermuda is approximately 950 km due east of Charleston, South Carolina. Bermuda has a year-round tropical climate, but Charleston does not. Why?
2. The insides of electric kilns are lined with firebrick to help retain heat and prevent rapid temperature changes. Why are kilns lined with brick rather than with a thick layer of shiny metal which would reflect the heat?
3. If a large aluminum skillet and a small iron skillet of equal masses are placed on heating elements of the same size and the same temperature at the same time, which skillet will heat more quickly? Why?
4. In winter, a wooden floor will feel warmer to your bare feet than a tile floor will, even though they are actually the same temperature. Why does the wood feel warmer?
5. Examine the following list of phenomena. Decide whether each is an example of conduction, convection, or radiation. Explain your decision.
   a. Ice forming on an automobile at night when the temperature of the air is above freezing
   b. Ocean breezes cooling the land
   c. A flame heating a nail
   d. An electric heater heating a room
   e. The sun heating the earth

ELECTRICITY

CHAPTER
16

Brrrrrring! The alarm goes off at 6:30 A.M. You crawl out of bed, feel your way to the light switch, grab your robe, and head for the shower. Brrr, the bathroom tile is cold, so you switch on the electric wall heater. After a hot shower, you put on the clean clothes that your mom washed, dried, and hung up the night before. The smell of sizzling bacon calls you to the kitchen. As you sit down, your mom pours a glass of cold orange juice for you. The radio announcer reports that a light snow is falling over most of the county, but school officials have not canceled classes. After a sigh of disappointment, you kiss your mom good-by and run to the car. As you ride to school, the streetlights blink off like strings of defective Christmas lights.

Does this sound like a typical winter morning? Did you notice how many of your morning activities depend upon electricity? In a little over an hour, you benefited from over ten different applications of electricity!

Because electricity plays a key role in our lives, we should have a basic understanding of what it is and how it works. The various forms of electricity can be divided into two broad categories—**static electricity** and **current electricity.**

Static Electricity

On cold, dry winter days, static electricity is probably your least favorite form of electrical energy. Your pants cling, your sweaters give you shocks, and walking across a carpet can result in a nasty sting if you happen to touch a metal doorknob or another person. Static electricity has been observed throughout history. Moses described lightning—one of the most spectacular forms of static electricity—as early as 1446 B.C. (Exod. 19:16). Over two thousand years ago, the Greeks observed that a piece of amber that had been stroked with wool or fur could "magically" attract certain lightweight objects—even against the force of gravity. Today we still encounter this effect of static electricity; we call it static cling.

Identifying charges

Static electricity is caused by **stationary electric charges**, or electric charges that are at rest on an object. Where do these charges come from? Scientists picture the atom as consisting of electrons spinning about a central nucleus of neutrons and protons. Two of these three types of particles play a role in the electrical phenomena that we observe in matter. An electron is a tiny particle that carries a negative electrical charge. A proton is a relatively massive particle that carries a positive electrical charge. Neutrons are also massive, but they carry no charge and are electrically neutral.

In some materials the valence electrons are held only loosely to the nuclei of the atoms. These electrons can be removed from the nuclei with little effort. However, in all substances the heavier, positively charged protons and neutral neutrons are much less free to move. Therefore, an electrical charge is usually produced by the removal or addition of *electrons.* The electrical characteristics of any substance depend directly on how easily its valence electrons can be removed from their atoms.

16-1 When you walk across a carpet, you sometimes acquire a static charge. Your shoes remove electrons from the carpet. If you touch a metal object, you are in for a shock as the electrons rush from your finger into the metal.

16-2 A static charge can also be produced by rubbing a hard rubber rod with wool. The rod picks up electrons from the wool and receives a negative charge.

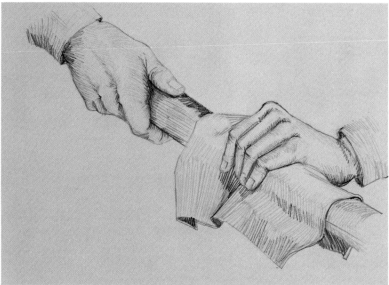

When two different materials are rubbed together, the frictional force is often strong enough to loosen the outer electrons of one or both of the substances. When this happens, some of the electrons from one substance are transferred to the other substance. The material that gains extra electrons becomes *negatively charged*; the material that loses some of its electrons becomes *positively charged*.

16-3 The law of charges states that opposite charges attract and like charges repel. The opposite charges are drawn toward each other. The forces produced by like charges tend to push them apart.

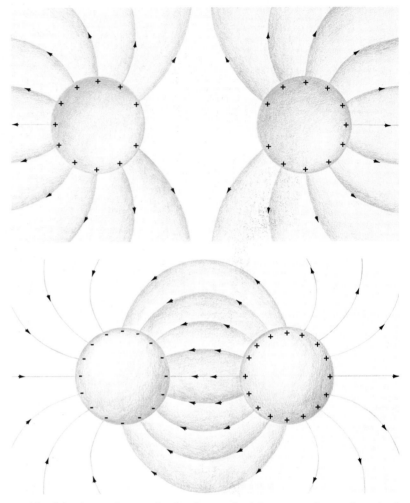

Positively and negatively charged objects produce *electrical forces.* Two objects that have the same charge (both positive or both negative) produce a force that pushes them away from each other. When you pull a wool sweater over your clean, dry hair, each of your hairs gains electrons (and a negative charge) from the wool. Because the negatively charged hairs repel one another, they stand out. Two objects that have opposite charges (one positive and one negative) produce a force that pulls them toward each other. This attraction of oppositely charged objects causes the "cling" when your clothing sticks to your socks or hose. The principles behind both types of electrical forces are expressed in the **law of charges:** like charges repel; unlike charges attract.

FACETS
OF BASIC SCIENCE

How Strong Is An Electrical Force?

Consider the atoms that make up your body. They all consist of protons, neutrons, and electrons. Because God established that atoms should contain an equal number of protons and electrons, the positive and negative charges in your body balance each other. Consequently, your body is balanced; it has no excess charge, and it produces no significant electrical force.

What do you think would happen if suddenly your body acquired just 1 percent more electrons, giving you 1 percent more negative charges than positive charges? How strong would be the electrical force produced by these negative charges? Strong enough to lift a pebble? Strong enough to push a Mack truck? Strong enough to topple the Alps?

No!

The electrical force produced by an imbalance of just 1 percent of the electrons in your body would be strong enough to push two earth-size planets apart!

Transferring charges

Substances can be classified into three basic categories according to their electrical behavior: conductors, insulators, and semiconductors. Which category a substance belongs to depends on how easily the valence electrons in the substance can be removed from their paths around their nuclei. Substances that hold their valence electrons loosely are electrical **conductors**. Substances that hold their valence electrons tightly are electrical **insulators. Semiconductors** fall into a class between conductors and insulators, holding their valence electrons more tightly than conductors, but less tightly than insulators.

Table 16-4

Relative Conductivity of Various Substances		
poor conductors **—good insulators**	rubber glass wood	10^{-16}
semiconductors	silicon germanium	1.0
good conductors **—poor insulators**	iron aluminum copper silver	10^8

Although the charges involved in static electricity are stationary, they can be momentarily shifted from one object to another, or even from place to place in the same object. When the charges of static electricity are transferred from place to place, they move until they are equally distributed on all the substances involved, and then stop moving. Static electricity never involves a continuous flow of charge.

Exactly what happens when electric charges are transferred? When a negative charge is applied to a neutral object, electrons flow from the negatively charged object to the neutral object until both objects have the same concentration of extra electrons. When a positive charge is applied to a neutral object, electrons flow from the neutral object to the positively charged object until both objects have the same shortage of electrons per unit area. Thus, when we say that charge flows or is transferred from one object to another, we mean that electrons move from a place with a higher concentration of electrons to a place with a lower concentration of electrons.

The more strongly a substance holds its valence electrons, the harder it is for charge to move within or through the material. Since conductors hold their valence electrons loosely, charge moves very easily through them. Insulators hold their valence electrons extremely tightly. Very little charge can be made to flow through them. Semiconductors hold their electrons moderately tightly. Charge flows through them moderately easily.

As a general rule, the elements on the left-hand side of the periodic table (metals) are conductors, those on the right-hand side (nonmetals) are insulators, and those near the middle of the table (metalloids) are semiconductors.

Table 16-5
Relative Conductivities of the Elements

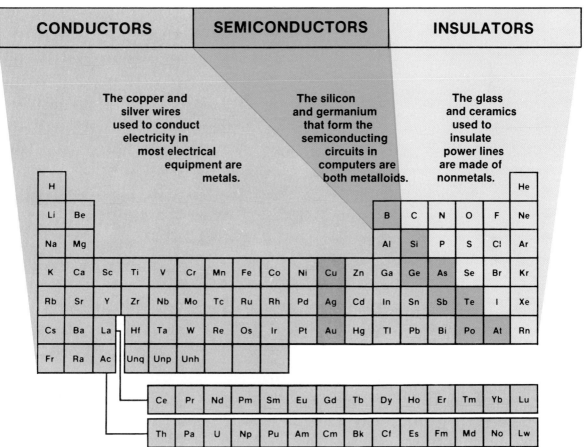

Producing charges

To produce a negative charge on a substance, electrons must be added to it. To produce a positive charge, electrons must be removed from the substance. Often two objects become charged simultaneously: one acquires a positive charge as it loses electrons, and the other receives a negative charge as it gains those electrons.

FACETS OF BASIC SCIENCE

Sparks Are Flying—The Van de Graaff Generator

Robert Van de Graaff (VAN deh GRAF), a Princeton physicist, invented one of the first devices that produced charges faster than they could escape. In the *Van de Graaff generator*, a motor-driven belt passes over two pulleys made of insulating materials. At one point, the belt receives negative charges from an electron source called a comb. The moving belt carries the negative charges to a metal "collector comb." Since the charge on the belt is more negative than the charge on the comb, electrons flow from the belt onto the collector comb. From the collector comb the electrons flow onto a large metal sphere. The longer the Van de Graaff generator operates, the more negative charge collects on the large metal sphere. The charge cannot flow off the metal sphere because the support for the sphere is made of an insulating material, which does not conduct charge well. Of course, there is a limit to the amount of charge that can be collected on the metal sphere.

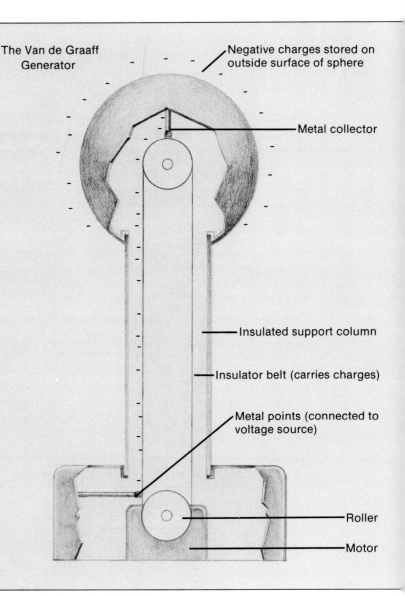

The Van de Graaff Generator

Negative charges stored on outside surface of sphere

Metal collector

Insulated support column

Insulator belt (carries charges)

Metal points (connected to voltage source)

Roller

Motor

Walking across a rug in dry weather often results in charges in both the rug and your shoes. Contact between these two objects produces these charges by allowing electrons from one object to move to the other. Friction produces the most charge when two insulators (both the rug and your shoes are insulators) are rubbed together. Whether the final charge on each insulator is positive or negative depends on the types of substances used.

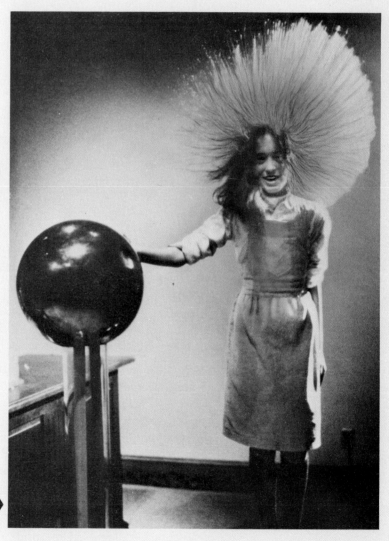

As soon as the concentration of negative charge on the sphere and collector comb has reached the same level as the concentration of negative charge being delivered by the moving belt, no more negative charge will flow from the belt into the sphere.

The charge that accumulates on the metal sphere of a large Van de Graaff generator can produce a tremendous electrical force. Sparks up to 4 m long can be produced between a Van de Graaff generator and a grounded object. (A *spark* is a visible transfer of charge from one object to another.)

As the negative charges flow from the generator, they collect ▶ on the individual fibers of hair. What makes the hairs stand out?

Rubbing a Lucite (LOO site) (plastic) rod with wool produces a positive charge on the rod and a negative charge on the wool. Rubbing an ebonite (EB uh NITE) (hard rubber) rod with wool, however, produces a negative charge on the rod and a positive charge on the wool. Which substance do you think holds its electrons more tightly, ebonite or Lucite?

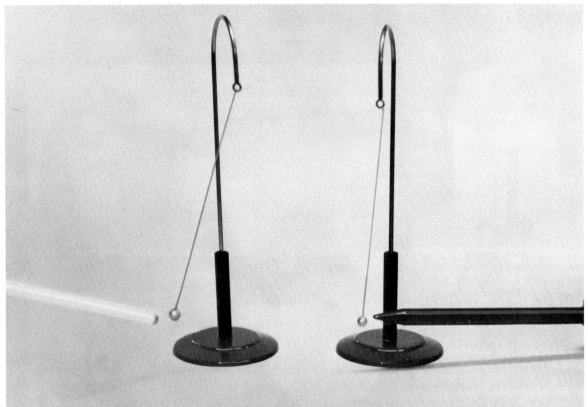

Rubbing two insulators together produces charge on the insulators relatively easily. This charge, however, quickly leaks away as it is transferred to ions in the atmosphere. Static cling, the attraction between two oppositely charged insulators, is worse in winter than in summer because winter air is drier than summer air and contains fewer ions. Because winter air contains fewer of the charge-absorbing ions, charge remains on a charged insulator longer in winter than in summer. In everyday situations, we prefer that the charges of static electricity leak away as quickly as possible. However, in order to study static electricity, scientists have devised methods of producing electric charges faster than they can leak away.

Storing charges

Paper is not a conductor, but it stores charges well. It does not store charges by gaining or losing electrons; the individual molecules of paper hold their electrons too tightly for that. If its electrons cannot move away from the nuclei of its atoms, how does paper store charge?

Imagine that a negatively charged rod is brought near a piece of paper. The negative charge of the rod will repel any other negatively charged particles. The electrons in the paper are negatively charged. As a result, the paths of the electrons in the paper will be shifted slightly away from the rod (repelled). After the electrons have moved slightly away, the protons of the paper molecules will be left relatively closer to the rod. When this occurs, the negatively charged rod and the positively charged protons at the surface of the paper will attract each other. The two oppositely charged materials will cling together. Would a similar attraction result if the rod were positively charged? In this case, the electrons in the paper would be attracted toward the rod, causing the surface of the paper to be negatively charged. Then the positively charged rod and the negatively charged paper surface would attract each other.

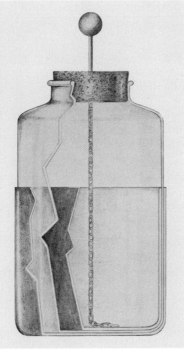

16-6 The Leyden (LY den) jar was invented in 1746 for the purpose of storing electrical charges. It consists of a glass bottle coated both inside and outside with tin or lead foil. The inner layer of foil is positively charged. The outer layer of foil is negatively charged. Because of induction, the outer surface of the glass is positively charged and the inner surface is negatively charged. Because some of the electrical energy from the layers of foil is used to shift the paths of the electrons in the glass, much charge can be stored on the layers of foil without electrons penetrating the glass.

Charging an object by shifting the paths of its electrons is called **induction** (in DUK shun). As long as a charged rod is held close to a piece of paper, the electrons in the paper will be held in their shifted positions. When the charged rod is removed, induction ceases and the electrons return to their normal paths within the paper molecules. Therefore, induction produces only a temporary storage of charges.

Scientists use the induction principle to build charge-storing electronic components called **capacitors** (kuh PAS ih turz). In a capacitor, a positively charged conductor is separated from a negatively charged conductor by an insulator. Without an insulator, the charge might jump between the two oppositely charged conductors. As the charges on the conductors increase, the likelihood that this will happen becomes greater. The insulator prevents the charge from jumping by absorbing some of the electrical energy of the charges. Some of the attractive force between the two conductors is used to shift the insulator's electrons toward the positive conductor, giving the insulator an induced charge. Therefore, both induced and free charges can be stored in a capacitor.

One of the first insulators that was used to store charge by induction was glass. Today, capacitors use insulators such as

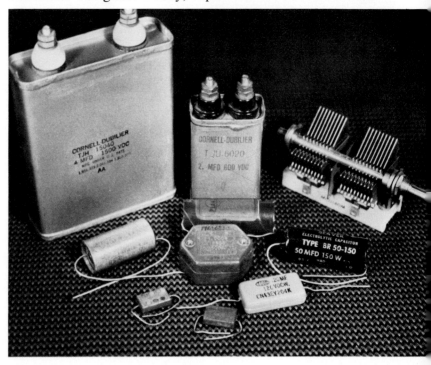

16-7 The dial tuners on many radios are capacitors. Layers of metal conductors are separated by air spaces which act as insulators to cause a capacitor to store charges.

paper, selenium, air, and even electrolyte solutions to store charge. Televisions, tape recorders, radios, computers, and car ignitions all store charge in capacitors.

Detecting charges

How can you tell whether an object has a positive charge, a negative charge, or no charge at all? Scientists have designed an instrument called an **electroscope** (ih LEK truh SKOAP) that uses the law of charges to detect charge. The simple electroscope shown in Figure 16-8 consists of a flask with a one-holed rubber stopper, a metal rod, a few leaf-shaped pieces of aluminum foil, and a metal sphere.

The metal rod in the electroscope not only serves as a support for the metal leaves and metal sphere, but also conducts to the leaves any charge that is placed on the sphere. If a negative charge (extra electrons) is placed on the sphere, extra electrons are redistributed through the rod to the metal leaves, making both leaves negatively charged. In accordance with the law of charges, the leaves will repel each other and swing apart. On the other hand, if the sphere is positively charged, the metal rod will conduct electrons from the leaves, making them both positively charged. Once again, the leaves will swing apart because of their like charges.

16-8 When a simple electroscope is uncharged, the foil leaves stick together. When a charged object touches the metal rod connected to the foil, a charge will be conducted to the leaves and will cause them to separate. What force causes the leaves to spread apart?

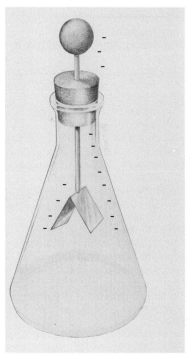

FACETS
OF BASIC SCIENCE

Lightning

Lightning strikes somewhere on the earth about 100 times every second. Most lightning is *forked lightning*, easily recognized by its zigzag streaks of light. Less common is *sheet lightning*—flashes of light over large areas of the sky. Some scientists believe that sheet lightning is a reflection of forked lightning striking beyond the horizon; others, that sheet lightning is an electrical discharge over a large area in the atmosphere. *Ball lightning*, the least common type of lightning, occurs so rarely that scientists know very little about it. Observers describe ball lightning as round, luminous balls of reddish light about 20 cm in diameter that explode soon after they descend from a cloud.

Lightning can strike from clouds to the ground, from the ground to clouds, between clouds, or between parts of the same cloud. In less than a second, a single lightning bolt may jump up to 3000 m and heat the air along its channel up to 15,000° C. The tremendous increase in pressure generated by the sudden expansion of this heated air produces a clap of thunder often audible over 25 km away. One lightning stroke is usually followed by another stroke along a slightly different path. Scientists have detected up to forty strokes in less than a second.

Occasionally Scripture uses lightning to symbolize judgment. For example, in Psalm 18:14 David exclaims, "Yea, he sent out his arrows, and scattered them; and he shot out lightnings, and discomfited [vanquished] them." Lightning is a fitting symbol for judgment because it possesses not only great destructive power but also great speed.

In 1752 Benjamin Franklin demonstrated by his famous kite experiment that lightning is a form of electricity. During the downpour of a thunderstorm, Franklin flew a kite from a long length of wet twine. Stationing himself under a dry shed, Franklin held a dry silk string attached to a key connected to the twine that held the kite. He observed that sparks flew from the key whenever he brought it near objects physically attached to the ground. He wondered if these sparks were identical to the electrical charges he could store in his Leyden jars. He

tested his hypothesis by touching the key to a grounded Leyden jar. As Franklin suspected, charge flowed from the key to the jar just as it did from other sources of static electricity. His conclusion: lightning is static electricity. (Warning: Do not attempt to repeat Franklin's experiment! Many people have been killed trying to duplicate his results.)

What causes lightning? Most lightning occurs during a thunderstorm as rain falls over an area of warm, rising air. When droplets of water fall from a cloud through a rising column of air, they are broken into smaller droplets of unequal size. The smaller, lighter droplets of water acquire a negative charge and are carried back up to the cloud by the rising air. The heavier droplets acquire a positive charge and fall to the earth. These opposite charges continue to accumulate in the cloud and the earth until their force breaks down the insulating capacity of the air. The bolt of lightning produced as charge jumps from the cloud to the earth may release more power than the combined peak capacity of all the electric power plants in the United States. However, because the bolt lasts less than a second, the energy it releases is worth less than $20.

Benjamin Franklin also invented one of the best protections against lightning, the lightning rod. A *lightning rod* is a pointed, upright metal rod fastened to the roof of a building and connected to the ground by a wire leading from the base of the rod. The

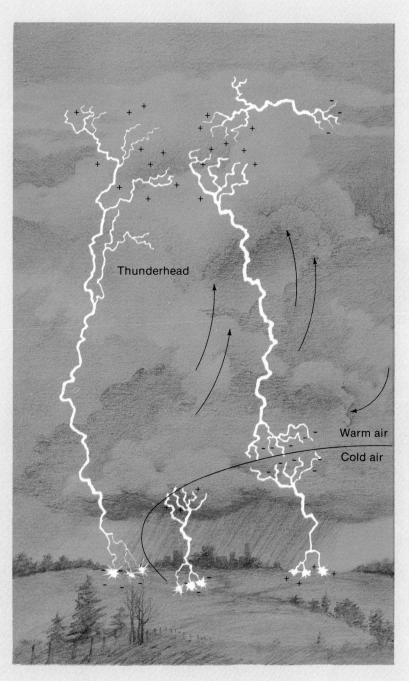

Thunderhead

Warm air

Cold air

lightning rod serves to conduct charge to the ground. If lightning does occur near the rod, it will be attracted to the highest object in the area (the lightning rod) and will be conducted harmlessly to the earth through the wire.

Here are some important safety rules that will help you protect yourself from lightning during a thunderstorm:

1. The safest shelter during a thunderstorm is a building protected by lightning rods, or a shielded metal enclosure such as a car. Stay in a protected place if you can.

2. Stay away from isolated trees, high points of land, and bodies of water, because lightning is most likely to strike these locations.

3. If you are caught in an open area, squat down. Do not lie down because lightning striking the ground near you could electrocute you if a large portion of your body is in contact with the ground.

4. Indoors, keep away from windows and outside doors. Close all windows; lightning has been known to enter buildings through open windows. Avoid using electrical appliances and touching plumbing. Lightning can strike and kill or seriously injure you as you touch a faucet or telephone.

Mechanical electroscopes can detect only relatively large charges. This shortcoming is the result of the fact that tiny electrical charges produce only tiny electrical forces of repulsion, which cannot move the relatively large mass of a metal leaf or pointer. Today, most laboratories use electronic electroscopes. Instead of relying on mechanical movement, these electroscopes measure the charge on an object by applying the charge to a capacitor and then measuring how long it takes the capacitor to lose the charge.

16-9 In a Braun electroscope, a charge applied to the metal plate is conducted to a "stem" and pointer instead of to metal leaves. As the law of charges predicts, the pointer swings away from the "like-charged" stem.

Using charges

You probably benefit from static electricity—stationary electric charges—every day. For example, thousands of photocopying machines in offices and public buildings use static electricity to make millions of paper copies of original documents each year. To produce a photocopy, an image of the original is reflected onto a positively charged, photosensitive drum by means of a very bright light. Wherever this light hits the drum's surface, electrons are released to the drum. As a result the drum becomes electrically neutral at all points where light has touched it. Next, the drum rolls past negatively charged ink particles, which stick to all the positively charged places on the drum. Finally, the drum rolls across positively charged paper, which attracts the ink particles from the drum. Before the paper leaves the photocopying machine, a heated plate bonds the ink particles to the paper. In some high-speed copying machines, a laser replaces the bright light source. Such machines can reproduce up to 28,000 lines per minute. They could reproduce an entire Bible in less than five minutes.

16-10 A Xerox copier.

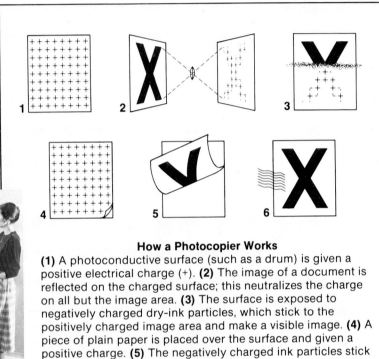

How a Photocopier Works

(1) A photoconductive surface (such as a drum) is given a positive electrical charge (+). **(2)** The image of a document is reflected on the charged surface; this neutralizes the charge on all but the image area. **(3)** The surface is exposed to negatively charged dry-ink particles, which stick to the positively charged image area and make a visible image. **(4)** A piece of plain paper is placed over the surface and given a positive charge. **(5)** The negatively charged ink particles stick to the positively charged paper. **(6)** Heat bonds the image to the paper.

Electroscopes can be used to measure radioactive decay. As radioactive substances decay (break down into other substances), they give off ions. When a charged electroscope is placed near a radioactive substance, the ions released by radioactive decay will either donate electrons to or remove electrons from the electroscope, depending on the charge on the electroscope. The strength of the radioactive substance (how quickly the substance is decaying) can be determined by measuring how quickly the electroscope discharges. You can observe a similar event by holding a lighted match near the plate of a charged Braun electroscope. Ions produced during combustion (burning) will remove charge from an electroscope in the same way as ions from radioactive decay do.

Electrostatic (ih LEK tro STAT ik) principles also operate in the pollution-control systems of many factories. As industrial smoke travels from machinery to the smokestacks, it passes charged electrodes that give the smoke particles a static charge. Just before the smoke enters the smokestacks, the charged particles are collected on oppositely charged metal plates. Much of the remaining "smoke" that is released through the smoke-stack is harmless steam. Frequently, the particles attracted to the electrodes contain valuable chemical substances that can be reclaimed. This type of antipollution device, called an *electrostatic precipitator* (prih SIP ih tay tur), substantially reduces air pollution from many factories.

High-quality stereo systems often use electrostatic speakers to reproduce sound with great clarity. Electrostatic speakers are built like large capacitors. One electrode in each speaker is nonmovable; the other electrode vibrates freely, producing sound by causing the surrounding air to vibrate.

16-11 An electrostatic precipitator filters smoke particles from air by using the law of charges. Negative electrodes give the smoke particles a negative charge so that they will be attracted to positively charged collection plates. When the plates are coated with particles, they are cleaned and put back in place. This unit is used to clean the air from a home furnace.

Current Electricity

Modern civilizations could not exist without electricity. Cars, elevators, freezers, hair dryers, fluorescent lights, and hundreds of other convenient and time-saving devices require electricity to operate. In almost all these devices, moving charges provide the energy for the work that is accomplished. Electricity that involves continuously moving charges is called current electricity.

16-12 Looking at a city at night will tell you how much modern society depends on electrical power.

Identifying current

Because of their tiny size, light weight, and location in the atom, electrons move through substances much more easily than protons do. Therefore, most of the moving charges that we discuss are actually moving, negatively charged electrons—not moving, positively charged protons. Because conductors hold their valence electrons very loosely, electrons (and therefore charges) flow easily through conductors. When enough electrical energy is applied to a conductor, its valence electrons are stripped from their nuclei, and negative charges are forced to move along the conductor. When enough energy is constantly applied to keep the charges moving continuously, an electrical **current** occurs. In most electrical devices, the electrical current is forced to flow in a circular path called a **circuit** (SUR kit). The simplest circuit is a wire connected to the two terminals of a source of electrical energy. How does this type of simple circuit work?

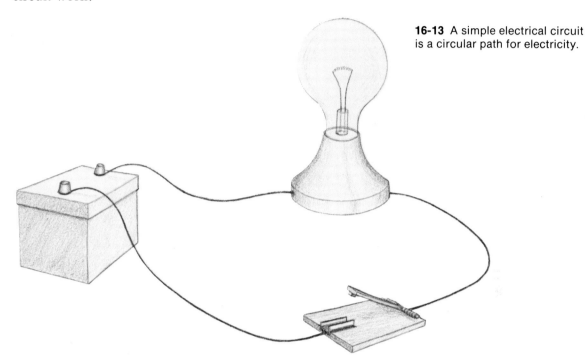

16-13 A simple electrical circuit is a circular path for electricity.

A **battery** is a typical electrical energy source. It can supply the electrical energy to force electrons through a circuit. The battery chemically "pumps" electrons from its negative terminal into a wire or some other conductor. These electrons repel the like-charged electrons already in the conductor, shoving electrons out the other end of the conductor, into the *positive terminal* of the battery. Once electrons enter the positive terminal of the battery, they make their way back to the *negative terminal*.

Any break in the conductor keeps electrons from flowing around a circuit. A circuit can be broken intentionally with a **switch**. A simple switch is a conductor that can be moved so that it either bridges or does not bridge the gap between two wire conductors. When the conductors do not make contact, electrons cannot flow across the break, and both the circuit and the switch are said to be *open*. When the conductors do make contact, electrons can flow through the connected conductors, and the circuit and switch are said to be *closed*. A switch acts like

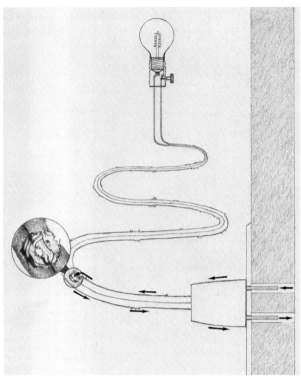

16-14 A short circuit occurs when electricity is able to find a path shorter than the one it is supposed to travel. The frayed wires of this lamp allow the current to "take a short circuit" through the spot where the two wires touch.

a drawbridge. When the switch is open, the drawbridge is up and the electrons cannot jump the wide gap. When the switch is closed, the drawbridge is down and electrons can "march" across. The spark that often occurs when a switch closes is really a stream of electrons jumping across the narrowing gap.

Electrons will take the easiest path whenever possible. This tendency is frequently to blame when electrical appliances break down. For example, picture a lamp cord that has frayed so badly that the wires inside it touch each other. If the electrons flowing into the cord flowed all the way through the lamp, it would convert some of their energy into light. But rather than traveling the entire circuit, the electrons take a short cut through the point where the wires touch. This shorter path for the electrons is called a **short circuit.**

Causes of current

Electrons move through a circuit only if they are pushed by an *electrical force.* What is an electrical force? Where does it come from? And what part does it play in electrical circuits? We can compare current electricity to a water-pump system. A pump can push water through pipes from a low elevation to a higher elevation. The higher the pump pushes the water, the more work the pump performs. As it is raised, the water gains potential energy. As it falls back to its original level, it can be used to do work.

A battery is an electrical pump. Instead of pumping water, a battery pumps electrons. Inside a battery, electrons are pushed from one place to another by a chemical reaction. As this process continues, the place losing electrons becomes positively charged, and the place gaining electrons becomes negatively charged. The positively charged place, called the *positive terminal*, has a shortage of electrons. The negatively charged place, called the *negative terminal*, has an excess of electrons. These electrons are ready to go through a circuit.

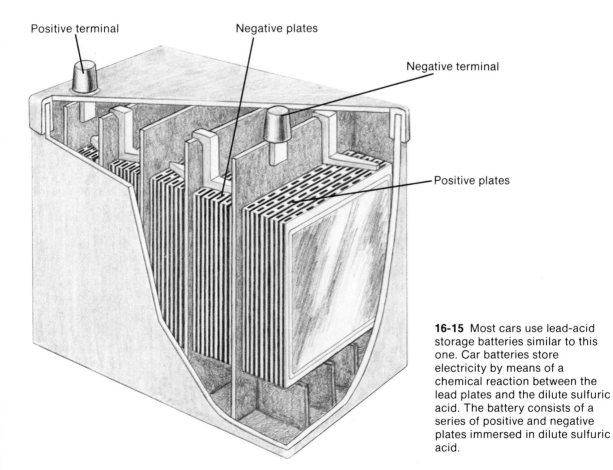

Positive terminal

Negative plates

Negative terminal

Positive plates

16-15 Most cars use lead-acid storage batteries similar to this one. Car batteries store electricity by means of a chemical reaction between the lead plates and the dilute sulfuric acid. The battery consists of a series of positive and negative plates immersed in dilute sulfuric acid.

How is the movement of electrons within a battery and circuit similar to the work done in a water-pump system? The water pumped to an elevation will do work if it is allowed to flow downward. Similarly, the electrons that a battery pushes onto its negative terminal will do work if they are allowed to flow through a circuit.

If you wanted to build a water-pump system that would give the water a large amount of potential energy, you would find a location where the water could be pumped up a very high mountain. When the water was released, it would be capable of doing a large amount of work. But to pump the water up the mountain you would need a strong water pump. If you want a large amount of electrical energy to flow through a circuit, you also need a strong "pump." Some batteries are stronger than others: the stronger the battery is, the more electrons it can push onto its negative terminal. Which is a stronger "pump"—a flashlight battery or a car battery?

The negative terminal of a strong battery contains many mutually repelling electrons. Therefore it possesses a great amount of electrical potential energy, or as scientists say, a *high electrical potential.* On the other hand, the positive terminal of a battery gains electrons very easily. In fact, it attracts electrons. Because it requires very little energy to add electrons, a positive terminal has a very *low electrical potential.*

Every object has an **electrical potential.** The more negatively charged an object is, the more electrical potential it has. A very negatively charged object has a higher potential than a less negatively charged object. And any negatively charged object has a higher electrical potential than a neutral or positively charged object.

16-16 The glow in this tube is caused by a stream of electrons that jump from one electrode at a high electrical potential to another electrode at a lower electrical potential. The potential difference between the two electrodes is 20,000 V.

Current always flows from places with higher electrical potentials to places with lower electrical potentials. These places may be different objects or different points in the same object. In Figure 16-16 the line of blue light in the tube is given off by a stream of electrons flowing from an electrode with a high potential to an electrode with a low potential.

The difference between the electrical potentials of two different points or objects is called the **potential difference** or **potential drop** between the two places. Potential difference is measured in units called **volts (V)**. A potential difference of 1 volt uses only 1 J of energy to move 6,250,000,000,000,000,000 (6.25×10^{18}) electrons through a circuit. Since 6.25×10^{18} is an awkward number to use regularly, the SI system of measurement calls this number of electrons 1 **coulomb, (C)** (KOO lahm) of charge. Therefore, 1 V gives 1 J of energy to 1 C of charge.

When a conductor is connected to an electrical energy source so that a circuit is formed, the potential difference between the two ends of the conductor is known as the **voltage** of the circuit.

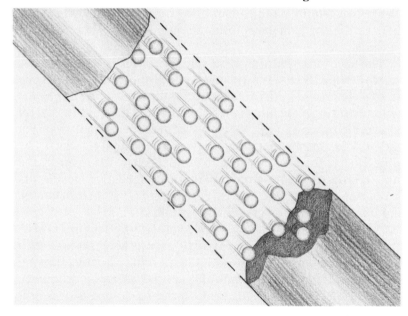

16-17 Voltage can be described as the amount of work available to push electrons through a circuit. The greater the voltage is, the more electrical force is pushing the electrons through the circuit.

The larger the potential difference is between two points, the more the electrical force pushes electrons from the point with higher potential to the point with lower potential. Therefore, voltage can also be described as the amount of work available from an energy source for pushing electrons through a circuit. In practical terms, a 6-V battery (a battery with 6 volts of potential difference between its terminals) will push electrons through a wire twice as fast as a 3-V battery will.

The greater the number of electrons that flow through a circuit in a given amount of time, the greater the amount of current that flows through the circuit. We measure current in units called **amperes** (**A**) (AM pihrz). Measuring electrical current in amperes is like measuring water current in the number of liters of water that pass a point in a pipe every second (liters per second). A simple electrical circuit with a current of 1 ampere has 1 C of charge (6.25×10^{18} electrons) moving past any given point in the circuit every second. How many coulombs of charge flow in one second past a point in a circuit with 2 A of current?

Controlling current

How do the moving charges of current electricity accomplish work in electrical devices? Again compare electricity to water. Moving water can do work. For instance, the water falling down a mountain can turn a paddle wheel. The water uses some of its energy to push the paddles as it flows by. The paddle wheel can then use the energy it gains from the water to do work by turning a grindstone.

The electrical parallel to a paddle wheel is a resistor. A **resistor** (rih ZIS tur) is any object or substance that resists the flow of electrons. Resistors that accomplish work in your home include heating elements, light filaments, and the volume dial on your radio or television. Just as water uses energy to flow past a paddle wheel, electrons use energy to flow through resistors. The more energy the electrons use to flow through the resistor, the more **resistance** the resistor has. As you might expect, insulators have large resistances, semiconductors have medium resistances, and conductors have very small resistances.

A German schoolteacher named Georg Simon Ohm (OME) observed that resistance, potential difference, and current are all related. He found that the amount of current (amperes) flowing through a circuit depends not only on the potential difference (voltage) of the circuit, but also on the resistance of the substances in the circuit. Today we measure resistance in units called **ohms** (Ω). It takes 1 V of potential difference to push 1 A of current through a resistor with a resistance of 1 Ω. It takes 2 V to push 2 A of current through a 1 Ω resistor. How many volts would it take to push 10 A through a 2 Ω resistor?

The relationship between the potential difference, the current, and the resistance in a circuit is known as *Ohm's law.*

16-18 Resistors are coded by colored bands. You can tell how much resistance a resistor has by checking the table in Appendix C.

Ohm's law may be expressed mathematically as follows:

potential difference = current x resistance

This equation may also be written in symbols:

$$V = I \times R$$
$$V = IR$$

In these equations V equals the potential difference in volts, I equals the current in amperes, and R equals the resistance in ohms. If we know any two of these properties of a given circuit, we can find the third property by using Ohm's law. In the following example, the current and potential difference of a circuit are known, and Ohm's law is used to find the resistance.

16-19 Georg Simon Ohm.

A circuit through a lamp has a current of 2 A and a potential difference of 120 V. What is the resistance of the circuit?

Ohm's law: $V = IR$ $V = 120V$

 $120V = (2A)(R)$ $I = 2A$

$$\frac{120V}{2A} = R$$

$$\frac{60V}{A} = R$$

In this equation, the resistance of the circuit is 60 V per ampere. But the normal units for measuring resistance are *ohms.* Why is this answer expressed in volts per ampere? According to Ohm's law and the definitions of volts and amperes, $1\,\Omega$ is the same as 1 V per 1 A:

$$1\Omega = \frac{1\ V}{1\ A}$$

Therefore, the circuit in our example has a resistance of $60\frac{V}{A}$, or 60Ω.

All electrical devices have some resistance. Therefore electrons always lose energy as they pass through electrical devices.

FACETS
OF BASIC SCIENCE

Watch the Needle: Electrical Measuring Devices

Three different devices are used to measure various electrical quantities in a circuit.

An **ohmmeter** (OME MEE tur) is a device that measures resistance. An ohmmeter consists of a battery with a known electrical potential in series with an ammeter. When the ohmmeter is connected to a circuit load, it forces its known voltage through the load and then through the ammeter of the ohmmeter. From the known voltage of the ohmmeter's battery and the current detected by the ammeter, the resistance of the circuit can be calculated by Ohm's law. Since an ohmmeter provides every circuit with the same voltage, the current in such a circuit varies directly with the resistance. Consequently, the ammeter of an ohmmeter is calibrated directly in ohms.

An **ammeter** (AM MEE tur) measures the flow of current through a circuit. Ammeters must be placed in series with a circuit to measure current. A single branch of a parallel circuit receives only some of the circuit's current. Therefore, an ammeter connected in parallel detects only the current flowing through the branch of the circuit that the ammeter forms. A needle in an ammeter deflects according to the amount of current flowing through the

instrument. Most ammeters have both a red and a black connecting post. The black post is the negative terminal and must be connected so that current flowing from the negative terminal of the battery enters the ammeter through this post. The red post is the positive terminal. Current should leave the ammeter through the red post on its way to the positive terminal of the battery. Connecting an ammeter to a circuit in the wrong direction can damage the ammeter.

HEY, BRING THAT OHMMETER UP HERE; I THINK I FOUND THE SHORT.

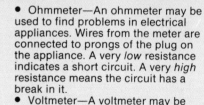

- Ohmmeter—An ohmmeter may be used to find problems in electrical appliances. Wires from the meter are connected to prongs of the plug on the appliance. A very *low* resistance indicates a short circuit. A very *high* resistance means the circuit has a break in it.
- Voltmeter—A voltmeter may be used to test how much "life" is left in a battery. Batteries should be tested while in use for accurate results.
- Ammeter—An ammeter can be used to find out how much current is going into a car battery as it is being charged.

A **voltmeter** (VOALT MEE tur) is used to measure the potential difference between two points in a circuit. Voltmeters must be placed in parallel with the section of the circuit containing the load for which the potential difference is to be measured. Remember that the potential drop across two branches of a parallel circuit is the same for both branches. [Never use a voltmeter in series; it will give you a wrong reading. Never use an ammeter in parallel; it will give you a wrong reading and doing this will perhaps damage the ammeter.]

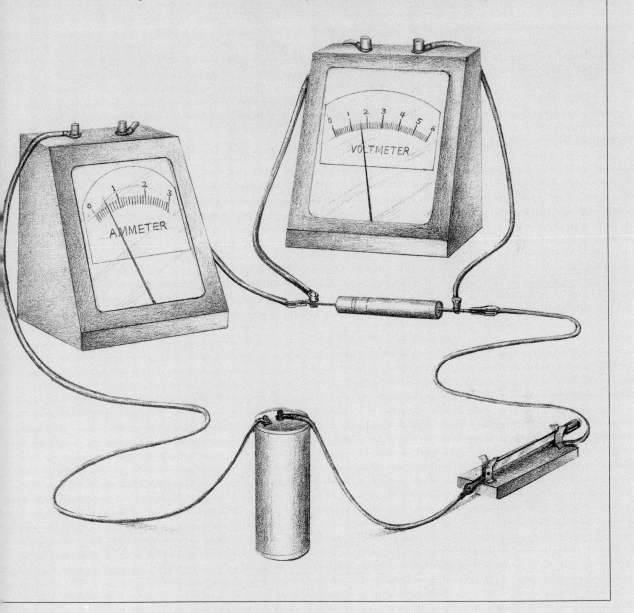

16-20 The high resistance of the material in the heating element of this oven produces the heat that baked the cake.

Often the energy lost by the electrons is converted into other forms of energy in the device. For example, if you are making a coffee cake, you may use an electric mixer to convert electrical energy into the mechanical energy necessary to spin the beaters. Your oven converts electrical energy into the heat energy that bakes the cake.

The resistance in an electrical device is called a **circuit load**. We measure circuit load in *ohms,* the same units we use to measure resistance. A circuit may contain more than one load and may be arranged in two different ways. In a **series circuit** there is only one path for the electrons to follow. All the electrons from the source flow through all the loads in sequence and then return to the source. In a **parallel circuit**, the electrons have

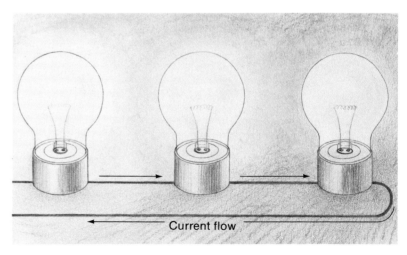

Current flow

16-21 What would happen if the filament in one of the bulbs burned out?

several paths to follow. Only part of the electrons pass through any one load. The rest of the electrons flow through the other load or loads.

For example, if two or more light bulbs are connected in series (Figure 16-21), the electrons that pass through the first bulb must also pass through the second and third bulbs. Therefore, the same amount of current flows through all the light bulbs. They will evenly divide the available energy and burn equally bright. If any one bulb burns out (the thin, current-conducting wire breaks), the circuit is broken and the current stops flowing through all the bulbs.

If two or more bulbs are connected in a parallel circuit (Figure 16-22), some of the electrons flowing through the circuit pass through the first bulb while the same amount of electrons pass through the second and the third bulbs. The two branches of the parallel circuit are like two branches of a water pipe. Since the same electrical potential (voltage) pushes electrons through both branches, the electrons in each branch have equal amounts of force pushing them forward. Even if the branches do not have equal resistance, the same amount of energy is used up in each branch. Therefore the same potential drop occurs in each branch of a parallel circuit.

If either of the light bulbs in the parallel circuit burns out, breaking the circuit in that branch, electons will continue to flow through the other branch, and the other bulb will continue to burn. Only if all bulbs are burned out will the circuit be completely broken. Houses are usually wired in parallel for this reason.

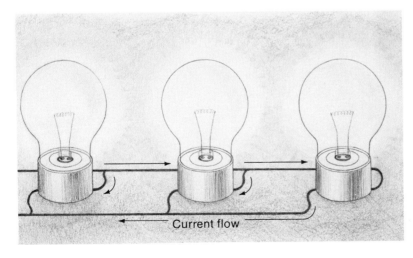

Current flow

16-22 What would happen if the filament in the first bulb burned out? The second?

FACETS
OF BASIC SCIENCE

Bright Ideas

Many of the appliances we use daily—toasters, irons, electric stoves and ovens, fluorescent and incandescent lights, to name a few—produce heat or light from electrical energy. How does electrical current produce light and heat?

We know that electrons lose energy as they pass through a resistor. Where does this energy go? Most of the energy of the electrons is converted into thermal energy in the resistor. The more resistance the resistor has, the more thermal energy the electrons produce as they pass through it. Similarly, the more current is pushed through any given resistor, the more thermal energy is produced.

Forcing electrical currents through high-resistance resistors produces heat efficiently. In toasters, irons, stoves, and similar appliances, electrical current passes through materials such as nichrome (an alloy of nickel, iron, and chromium) or carbon. When enough current flows through a heating element made of one of these substances, the element glows red-hot.

Forcing current through an electrical device can also produce light. The first electrical lights were arc lights. The British chemist Sir Humphrey Davy found that a bright spark would flash continually between two carbon rods if they were connected to the terminals of a high voltage battery. Lights based on this principle produced a very bright but glaring light. Consequently, arc lights were not often used in homes. Today carbon arc lights provide extremely bright light for large motion-picture projectors, searchlights, and spotlights.

Current flowing through wires can also produce light. The word *incandescent* means "glowing with great heat," and lights made from wires that glow when current passes through them are called *incandescent lights*. As nineteenth-century scientists learned more about electricity, they realized that incandescent light was a promising way to produce light efficiently. Unfortunately, their tests quickly revealed an obstacle: each wire that produced a fairly bright light also burned out quickly. During the last half of the nineteenth century, Thomas Alva Edison tested thousands of different substances as the conductors in incandescent light bulbs. Platinum, human hair, cotton, and bamboo were just a few of the materials he tried. Finally, in October 1879, he succeeded: a carbonized thread formed a long-lasting incandescent filament. Edison found that if he enclosed the carbonized filament in a glass bulb and removed the air from within the glass, the filament lasted even longer. The lack of oxygen in the bulb kept the thread from oxidizing and burning out quickly. In the wake of Edison's discovery, light bulbs rapidly became the major source of light in American homes.

free electrons and the mercury ions in the tube. Periodically, free electrons rejoin the mercury ions and produce invisible ultraviolet light. When the ultraviolet light strikes the inner coating of the tube, a bright, uniform, bluish green light is given off.

Today carbon filaments have been replaced by more sturdy and efficient materials, primarily tungsten wire. Tungsten wire has a very high resistance and requires a relatively small amount of current to become brightly incandescent. In addition, tungsten's very high melting point (about 3410° C) keeps tungsten filaments from burning out quickly.

Fluorescent light bulbs produce light from current much differently from the way incandescent light bulbs do. In fluorescent lights, mercury vapor fills a long tube that has electrodes at each end. When enough voltage is supplied to the electrodes, the mercury molecules are ionized; that is, valence electrons in the mercury atoms are removed from their paths. Current then flows through the tube, carried by the

Because wires made of conductors have very little resistance, they are used to carry current between electrical energy sources and loads. Each type of wire can carry only a limited amount of current without overheating and possibly starting a fire. **Fuses** were invented to prevent electrical fires by breaking circuits before the wires become too hot. Fuses are made of metals with low melting-point temperatures and are rated according to how much current they can carry without melting and breaking the circuit. For example, if *more* than 10 A of current pass through a fuse with a current rating of 10 A, the wires in the fuse will melt and break the flow of current in the circuit. Most houses have fuses with current ratings of 20 to 30A. Since replacing burned-out fuses can become tedious and expensive, another device, known as a **circuit breaker**, has been designed to temporarily open a circuit that is carrying too much current.

16-23 Types of fuses.

Household fuses like these are often found in the fuse boxes of older homes. When too much current passes through the small metal filament in the fuse, the filament melts and breaks the circuit.

Cylinder fuses protect major appliances, which demand high voltage and high amperage. The alloy core of a cylinder fuse will melt to protect the appliance. If a surge of current is pulled through the circuit, the fuse will "blow out."

Circuit breakers contain heat-sensitive springs which switch off the circuit if the spring is heated past a certain temperature by too large a load of current. Most modern homes have circuit breakers.

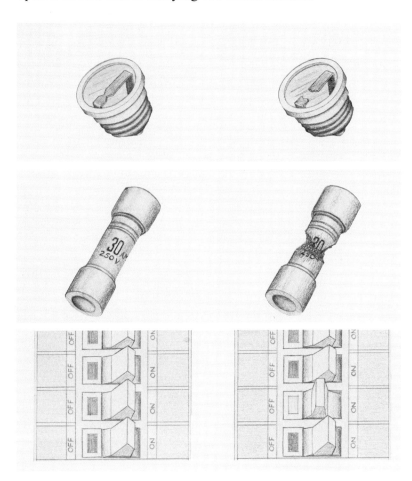

16-24 An electrical meter like this one records how many kilowatt-hours of electrical power are used in your home.

Power and current

Power measures how fast work is done. The unit of power is the watt. A machine that performs 1 J of work in 1 s uses 1 W of power. The more quickly a circuit uses energy, the more power it needs. For example, a 100-W light bulb uses twice as much energy per unit of time as a 50-W light bulb. The extra energy is used to produce more light in the 100-W light bulb. Machines in many factories use thousands of watts of power. The power ratings of these machines are expressed in **kilowatts (kW)**, or units of 1000 W.

We often refer to companies that sell electrical energy as "power companies." However, the "power meter" behind your house measures not electrical *power* (the rate of use) but electrical *energy* (the amount used). The electric company charges you according to how much energy you use, not according to how fast you use it. Therefore, it costs just as much to operate a 100-W light bulb for ten hours as it does to run a 1000-W blow dryer for one hour. The light bulb uses 100 J per second; the blow dryer uses 1000 J per second. The light bulb has to run ten times longer than the blow dryer to use an equal amount of energy (the same number of joules).

FACETS
OF BASIC SCIENCE

Electrical Safety

Electricity has become such a permanent part of our modern civilization that we use it without thinking about it. A lack of knowledge about electricity, however, can be hazardous to your health! Each year many people die of electrical shock and in electrical fires because they neglect to follow the rules for using electricity safely.

Electrocution (death by electric shock) occurs when the human body completes an electrical circuit and current flows near the heart muscles. How does such a tragic event occur?

Electrocution is usually caused by the careless use of electrical appliances. When the cord to an electrical appliance frays, the wires in the cord may touch the body of the appliance. If the body of the appliance is metal, it can acquire a fairly high electrical potential. If you touch the metal appliance and an electrically grounded object at the same time, electric current flows from the appliance through your body. If this current flows anywhere near the heart muscles, it interferes with the normal currents in the muscle, causing the heart to beat erratically. This condition, which doctors call ventricular fibrillation, can reduce the flow of blood to the body and eventually cause death.

Observing several basic safety rules can help prevent electrocution:

1. Never touch a metal appliance and a grounded object at the same time. For example, never touch a water spigot or a concrete floor (if you are barefoot) while your body is in contact with any electrical appliance. A water pipe and a concrete floor are both grounded objects; they are both in contact with the earth. Washing machines and similar appliances are especially dangerous in this type of situation because they operate at a fairly high voltage.

2. Check all appliances for frayed cords. Do not use an appliance that has a frayed cord until it has been repaired. A tingling sensation in your fingertips when you touch an appliance usually indicates that the appliance has a frayed cord.

3. Use grounded plugs whenever they are available. A grounded plug includes a third wire called a *ground wire*. When a grounded plug is plugged in, the ground wire connects to a metal pipe or metal stake driven into the ground. Grounded plugs allow the current from a charged appliance to flow into the ground instead of through your body.

Each year electricity claims many lives through electrical fires (fires started by a malfunctioning electrical device). Electrical fires are also easy to avoid by taking a few simple precautions.

1. Check for cracked or dried-out electrical cords. Once an electrical cord cracks, the wires may come close enough

together to produce sparks. Sparks, in turn, can produce fires.

2. Never place an extension cord under a rug. If sparks fly from the cord, the rug can easily catch fire. Also, because some extension cords are made with fairly small wires, their resistance is high and they become hot very quickly. In some cases, the wire can become hot enough to cause the rug to burn.

3. Check the current rating of each circuit you use. If you draw more current through a circuit than the circuit is designed to carry, the wires can become hot

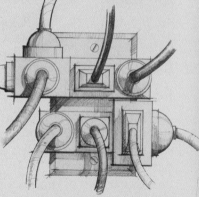

enough to start a fire. Fuses and circuit breakers are designed to protect circuits by breaking the circuits if too much current is drawn through them. Do not try to shunt an electrical current around these safety devices.

4. Do not allow flammable objects to come close to open heating elements. For example, keep curtains and sheets away from the heating elements of electric heaters; unplug an iron after you are finished using it.

Scientifically Speaking

static electricity
current electricity
stationary electric charges
law of charges
induction
capacitors
electroscope
current
circuit
battery
switch

short circuit
electrical potential
potential difference
potential drop
coulomb (C)
voltage
amperes (A)
resistor
resistance
ohms (Ω)

ammeter
voltmeter
ohmmeter
circuit load
series circuit
parallel circuit
fuses
circuit breaker
kilowatts (kW)
ground wire

Questions to Talk Over

1. Outside the wind drifts snow against your car, but inside the beautifully carpeted store, you are comfortably warm as you rush to finish your Christmas shopping. At last you have found your final gift. As you hand the cashier your money, a spark jumps from your finger to the cashier's finger, startling both of you. Explain exactly what happened when the spark jumped and why.

2. Sometimes large metal objects can collect an electrical charge and act as giant capacitors. If you observed the refueling of a jetliner at a large airport, you would see the fuel operator connect cables from the ground to the fuel truck and the airplane before refueling begins. Why do you suppose he does this?

3. The negative terminal of a car battery is connected directly to the metal chassis of the car, while the positive terminal is said to be "hot." If you were installing a radio in a car, you would energize the radio by bolting one wire from the radio to the chassis and running another wire from the radio to the battery. To which battery terminal would you attach this wire? Why can you use this system of wiring in a car but not in a metal frame building?

4. As you add more resistors in series in a circuit, the total resistance increases. Ed and Louis discovered this principle the hard way when they decided to add more lights to their clubhouse. As they added more lights to the circuit, all the lights became dimmer. Finally, all the lights went out! What happened? How should the boys have wired their clubhouse?

5. Susan decided that to do her part to save electrical power, she would use her electric blow dryer on the medium setting of 800 W instead of the high setting of 1200 W. Now it takes Susan twice as long to dry her hair. Has she reduced her power consumption? Which setting is more efficient?

MICHAEL FARADAY
ENGLISH PHYSICIST (1791-1867)

What do silver-plated spoons, electric generators, polarized sunglasses, and liquid ammonia have in common? The answer is Michael Faraday (FEHR uh DAY). His work made possible these and many similar innovations. Science historians rate this man as one of history's greatest experimental physicists.

Faraday's pioneering work in electrochemistry showed that compounds can be broken down into elements by an electrical current. Faraday called this decomposition reaction *electrolysis*. Today many industries use electrolysis in processes that range from plating spoons with silver to powering batteries and extracting aluminum from its ore.

While experimenting with magnets, Faraday also uncovered a new way to produce electricity. This discovery is the basis for electric generators, transformers, and electric motors. Faraday also contributed to the study of polarized light and the liquification of gases. Perhaps most noteworthy of all is Faraday's discovery of the "field" of force that surrounds a magnet. This concept became one of the major developments in the history of physics. Field theory is still employed today at the forefront of theoretical research.

What made Michael Faraday the successful scientist that he was? Faraday had the right attitude toward science, himself, and God. A devout Christian, Faraday based his attitudes on

the firm foundation of Scripture. He viewed science as a constant search for truth about God's creation. Faraday wanted to discover and understand as much as he could about God's universe. To do this, he disciplined himself to become a model researcher. Faraday believed that the ideal scientist should be enthusiastic but always careful; he must constantly test his theories against the facts. If fact and theory do not match, theory must be discarded. These were high standards, but Faraday drove himself to meet them.

Faraday's Christianity motivated him not only to excellence, but also to humility. Despite his notable achievements, Faraday never forgot that he could make

mistakes, and as a result he carefully scrutinized his work for errors. In the words of one of his biographers, Faraday led a "life-long strife to seek and say that which he thought was true, and to do that which he thought was kind." Faraday's humility made him both an exemplary scientist and a shining testimony for Christ.

Faraday's contributions to science were firmly rooted in his faith. As an earnest student of the Bible, Faraday made nearly 3000 notes in the margin of his Bible. To his knowledge of the Bible, he added enthusiasm and an intense love for God. Even his heavy research schedule could not distract Faraday from the all-day Sunday services and midweek prayer meeting of the small fundamental church he attended in London. Another great scientist, John Tyndall (TIN dul), noted that "a good deal of Faraday's weekday strength might be attributed to his Sunday exercises. He drinks from a fount on Sunday which refreshes his soul for the week."

Faraday knew that God's Word is sure. While he carefully searched out and analyzed scientific knowledge, he realized that knowledge of God comes from the Bible by simple faith. A reporter once asked Faraday about his speculations on the hereafter. "Speculations?" replied the astonished physicist. "I have none. I am resting on certainties. 'I know whom I have believed, and am persuaded that he is able to keep that which I have committed unto him against that day' " (II Timothy 1:12). Although some of Faraday's scientist friends smiled scornfully at his beliefs, they could not say that they were the product of a weak mind or that they failed to produce a godly life.

Michael Faraday commanded respect and admiration from across the globe. For many years he served as director of the Royal Institute's laboratory in London. His election as a Fellow of the Royal Society was only one of about ninety-five honors he received for his outstanding achievements. Psalm 1:2-3 promises a man who delights in the law of the Lord that "whatsoever he doeth shall prosper." Certainly this promise was fulfilled in the life of Michael Faraday. He stands both as a scientific hero and as an inspiring example of a Christian who applied his faith to everyday life.

MAGNETISM
CHAPTER
17

Magnetism

The properties (both real and imagined) of magnets are woven throughout the lore of antiquity. Ancient Greeks first described magnetism in their early writings. The Greeks found "lodestones" in Magnesia in Asia Minor. These mysterious stones could attract and hold iron shavings.

To ancient men, these magnetic properties seemed magical. Some proposed that magnets were evil objects possessed by invisible spirits. Others claimed that magnets could heal sickness and cure headaches. In the Middle Ages the superstitions associated with magnetism made owning a magnet hazardous to your health! Possessing a lodestone might brand you as a wizard or a witch and earn you a fiery reception from an angry crowd. Yet it was during this time that man discovered the first practical uses for magnets.

Until then, sailors had navigated the oceans solely by visual observations of the sun and the stars. A sudden storm or an overcast sky was sometimes fatal for these early travelers. Without their celestial guideposts, sailors had no way to keep their ships from drifting many miles off their appointed courses.

Sometime during the Middle Ages, an inventive person noticed that if a lodestone were placed on a piece of wood and floated on water, it would always orient itself in a north-south direction. Using this property of lodestones, men designed crude compasses that gave sailors and other travelers accurate directions, regardless of the atmospheric conditions.

In 1269 Petrus Peregrinus de Maricourt (MAH REE KOOR) of France observed that iron shavings sprinkled near a lodestone were attracted primarily to two separate spots on the lodestone. From this observation, Maricourt determined that the magnetic force of the lodestone was concentrated at these two locations. Today we call the two areas of concentrated magnetic force on a magnet *magnetic poles*.

In 1600 Maricourt's discovery was followed by another important step toward understanding magnetism. William Gilbert, an English physician, was fascinated by magnets. He compiled a book that listed all of the then-known properties of magnets. Actually, only a few of the "facts" in Gilbert's book were scientific. Yet Gilbert had brought the study of magnetism to the attention of the scientific world.

Identifying Magnetism

Electrical effects depend on positive and negative electrical charges. Could magnetic effects be caused by "magnetic charges"? This possibility directed the efforts of many early investigators.

Positive and negative electrical charges can be separated onto separate objects. An object can have a positive charge in one area without having a negative charge in another area. Early investigators thought the same was true of magnets. These scientists believed that large concentrations of "boreal (BOR ee ul) charge" (from *Boreas,* the Greek god of the north wind) formed north magnetic poles and that large concentrations of "austral (AWS trul) charge" (from the Latin word *auster*, meaning "south wind") formed south magnetic poles. Theoretically, these "magnetic charges" could be separated onto different objects, giving an object only one type of magnetic pole. Yet objects that have a north magnetic pole also have a south magnetic pole. If you divide a magnet in half, you will end up with two smaller magnets—each with a north and a south magnetic pole. Scientists have found that even when magnets are divided as many times as is physically possible, each of the microscopic fragments has both a north and a south magnetic pole. This evidence has caused scientists to conclude that "magnetic charges" probably do not exist.

Electric and magnetic fields

The effects of magnetism are very similar to the effects of static electrical charges. A negative electrode produces an electrical force that attracts positive electrical charges and repels negative electrical charges. The strength and direction of this force vary at different places around the electrode.

The strengths and directions of the electrical force at every point around the electrode are collectively called the **electric field of force**. The lines drawn around the electrode in the figure below are called **lines of force**. Scientists place arrows on each line of force to show in which direction the electrical force will move a positive charge. Electric fields are always directed away from a positive charge and toward a negative charge. (A negative charge would be moved in the opposite direction.) The direction of these arrows at any given point gives the direction of the electric field at that point. In an area where the lines of force are close together, the electric field exerts a very strong force. The closer the lines, the stronger the force. Where is the electric field strongest?

17-1 The lines of electrical force surrounding a negative electrode.

FACETS
OF BASIC SCIENCE

Magnetic Poles

As you know, magnets tend to align themselves in a north-south direction. Scientists call the end of the magnet that orients itself toward the north the *north magnetic pole*. The north magnetic pole of the magnet in the figure is marked with an N. The other end, marked with an S, is called the *south magnetic pole*.

Although the poles of magnets are not produced by electrical charges, they behave much like positively and negatively charged objects. North poles repel each other, and south poles repel each

other; yet a north pole attracts a south pole. These properties demonstrate the **law of magnetic poles**: unlike magnetic poles attract; like magnetic poles repel.

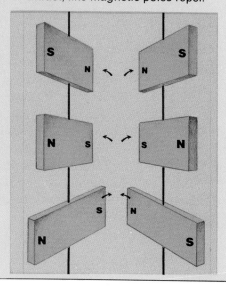

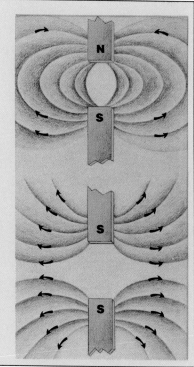

Lines of force are different for different electric fields. Notice the direction of the lines of force in the field around the two electrodes in the figure below. The arrows on lines of force show the direction in which the electrical force will move positive charges. Which electrode in this figure has a positive charge? Which one has a negative charge?

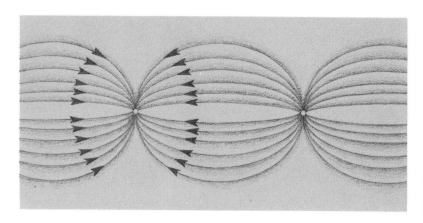

17-2 The lines of electrical force point toward the negatively charged electrode.

413

The figure below pictures the electric field around two adjacent, positively charged electrodes. Notice that the lines of force point *away* from both of them.

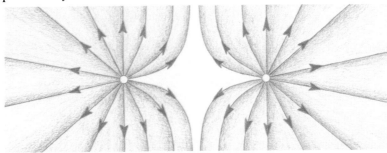

17-3 Iron filings reveal the magnetic fields of force created by the poles of a magnet hidden beneath the paper. The filings act as tiny bar magnets, aligning themselves with their north poles pointing in the same direction as the lines of force. Where the iron filings are closest together, the magnetic force is strongest.

Scientists use **magnetic fields of force** to show the strength and direction of *magnetic forces*. In magnetic fields, the lines of force point in the direction in which the magnetic forces would move a north magnetic pole. Since opposite magnetic poles attract each other, magnetic lines of force always point toward south magnetic poles and away from north magnetic poles.

Magnetic materials

Magnets attract only a small group of materials. These magnetic materials include iron, cobalt, nickel, gadolinium, and a few alloys of these elements. Steel (an alloy of carbon and iron) and alnico (an alloy of aluminum, nickel, cobalt, and iron) are commonly used to form the powerful magnets in motors and meters.

Magnetic materials fall into two categories. **Ferromagnetic** (FEHR oh mag NET ik) materials are strongly attracted to magnets. **Paramagnetic** (PEHR uh mag NET ik) materials are only slightly attracted to magnets. These two types of magnetic materials affect magnetic fields differently. When ferromagnetic materials, such as steel and iron, are placed in a magnetic field, they greatly increase the strength of the magnetic force in the field. Paramagnetic materials, such as wood and aluminum, only slightly increase the magnetic force of a surrounding magnetic field.

The photograph below contrasts the effect of ferromagnetic and paramagnetic materials on magnetic fields. Each magnetic field is created by a coil of current-carrying wire. When a paramagnetic material (aluminum) is placed in the center of a coil, the magnetic field becomes weak. But when a ferromagnetic material (iron) is placed in the center of a coil, the magnetic field grows stronger. The iron filings around each of the bars indicate the relative strengths of the fields.

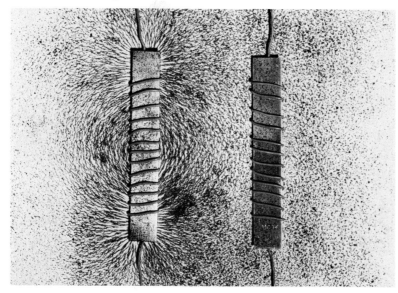

Diamagnetic (DY uh mag NET ik), or **nonmagnetic**, materials are not at all attracted to magnets. Some diamagnetic materials, such as table salt and mercury, are actually repelled from the magnetic field of a strong magnet. If you placed salt crystals in a magnetic field, the salt would weaken the magnetic field noticeably. Many scientists believe that the domains in the salt actually line up against the lines of force in the magnetic field.

Inducing magnetism

Some materials, especially iron and steel, can be magnetized by a process known as *induction* (in DUK shun). These temporary magnets usually lose their magnetic fields shortly after they are magnetized. How does induction produce a *temporary magnet*?

If an iron nail is stroked in one direction with a magnet, the nail is magnetized. Materials that can be magnetized contain microscopic regions called **domains** (do MAYNZ). Scientists suspect that each domain acts as a tiny magnet. In an unmagnetized material the domains are pointed in hundreds of different directions. When the magnetic forces from all the domains interact, the effects of the magnetic forces are canceled.

17-4 The magnetic domains in an unmagnetized material point in random directions. But when a magnetic field acts on the material, it induces the domains to align themselves in one direction, creating a magnet.

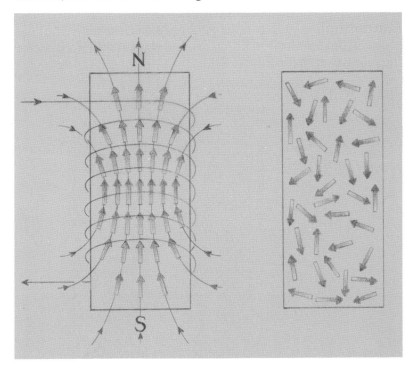

When you rub a magnet along a nail in one direction, many of the domains in the nail line up. In which direction will the domains point? If the north pole of a magnet is stroked along the nail, the south poles of the domains will turn to point toward it. If the south pole of a magnet is stroked along the nail, the north poles of the domains will turn toward it. Eventually, the magnetic field of almost every domain will be pointed in the same direction.

Temporary magnets gradually lose their magnetism after the process of induction stops. What do you think happens to the domains in a temporary magnet as it becomes demagnetized?

Experimental evidence supports the *theory of magnetic domains*. When a highly polished piece of iron is coated with a mixture of glycerin and iron oxide, the particles of iron oxide line up in definite lines around microscopic regions. These lines indicate the boundaries between the domains. When a magnetic field is applied to the iron, the lines of iron oxide particles shift, showing the changing positions and directions of the domains.

Some materials possess a magnetic field without being magnetized by an outside force. These permanent magnets retain their magnetic fields for long periods of time. Some permanent magnets have lasted for centuries! However, permanent magnets can lose their magnetic fields if they are heated to high temperatures, dropped, or hammered.

17-5 An iron nail can be magnetized by a strong magnet. If the nail is stroked over the magnet several times, the domains of the nail will align, and the nail will display magnetic properties.

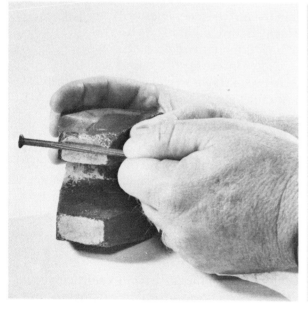
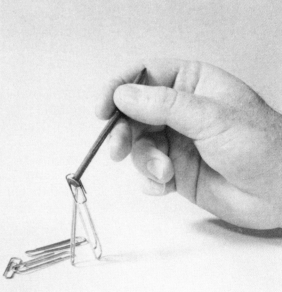

Impacts or large amounts of thermal energy disrupt the alignment of the domains in a magnet. The temperature at which the domains are disrupted is called the **Curie temperature** of the magnet. When a material is hotter than its Curie temperature, it cannot hold a magnetic field.

Earth's magnetic field

What makes compasses point toward the magnetic north pole? Our planet behaves like a huge bar magnet. Its magnetic field is aligned in a generally north-south direction. A compass contains a very light bar magnet positioned so that it can turn easily on a pivot. This bar magnet aligns itself along the north-south direction of the earth's magnetic field. Then, when the "N" marking on the compass dial is lined up with the north pole of the compass magnet, all the directions on the compass dial can be read.

If you lived in Barrow, Alaska, your compass would point 30° E! Is this problem caused by the extreme cold? No, in spite of the cold, the magnet in the compass is attracted directly toward the magnetic north pole. The problem is that the magnetic north pole lies to the east of Barrow, Alaska. The magnetic north pole is located near Prince of Wales Island. This Canadian island is located in the Arctic ocean, 1920 km south of the geographic North Pole.

Compasses point toward the magnetic north pole. Depending on where you are located, this might not be true north. How can you find true north with a compass no matter where you are? Scientists have developed tables of corrections that allow you to find the difference between true north and magnetic north. The values given in these tables are called **declinations** (DEK luh NAY shunz).

To determine directions accurately from a compass reading at any given point on the earth, the magnetic declination at that point must be added to or subtracted from the compass reading. For example, a declination of 10° W indicates that the magnetic field at that point points 10° W of the direction of true north. If a compass reading at that point showed a certain direction as 30° E, the actual direction would be 10° less, or 20° E. If, however, the reading were 30° W, the actual direction would be 10° greater, or 40° W.

Is the magnetic north pole of the earth really a north magnetic pole? Remember that it attracts the north poles of magnets. Are

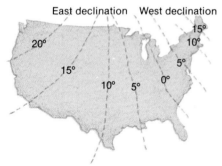

17-6 The map shows the lines of declination for the United States.

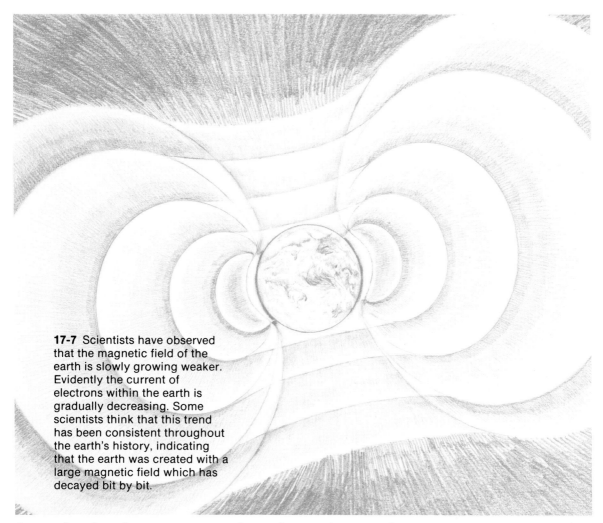

17-7 Scientists have observed that the magnetic field of the earth is slowly growing weaker. Evidently the current of electrons within the earth is gradually decreasing. Some scientists think that this trend has been consistent throughout the earth's history, indicating that the earth was created with a large magnetic field which has decayed bit by bit.

the north poles of magnets attracted to other north magnetic poles? No! What we refer to as the magnetic north pole of the earth actually *behaves* like a south magnetic pole. What we call the earth's south magnetic pole is actually a magnetic north pole because it attracts a magnet's south pole.

Observations from 1835 to the present indicate that the earth's magnetic field will vanish completely in only 3000 years! If this pattern of magnetic decay has been similar in the past, it places a definite limit on the age of the earth. Creationist scientists who have studied the question find that these observations fit the view of a young earth (measured in thousands of years) far better than that of an old earth (measured in billions of years).

Electricity and Magnetism

In 1819 the Danish physicist Hans Christian Oersted (UR *stith*) accidentally discovered that a wire carrying an electric current produces a magnetic field. During a classroom demonstration, Oersted stated that electricity and magnetism were completely unrelated. To illustrate his point, he held a compass near a current-carrying wire. Imagine his surprise when he found that the current-carrying wire altered the direction of the compass magnet! When Oersted turned off the electric current, the magnetic field also disappeared. Oersted immediately began experimenting with the wire and the compass and found that the compass pointed in different directions depending on its position around the wire. From his observations Oersted determined that magnetic lines of force form circular loops about a current-carrying wire.

17-8 In his experiment, Oersted found that current flowing from a battery through a wire created a magnetic field that altered the direction of a compass.

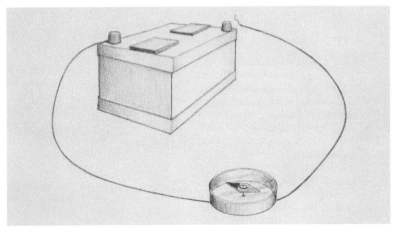

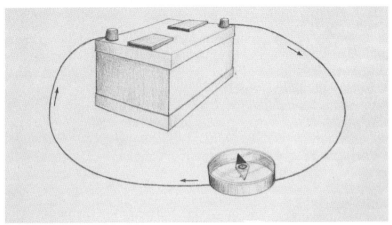

The figure below shows a current-carrying wire. The arrow along the wire shows the direction of the current. The direction of the magnetic lines of force around the current (the direction in which a north magnetic pole will be attracted) can be found by the left-hand rule. If you point your left thumb in the direction of the flow of the electrons, the magnetic lines of force will point in the direction in which the rest of your curled fingers point. The effect of these lines of force is evident in the directions of the north poles of the compasses at various points around the wire.

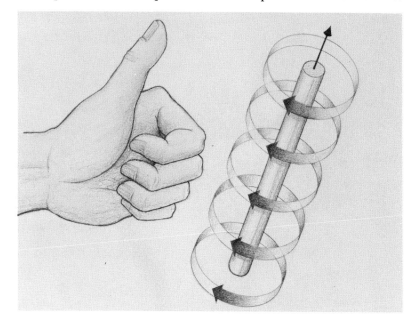

17-9 Whenever an electric current flows through a wire, a magnetic field is generated. The lines of this magnetic field form concentric circles around the wire. The left-hand rule helps you remember in which direction the magnetic fields move.

Magnetism from Electricity

Only a week after Oersted's discovery was announced in France, André Marie Ampère (AHM PEHR), a French physicist, announced that he had discovered a magnetic attraction between two parallel wires carrying current in the same direction. Ampère found that when he replaced one of the wires with a magnetic pole, the remaining current-carrying wire was deflected away from or attracted to the magnet. How the wire moved depended on the direction of the current in the wire.

Ampère also discovered that increasing the current in the wire increased the strength of the surrounding magnetic field. Later, scientists discovered that coiling a current-carrying wire increases the force of the magnetic field still further. Each loop of a coiled current-carrying wire produces an equal magnetic force. When the magnetic fields of each of these closely packed "magnets" are added together, the result is a fairly strong magnetic field. Coiled wires that are used as magnets are called **solenoids** (SO luh NOYDZ).

Special electrical switches called *solenoid relays* use solenoids to complete electrical circuits. When electrical current is passed through a solenoid relay, the magnetic force produced by the solenoid pulls a metal bar into place between two ends of a conducting wire, thus completing the electrical circuit.

17-10 In a solenoid relay, current flowing through the wire creates a magnet; this solenoid attracts the metal bar and completes the electrical circuit.

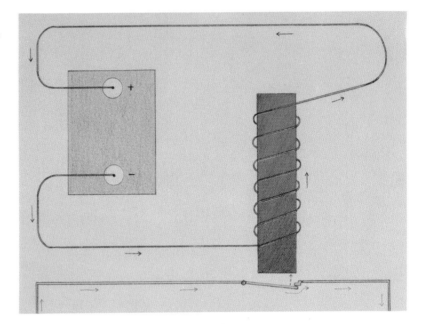

In 1823 an English experimenter named William Sturgeon (STUR jun) observed that placing a magnetic material inside a solenoid increased its magnetic field. In fact, a solenoid with an iron core produced enough magnetic force to lift a piece of iron twenty times as heavy as the iron core! We call solenoids with magnetic cores **electromagnets**. Electromagnets play a crucial role in many of the appliances you use daily.

Electricity from magnetism

The discovery that an electric current produces a magnetic field led some scientists to wonder if a magnetic field could produce an electric current. In 1830 an American scientist named Joseph Henry discovered that the magnetic field produced by a current-carrying wire coil produced a current in a nearby wire coil. He observed that this process took place for only a short time after a switch allowed current to begin passing through the first coil. Once the current reached a constant flow in the first coil, the current in the second coil died away. When the switch was opened, stopping the flow of current in the first coil, current flowed again in the second coil, but this time it flowed in the opposite direction. These observations led Henry to conclude that a *changing* magnetic field produces a flow of current in nearby conductors.

How does a magnetic field produce an electric current? The magnetic forces in a magnetic field affect the motion of electrically charged particles. When magnetic forces near a conductor increase or decrease, they set the charged electrons in the conductor in motion. The more quickly the magnetic force increases or decreases, the faster the electrons move.

There are several ways to produce a changing magnetic field near a conductor. Moving a loop of wire past a magnet changes the magnetic field around the loop of wire. Moving a magnet past a loop of wire produces the same effect. Also, changing the amount of current flowing through one coil of wire causes the magnetic field around the wire to change and affects the current in any nearby coil of wire. No matter which of these methods is used to change the magnetic field around a conductor, the result is always the same—the flow of electrons through the conductor.

17-11 A current is produced in a circuit if a magnet is moved up and down through a coil of wire in the circuit. A current is also produced when the coil is moved up and down around the magnet. This process is called magnetic induction.

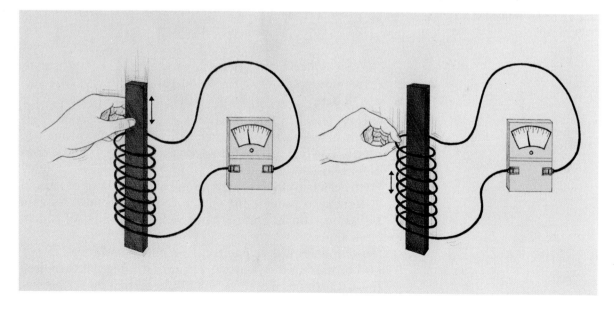

Generators

Devices called **generators** (JEN uh RAY turz) use magnets to convert mechanical energy into electrical energy. In a generator, some type of mechanically driven shaft rotates large numbers of wire coils through strong magnetic fields. As the coils experience changing magnetic forces, large amounts of current are produced in the coils. Most of the electricity we use each day is supplied by electrical generators.

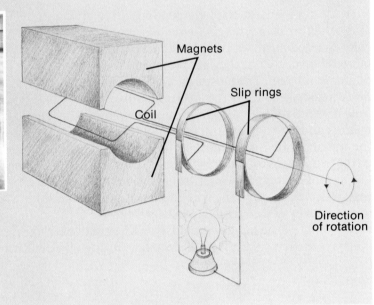

17-12 The huge generators of a modern power plant and this simple AC generator use the same principle to produce electricity: current is produced when a coil is rotated in a magnetic field.

The mechanical energy necessary to turn the generator shaft usually comes from one of three sources:

1. *Fossil fuels* are sometimes burned to produce thermal energy, which is then used to turn water into steam. This steam is forced through turbines, causing the turbines to rotate. The turbines, in turn, turn the shafts that rotate coils of wire inside the generators.
2. Hydroelectric plants use the *falling water* of dams or natural waterfalls to provide the energy to turn turbines. Niagara Falls and Hoover Dam are two well-known sites of hydroelectric plants.
3. *Atomic energy* derived from fissioning uranium-235 can also be used to turn water to steam. This steam is then used to turn turbines like those used in fossil-fuel power plants.

What kind of current does a generator produce? Since the wire coil in a generator rotates through a magnetic field, its position in the magnetic field is constantly being reversed. Consequently, the wire coil in a generator produces a current that moves first in one direction and then in the opposite direction in a repeating cycle. We call an electric current that regularly changes directions an **alternating current** (**AC**). The electricity that comes into our homes is alternating current. The graph below demonstrates the changing direction of alternating current. The current increases in one direction until it reaches a maximum and then it decreases to zero. Then the current begins to increase in the opposite direction. When it reaches a maximum current in that direction, it decreases to zero again. This cycle occurs over and over as the generator coil rotates through the magnetic field.

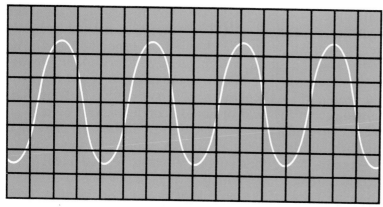

The current produced by a battery does not change directions and is called **direct current**, or **DC**. As the graph below indicates, direct current maintains a constant rate of flow in one direction.

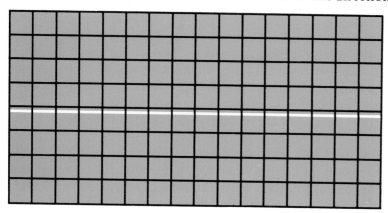

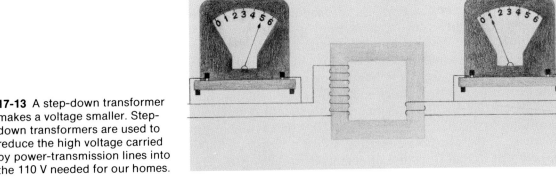

17-13 A step-down transformer makes a voltage smaller. Step-down transformers are used to reduce the high voltage carried by power-transmission lines into the 110 V needed for our homes.

Transformers

Because a DC circuit carries a steady flow of current, the magnetic field around a DC conductor becomes stable shortly after current begins to flow through the conductor. In an AC circuit, however, the direction of the current is constantly changing. Consequently, the direction and strength of the magnetic field around an AC conductor are constantly changing. The changing magnetic field of an AC conductor can be used to generate current in other conductors. For instance, if one coil of wire carrying an alternating current is brought very close to another coil of wire, the changing magnetic field around the first coil will induce an alternating current in the second coil. The voltage produced in the second coil depends on the ratio of the number of turns in the first coil to the number of turns in the second coil.

In the figure above, the first coil has more turns than the second coil. The alternating current in the first coil produces a very strong magnetic field. This field sets in motion many electrons in the second coil, but these moving electrons do not possess a large amount of energy. Therefore the voltage in the second coil is lower than the voltage in the first coil. Because this arrangement of conducting coils produces a smaller voltage in the second coil, it is known as a **step-down transformer.**

In Figure 17-14 the second coil has more turns than does the first coil. The magnetic field produced by the alternating current in the first coil sets in motion only a small number of the electrons in the larger second coil. Each of the moving electrons in the second coil gains a large amount of kinetic energy. Therefore, the voltage in the second coil is greater than the voltage in

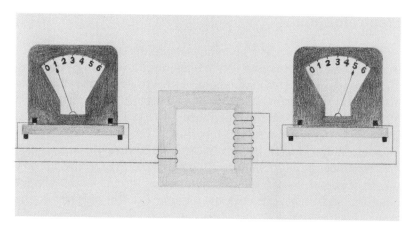

17-14 A step-up transformer increases voltage. Step-up transformers in neon signs produce the high voltage that causes the gas in the tube to glow.

the first coil. This arrangement of AC conducting coils is known as a **step-up transformer**.

Power companies use step-up and step-down transformers to conserve energy. Wires that carry electricity over long distances usually carry low-current, high-voltage electricity. If these wires were made to carry high-current, low-voltage electricity, much of the energy of the electrons would be converted into heat. When the current is kept low, the resistance of the wires has less effect on the electrons and much less energy is lost.

At a power plant, the alternating current produced by the generators is converted by step-up transformers into high-voltage, low-current electricity. The high-voltage power lines that crisscross the countryside carry voltages of up to 765 kilovolts (kV) to the areas where power is needed. In each of these areas, huge step-down transformers convert this electricity into high-current, medium-voltage (about 11 kV) electricity. The locations of these step-down transformers are commonly called *power substations*. Near individual homes smaller transformers reduce the electricity's voltage to 110 or 220 V, the voltage required by most household appliances. You may have seen these cylinders mounted on power poles near your house.

17-15 A power substation is really a collection of step-down transformers.

Using Magnetism

Magnetism plays a vital role in modern life. Hundreds of appliances, including electric drills, mixers, washing machines, and typewriters, depend on magnetically driven motors. Telephones, radios, and televisions all operate through the use of magnetic and electrical fields. What are some of the ways these devices use magnetism?

Electromagnets

Since 1823, when Sturgeon developed the first practical electromagnet, electromagnets have been built and utilized in many different ways. Electromagnets have proved especially useful for lifting sections of iron and steel. If you visit an iron reclamation plant (a junkyard), you will probably see a crane lifting cars and trucks by means of a large, flat disk. This disk is an electromagnet. When electric current is allowed to flow through it, the disk produces a magnetic force that can pick up extremely heavy pieces of metal. When the metal has been moved to the proper position, it can be released by turning off the current in the electromagnetic disk.

Electromagnets are also useful for sorting metals, particularly aluminum and iron. If a mixture of iron and aluminum materials is carried on a moving belt through a weak magnetic field, the iron pieces will be strongly deflected to one side, while the aluminum materials will pass on without being affected. Alumi-

FACETS
OF BASIC SCIENCE

Superconductors

You have just put the finishing touches on a giant electromagnet at the research facility. You give a signal and the switch is thrown. Power begins to course through the wires. The needles on the magnetometers (which measure the strength of the magnetic field) begin to twitch. As the power increases, the needles steadily climb. Soon the magnetic field will have the strength that you need to complete your research. Suddenly, however, the needles level off and begin dipping. You call to the power room; they assure you that the power supply is constant. Then what could be the problem? You order the power

Upper ring

Lower ring

num refineries use such electromagnetic sorters to keep iron products from contaminating the aluminum they reclaim from recycled aluminum cans.

Particle accelerators, large machines used in nuclear research, use electromagnets to bend the paths of moving electrons into a circle. As the current in the electromagnet is increased, the magnetic field becomes stronger and the path of the charged particles is bent into a smaller circle. The electromagnets in the particle accelerators act as shepherds, herding the electrons back into the path where they can be accelerated by the electrical field of the accelerator. Some of the particle accelerators constructed in recent years contain special electromagnets called **superconducting magnets.** Superconducting magnets have cores of tin, niobium, and certain other materials which have been cooled to temperatures of about 4 K. At such temperatures, these substances very strongly concentrate the magnetic field of the electromagnet. Therefore they greatly increase the magnet's ability to direct the paths of electrons.

17-16 A superconducting magnet used to focus the proton beam in a particle accelerator.

to be shut off and climb down the stairs to the electromagnet. You can feel the heat as you approach the mass of wires. Almost instantly you diagnose the problem: RESISTANCE.

All conductors have a certain amount of resistance to the flow of electrons. As this flow is increased, the resistance will create heat. Do you remember what thermal energy does to the molecules in matter? It causes them to move faster. As the vibrations of the molecules in the conductor steadily increase with the temperature, the resistance of the conductor grows. When very powerful currents are involved, this spiral may soon cause the conductor to melt.

What can be done to solve this problem? Often electrical devices such as electromagnets are equipped with cooling fans. These help to remove the excess heat. Yet in the case of the giant magnet, cooling fans would not do the job. For the giant electromagnet to produce a very strong magnetic field, resistance had to be reduced to a minimum. This is where superconductors come in.

Scientists have discovered that as the temperature of a conductor drops, the resistance also drops. In fact as the temperatures approach the coldest possible levels (near absolute zero), the resistance of a conductor suddenly vanishes. The conductor becomes a superconductor.

Now let us return to the research laboratory. If you supercool the conductors on your electromagnet, you will have a *superconducting electromagnet.* It will steadily produce a far stronger magnetic field than a regular electromagnet, using only a fraction of the electrical power—all because the superconductors present no resistance. The superelectromagnets that can be produced with superconductors are being used in fusion research and particle accelerators.

Superconductors have a wide variety of applications. One day soon superconductors may be used in computers to help speed computations beyond what we can imagine now. Supercooling conductors could also improve the efficiency of power transmission, and may someday make the electric car a practical reality.

◀ The tunnel of the main accelerator at the Fermi National Accelerator Laboratory in Batavia, Illinois. The upper ring of magnets is used to accelerate particles for study. The lower ring consists of new superconducting magnets that will be able to accelerate particles to half the speed of light.

You use an electromagnet every time you ring a doorbell. A doorbell is basically a switch (the doorbell button) connected in series with an electromagnet. When you push the doorbell button, the switch closes and electricity flows through the wire coil of the electromagnet. The resulting magnetic field around the electromagnet pulls a small metal clapper, causing it to strike a bell. However, the metal clapper itself is also part of the circuit. When the clapper moves to strike the bell, it breaks the circuit. Since current stops flowing through the electromagnet, the magnetic field begins to die away, and the clapper returns to its original position. This movement, in turn, closes the circuit, starting the entire cycle over again.

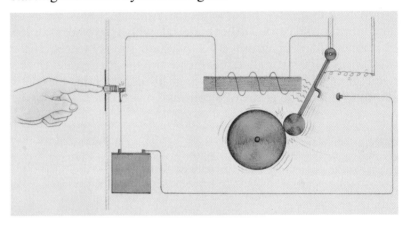

Galvanometers

Electric meters called **galvanometers** (GAL vuh NOM ih turz) use magnetism to measure slight changes in electrical currents. When a current-carrying wire coil is placed near a magnet, the magnetic field around the wire coil will either attract or repel the magnet. In most galvanometers the magnet is fixed in a certain position and the wire coil moves in response to the magnetic force between the magnet and the wire. The more current flows through the wire coil, the stronger the magnetic force will become, and the more the coil will be deflected. Since a coiled, current-carrying wire produces a concentrated magnetic field, even very slight changes in the current will produce noticeable changes in the deflection of the wire. If the current changes direction, the magnetic field around the wire will be reversed, and the wire coil will be deflected in the opposite direction. In most galvanometers, the deflection of the wire coil is detected by the movement of a needle that is attached to the wire coil.

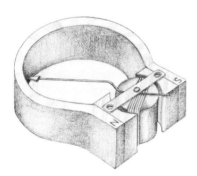

17-17 A galvanometer is a device that is sensitive to very small changes in electrical current. It uses an electromagnet fixed between the north and south poles of a permanent magnet to measure these changes.

Electric motors

Electric motors use the magnetic force between an electro-magnet and a permanent magnet (or in some cases a stationary electromagnet) to cause the electromagnet to rotate a shaft. The rotating electromagnet in an electric motor is called an **armature** (AR muh CHOOR) and consists of a current-carrying wire coil around a magnetic material. Some electric motors operate from direct current, some from alternating current, and others from both types of current.

In direct-current motors, some mechanism must be used to regularly change the direction of the current through the electro-magnet. Suppose that you connected a wire coil to a source of direct current. Since direct current is constant, the magnetic field produced around the coil would have a fixed direction and strength. If the coil were mounted on a shaft near a permanent magnet, the magnetic force between the coil and the magnet would cause the coil to rotate until its magnetic field was aligned with the magnetic field of the permanent magnet. At that point the coil would stop moving. The only way to keep the coil rotating would be to somehow continually change the direction of the current. As the direction of the current changed, the coil would continue rotating to align its changing magnetic field with the field of the permanent magnet.

DC motors are usually constructed according to the basic plan shown in Figure 17-18. Current flows into the wire coil of the armature through one metal brush and out of the wire coil through the other metal brush. However, between each brush and the coil, the current must pass through a **commutator** (KOM yuh TAY tur), a metal ring that rotates with the wire coil. The commutator is split into two halves. Since the two halves are separated by an insulating material, electric current cannot flow from one side of the ring to the other except through the wire coil. As current flows through the wire coil, it produces a magnetic field. The coil turns to align this field with the field of the nearby permanent magnet. As it does so, the commutator (turning with the wire coil) rotates just far enough so that each brush touches a different half of the commutator from the one it was touching before. This turn of events sends the current rushing through the wire in the opposite direction and changes the direction of the magnetic field. Consequently, the wire coil continues turning in an attempt to align its new magnetic field with the field of the permanent magnet. As this cycle continues,

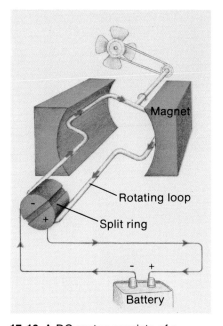

17-18 A DC motor consists of a current-carrying loop that rotates in a magnetic field because the current in the loop changes direction. The direction changes because the split ring, as it turns, reverses the electrical flow by reversing the wire connections.

431

the mechanical energy of the turning shaft can be used to perform useful work. Toy cars, windshield wipers, and disk drives for computers are only a few of the many devices that use DC motors.

AC motors receive current that is already changing direction regularly. Therefore the wire coil in an AC motor is connected to the electrical circuit through two separate metal rings instead of through a commutator. As the current inside the coil changes direction, the magnetic field of the coil also changes continually. As the magnetic force between the wire coil and the permanent magnet changes direction, the coil rotates and turns the shaft of the motor. AC motors provide energy for the moving parts in appliances such as dishwashers, blow dryers, and electric drills.

Scientifically Speaking

electric field of force
lines of force
law of magnetic poles
magnetic fields of force
ferromagnetic
paramagnetic
diamagnetic
nonmagnetic
domains
Curie temperature
declinations
solenoids

electromagnets
generators
alternating current (AC)
direct current (DC)
step-down transformer
step-up transformer
superconducting magnets
galvanometers
electric motors
armature
commutator

Questions to Talk Over

1. If you had only a piece of string and two identical bars of metal, one of which was magnetized, how could you determine which of the bars was a magnet?
2. The lines of force in a magnetic field show the direction in which the magnetic forces would move a north magnetic pole. Is it possible to have a north magnetic pole without a corresponding south magnetic pole? Why?
3. Will the lines of force for two magnetic fields cross each other? Suggest a way you could test your answer.
4. The first law of thermodynamics states that energy is neither created nor destroyed. How then is it possible for a step-up transformer to increase the voltage in a current from 50 V to 500 V? Is this a violation of the law of conservation? Explain your answer.
5. Compare an electric generator to an electric motor. Could permanent magnets be used to make both generators and motors? Explain your answer.

SAMUEL F. B. MORSE
AMERICAN INVENTOR (1791-1872)

You probably are familiar with the quotation, "What hath God wrought!" These were the first words ever sent by intercity telegraph. But can you name the source of the quotation—Numbers 23:23—or tell the story of how it was selected? This fascinating story begins with the labors of the great Christian inventor Samuel F.B. Morse (MAWRCE).

Samuel Morse was born in Charlestown, Massachusetts, in 1791. As the son of the town pastor, he was reared in a Christian home, but he did not accept Christ as his Saviour until early adulthood. He received his education at Philips Exeter Academy at Andover and at Yale University, both of which were fundamental Christian schools at that time.

Morse was actually trained as an artist rather than as a scientist. The year following his graduation from Yale, he traveled to England to study with Benjamin West, the most

respected artist of that time. The training Morse received during his four years abroad catapulted him into the ranks of America's foremost artists. He later painted such notables as President Monroe, Noah Webster, and General Lafayette. Also during this period, Morse came under the influence of William Wilberforce and his group of evangelical Christians known as the Clapham Sect. Morse was thoroughly impressed with Wilberforce and stated afterward, "What I saw of him in private gave me the most exalted opinion of him as a Christian." The godly witness of the Clapham Sect soon brought Morse to trust Christ as his own Saviour. Upon returning to America he lost no time in making a public profession of his faith at his own church.

While working in Concord, New Hampshire, Samuel Morse married Lucretia Pickering Walker. Theirs was a happy home, its bliss marred only by Samuel's long absences and the financial problems that accompanied his chosen profession.

But in spite of hard times Morse remained "satisfied that whilst engaged for God He will not suffer me to want."

On his second trip to Europe, the idea of the telegraph began to take shape in Morse's mind. In Paris he saw the French semaphore system of communication. Signals were relayed from mountaintop to mountaintop across the land. How much better this was, he thought, than the mail system back home. During the return voyage, Morse determined a specific plan of attack. When he disembarked in New York Harbor, his notebook contained sketches of the first crude electric telegraph.

Providentially, Morse received an appointment as professor of sculpture and painting at the University of the City of New York. This position provided him with a place to experiment and with a means of attracting assistants. After many months of labor, he was ready to demonstrate his collection of voltaic cells, coils, and wires for his colleagues at the university. Several showed interest in the invention, and he soon enlisted the help of a small group of

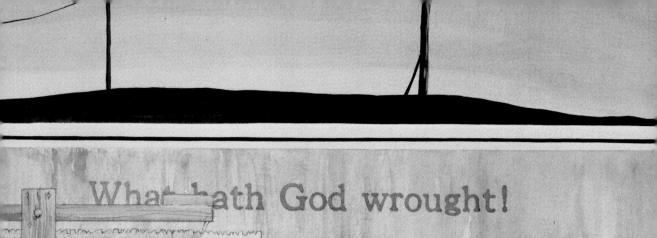

What hath God wrought!

friends. But only one, a fellow Christian named Alfred Vail, was to stick with him to the project's completion.

One of the earliest public demonstrations of Morse's telegraph took place in Vail's hometown, Morristown, New Jersey. The sender and receiver were both at the same location, but the signals traveled through some two miles of coiled wire between the two units. The spectators were enthusiastic, and the Morristown *Jerseyman* extravagantly praised Professor Morse and his invention. In 1838 Morse and Vail gave a demonstration at the Franklin Institute in Philadelphia. Again the equipment functioned successfully and a favorable report was issued—the first acclaim from representatives of the scientific community.

The next demonstration took place in Washington. Among those witnessing the demonstration were President Van Buren and several members of the cabinet. Morse and Vail hoped to secure funds for a trial line between two major cities some

distance apart. Unfortunately, the country was suffering a severe depression, and as one congressman informed Morse, "The treasury and the government are both bankrupt."

Morse, however, kept praying and persevering. Late in 1842 he set up a demonstration line between the rooms of the House Committee on Commerce and the Senate Committee on Naval Affairs. He remained faithfully on duty by his equipment, sending sample messages for the legislators and answering their questions. By the end of the year, the Committee on Commerce had submitted a favorable report on Morse's telegraph. Representative Ferris, the chairman of the committee, recommended that $30,000 be appropriated to set up a trial intercity telegraph system.

The committee's resolution passed fairly easily in the House. However, when the bill reached the Senate on the last day of the session, Morse prepared for the worst. In fact, by the end of the day, Morse believed the situation to be utterly hopeless. He returned to his hotel room, had his devotions, and retired for the night.

The next morning at breakfast a waiter informed Morse that he had a visitor in the hotel parlor. Much to his surprise, Annie Ellsworth, the daughter of the Commissioner of Patents, had come to bring the good news— his bill had passed around midnight and had been quickly signed by President Tyler. In appreciation for her message, Morse made Miss Ellsworth a promise—when the lines were finally completed from Washington to Baltimore, she would be allowed to choose the text for the first message. Thus, on May 24, 1844, the famous four words from the book of Numbers were transmitted from Baltimore to Washington and back again. Morse was delighted that these words of Scripture had been chosen for the first intercity telegraph demonstration. In a letter to his brother he wrote, "It is in my thoughts day and night, 'What hath God wrought!' It is *His* work, and He alone could have carried me thus far through all my trials and enabled me to triumph over the obstacles, physical and moral, which opposed me. 'Not unto us, not unto us, but to Thy name, O Lord, be all the praise.'"

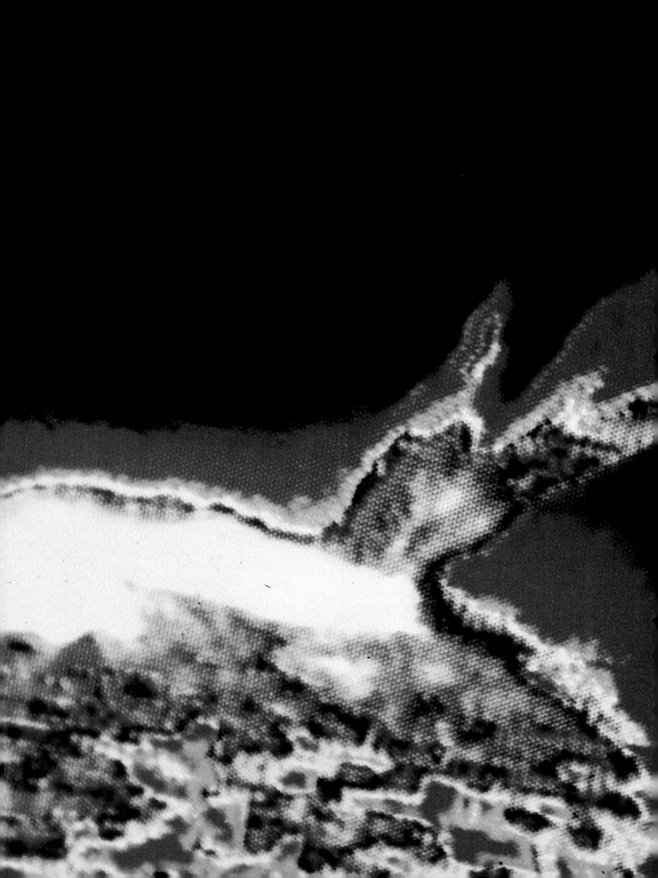

SEVEN

THE ENERGY OF WAVES

VIBRATIONS
CHAPTER
18

How does energy get from here to there? There are two ways to transmit energy between locations. Energy can be transmitted in the motion of matter. Electricity is the energy of the moving electrons that flow through wires to power the lights and appliances of our homes. You transmit energy to the head of a nail when you hit it with a hammer. In both cases matter moved from one place to another to accomplish work.

Yet energy can be transferred without the motion of matter. This form of energy transfer occurs through **waves**. Waves are rhythmic disturbances. Although some waves travel through matter, and other waves travel through empty space, all waves transfer energy.

Identifying Waves

Have you ever experienced the energy from waves as cheers pounded against your ears at a ball game? We hear by sound waves, see by light waves, and both see and hear entertainment by radio and television waves.

Waves can be generally classified into two different groups: mechanical and electromagnetic. **Mechanical waves** vibrate through a medium. Water waves, sound waves, and the vibrations of a string are all examples of mechanical waves. **Electromagnetic waves** do not need a medium. They can travel through a vacuum. Light waves, radio waves, television waves, and microwaves are all examples of electromagnetic waves.

The characteristics of waves

The figure below shows a cross-section of a typical wave. Scientists have given special names to the various parts of a wave. The highest points on a wave are called **crests**. The lowest points are called **troughs** (TRAHFS). The distance that a wave rises or falls from its normal rest position is called the **amplitude** (AM pli TOOD) of the wave. One wave is made up of a crest and a trough. Since the vibrations of a wave travel up and down in a repeating pattern, scientists call one wave a **cycle**.

The length of a wave can be measured in several different ways, but the most convenient way is to calculate the distance from one crest to the next crest or from one trough to the next trough. This measurement is called a **wavelength** (λ).

18-1 The structure of a wave.

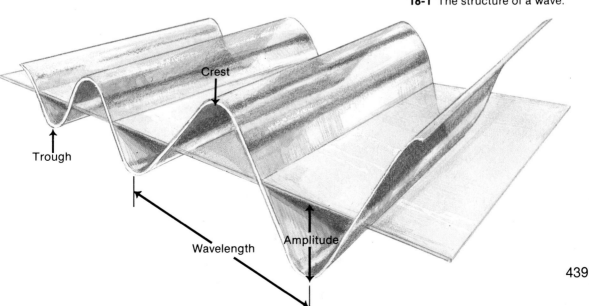

Crest

Trough

Wavelength

Amplitude

The number of wavelengths that pass a given point in one second is called the **frequency** (FREE kwun see) of a wave. Scientists measure frequency in units called **hertz (Hz)** (HURTZ), which stand for *cycles per second*. Two multiples of this unit are commonly used for waves that vibrate many times a second. One kilohertz (kHz) equals 1000 cycles per second, and 1 megahertz (MHz) equals 1,000,000 cycles per second.

The velocity of waves

Although waves travel from place to place, the individual particles of the material through which they move do not travel. How can this be? Figure 18-2 illustrates the movement of particles in a water wave. As the wave vibrates up and down, the particles move in a circular motion. They actually return to approximately where they began! Their forward motion is matched by the same amount of backward motion.

This idea is easier to visualize on a vibrating string. When you pluck a string, the vibrations clearly travel down the string, but does the string travel? Other than the up-and-down motion of the vibration, the particles of the string remain in place. The motion of a wave is different from the motion of the individual particles that are disturbed. The wave transfers energy by transporting vibrations, not by moving matter.

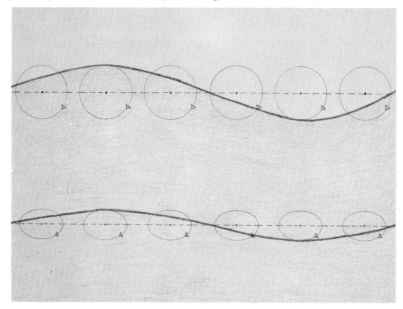

18-2 The individual particles on the surface of a water wave actually move in a circular path as the wave travels through the water. Particles below the surface move in an elliptical (oval) pattern.

How fast are these vibrations traveling? Waves travel at a variety of speeds. Water waves on the shoreline of a large body of water travel only a few meters per second. Sound waves in air move much faster. Under typical conditions, a sound wave can travel over 300 m/s. Light waves in space zip along at an incredible 300,000,000 m/s—fast enough to get from the earth to the moon in 1.3 s!

The *velocity* of a wave is mathematically related to two of its other characteristics: frequency and wavelength. The following equation ties these three quantities together:

$$v = f\lambda$$

The v represents the velocity in meters per second, the f stands for the frequency in vibrations per second, and λ, the Greek letter *lambda* (LAM duh), represents the wavelength in meters.

Suppose that waves on a beach are arriving 1 every 5 s and that the spacing between them is 20 m.

f = 1 wave/5 s = 1/5 waves per second = 1/5 hertz
λ = 20 m

Substitute the values into the equation:

v = fλ
v = (1/5 Hz) (20 m)
v = 4 m/s

We find that the waves are traveling at a velocity of 4 m/s.

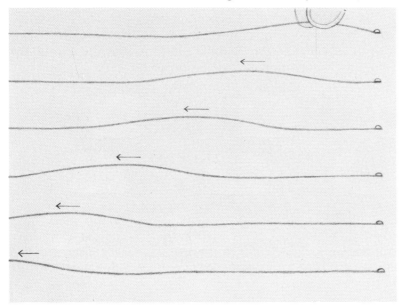

18-3 When a string is plucked, the vibrations travel down the string, but the particles in the string do not.

18-4 The vibrations of a transverse wave are at right angles to the direction of travel.

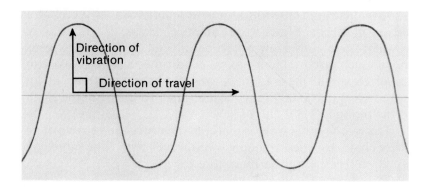

Types of waves

Most waves are classified into two major groups, depending on the direction of their vibration. If the vibration is at right angles to the direction of travel, the wave is said to be a **transverse** (trans VURCE) **wave**. Light waves and vibrations on a string are examples of transverse waves.

If the vibration occurs in the *same* direction that the wave is traveling, the wave is a **longitudinal** (LON ji TOOD un ul) **wave**. Examples are sound waves, *infrasonic* (IN fra SAHN ik) waves (waves similar to sound waves but too low in frequency for the ear to hear), and *ultrasonic* (UL truh SAHN ik) waves (waves similar to sound waves but too *high* in frequency for the ear to hear).

Water waves do not fit into either category. The individual particles in a water wave move in circles. Therefore, they have both transverse and longitudinal motion. They are constantly changing the direction of their motion.

18-5 A longitudinal wave vibrates in the same direction as it is traveling, as shown in these stages of a wave's travel.

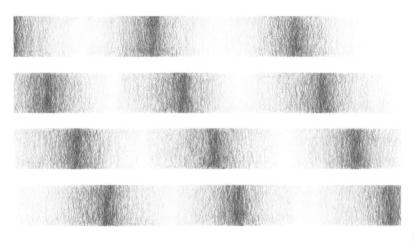

The reflection and refraction of waves

We can predict how waves react to different materials. If a wave of very short duration (called a **pulse**) travels down a stretched string and reaches the end, does it simply die out? According to the first law of thermodynamics, energy must be conserved. The pulse cannot just die out. What happens to the pulse? It is *reflected* along the string in the opposite direction. The reflected pulse is upside-down.

Water waves in a swimming pool rebound from the sides of the pool. Waves generated by a flashlight bulb reflect from the concave mirror behind the bulb to produce a beam of light. The "dishes" used for radar and television waves, the concave mirrors of large telescopes, and the "shells" placed behind bands and orchestras are all examples of wave reflectors. The "bouncing back" of waves from a surface is called **reflection.**

Another important phenomenon in waves is refraction. **Refraction** (rih FRAK shun) is the bending of waves as they pass from one medium to another. Light waves bend as they pass from the air into glass (a medium in which they travel more slowly) and into the air again.

18-6 The reflection of a circular wave **(a)**; light waves refracted by a calcite crystal **(b)**.

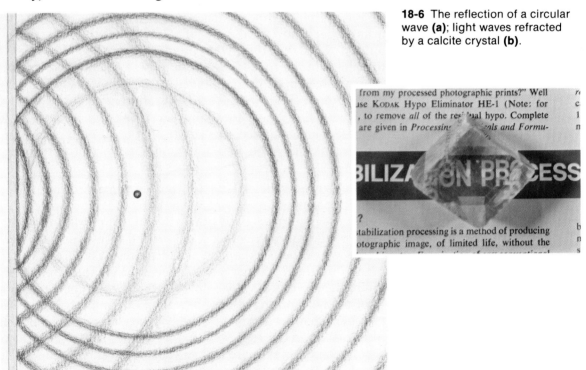

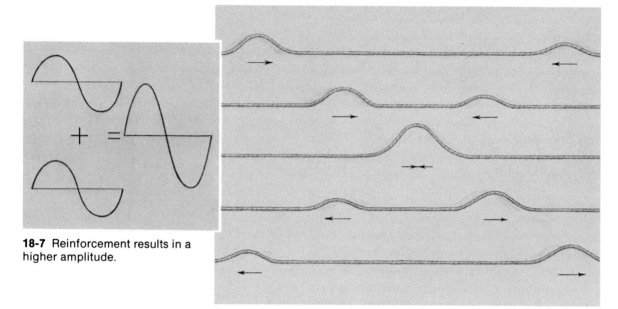

18-7 Reinforcement results in a higher amplitude.

The combination of waves

Picture a long rope stretched between two boys. At the same instant, each boy flicks his end of the rope upward, sending pulses toward the other. What happens when the pulses meet at the center of the rope? Since both pulses are upward displacements of the rope, they add together for a brief instant as they pass through each other. At that instant there is a single pulse as high as both the pulses together. They will pass through each other and continue. The ability of two pulses to encounter, survive, and move on as before comes as a surprise to many people.

Let us repeat the experiment, but this time have one of the boys flick the rope *downward* as the other flicks it upward. Two pulses now approach each other, the one an upward displacement of the rope, the other a downward displacement. What would you expect to happen as the pulses pass through each other this time? If they are of equal height but oppositely directed, as in this case (one up, the other down), there will be a brief moment during which they *cancel* each other. They will pass by each other and move on unchanged. During the moment of cancellation the rope will be approximately straight. However, since the waves are still traveling along the rope, all the energy of both waves is still present. *Cancellation* is the "sub-

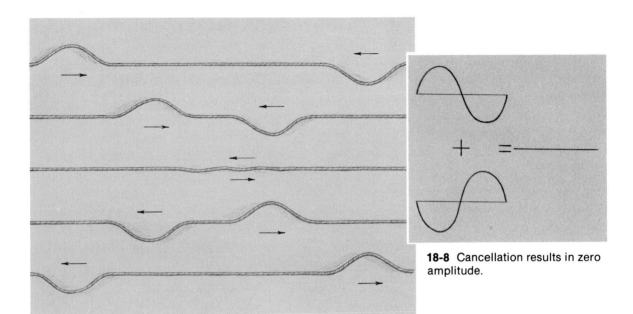

18-8 Cancellation results in zero amplitude.

traction" of the two pulses. It can also be thought of as the *addition* of a positive quantity and a negative quantity.

Pairs of longer waves and even larger numbers of waves can combine in much the same way. When waves from different sources cross paths, the resulting effect is called **interference** (IN tur FIHR unce). If the crests and troughs of the two waves exactly coincide with each other, the waves are in phase; they will add together. This reaction is called **constructive interference**. Inphase waves reinforce each other, producing higher crests and deeper troughs.

If the crests of one wave coincide with the troughs of another, they will cancel each other. These waves are out of phase. Out-of-phase waves create **destructive interference.** Often when waves interfere, both constructive and destructive interference can occur.

18-9 The waves in a ripple tank meet and reinforce or cancel each other, creating a pattern of constructive and destructive interference.

Some auditoriums have "dead spots" where it is difficult to hear even if the sound is amplified. Dead spots are caused by the destructive interference of the waves from two different loudspeakers. What do you think will happen where constructive interference occurs?

Constructive interference can cause danger at sea. Ship captains have seen small waves come together in phase to form waves 15 to 30 m high. Without warning, these waves can add together and capsize a small ship.

The Electromagnetic Spectrum

Light waves, television waves, and microwaves are members of the large family of *electromagnetic waves.* All of these travel at approximately the speed of light. Since all are capable of traveling through a vacuum, they are classified as radiant energy.

There is amazing variety in their wavelengths and in their frequencies, in how they are generated, and in their effects upon matter. God has designed tremendous diversity into His creation. He could have made just one kind of star, one kind of rock, one kind of plant, one kind of animal, and human beings looking exactly the same and having the same abilities. With just one kind of electromagnetic wave, we would not be able to both *see* and *keep warm*, for heat and light are two different kinds of electromagnetic waves.

Electromagnetic waves have both an electrical and a magnetic nature. These two natures—an electrical component and a magnetic component—vibrate at right angles to each other. As the waves become shorter and higher in frequency, they become more energetic. Thus radio waves are the least energetic and gamma rays the most energetic members of the electromagnetic family.

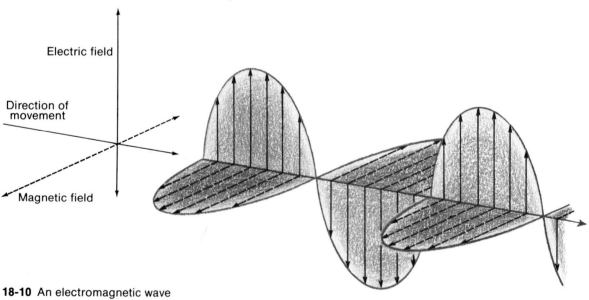

Electric field

Direction of movement

Magnetic field

18-10 An electromagnetic wave is a combination of a magnetic field and an electric field that are moving at right angles to each other.

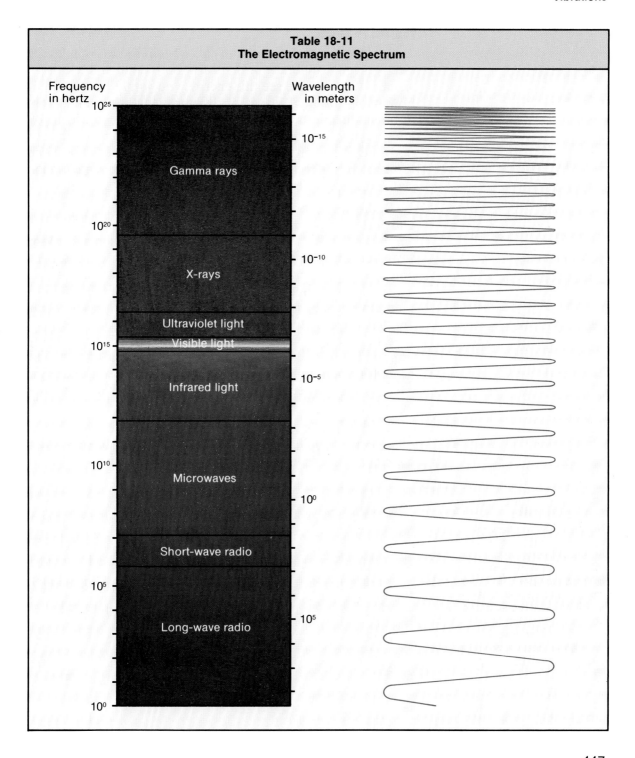

Table 18-11
The Electromagnetic Spectrum

Frequency in hertz

10^{25}

10^{20}

10^{15}

10^{10}

10^5

10^0

Gamma rays

X-rays

Ultraviolet light

Visible light

Infrared light

Microwaves

Short-wave radio

Long-wave radio

Wavelength in meters

10^{-15}

10^{-10}

10^{-5}

10^0

10^5

Radio waves

The portion of the spectrum called **radio waves** includes the electromagnetic vibrations that carry both radio and television signals. If you could see this energy, you would be amazed at how many different waves of different lengths, coming from different directions, are passing through the room in which you are studying. The idea that they are traveling right through your body might disturb you, but they are completely harmless. Even the relatively strong waves from nearby radio and television stations are weak enough to cause no dangerous side effects.

Radio waves are generated by accelerating electrons back and forth many times each second in a conductor called an *antenna* or *aerial*. This conductor may be a wire, a metal pole or tower, or some more elaborate geometric shape. Electrons in the antenna are accelerated back and forth by an electronic device called a **transmitter**. The number of back-and-forth motions made by the electrons in 1 s determines the frequency of the emitted wave. Although a portion of the electrons' energy is used in moving up and down the antenna, most of the energy imparted to the electrons is given off as radiant energy. The generation of radio waves is an amazingly efficient use of energy: a few watts of power can produce waves that travel for thousands of miles.

The frequencies of radio waves are specified in kilohertz or megahertz. A typical radio wave in the AM radio band is called a *medium wave*, a term referring to its "medium" wavelength. A

18-12 Some uses of radio waves. A short-wave transmission from North Africa **(a)** can be tuned in by a listener **(b)** in the United States. A pastor **(c)** can minister to shut-ins **(d)** by transmitting his message over AM radio, which can be tuned in on a medium-wave receiver. A pilot coming in for a landing **(e)** is guided by a long-wave directional beacon broadcast by airport control **(f)**.

a b c

1-MHz wave in the center of the AM band has a wavelength of 300 m.

Below the AM band (lower in frequency) is the *long-wave* region of the radio spectrum. These waves are long indeed. A 100 kHz wave has a wavelength of 3000 m! Long waves are used for submarine-to-shore communications systems, and beacons use long waves to guide planes into airports.

Above the AM band (higher frequency) is the *short-wave* region of the radio spectrum. A wave with a typical short-wave frequency, 10 MHz, has a wavelength of only 30 m. These shorter waves reflect back to the earth from the ionosphere (an ionized layer of the earth's atmosphere extending from roughly 100 km upward), allowing them to travel great distances. Short waves are used for a variety of services—international broadcasts, amateur radio, time signals, military communications, ship-to-shore radio systems, and citizens band (CB) radio. Still higher short-wave frequencies are utilized by FM radio stations, TV stations, police and fire departments, and mobile radio-telephone services. A 100-MHz wave, in the middle of the FM band, has a wavelength of only 3 m.

Radio waves are also received from astronomical bodies. A relatively new branch of science, **radio astronomy**, uses radio telescopes to receive these waves. These are not messages from space beings, but rather noises generated by molecules in space. By studying the frequencies and relative strengths of the noises, astronomers are able to get data about materials in interstellar clouds and other objects in space.

d   e   f

FACETS
OF BASIC SCIENCE

Radio image of Cas A, a supernova remnant in the constellation Cassiopeia.

The Very Large Array: The World's Largest and Most Powerful Radio Telescope

Twenty-seven identical reflector-dish antennas operate together in the desert near Socorro, New Mexico, to form the Very Large Array (VLA), the world's largest and most powerful radio telescope. This network of interconnected antennas is designed to pick up radio signals from very distant sources in space.

Because the radio emissions from these sources are faint when they reach the Earth, the

VLA system must be very large and very powerful. The huge antennas weigh 210 tons each and can be moved along 60 km of special double railroad tracks. The tracks form a Y shape with two 21-km arms and one 19-km arm. The antennas can be moved along the tracks to form four different configurations for different types of observations. The "A" configuration is the most extended and spreads out the antennas along the entire length of the arms. The "D" configuration is the most compact; the antennas are spread over only 0.6 km of each arm.

How do scientists use the VLA to make an observation? Usually they point all the antennas at the source to be studied and guide them by computer to track the source through the sky for several hours. The antennas act together in sets of two called interferometer pairs. During an observation, each pair of antennas sends a signal every ten seconds to the central computer system. At the end of the observation, the computers compile the data and produce a color-enhanced visual map of the radio source being studied.

These maps are often more detailed than the best photographs taken by the largest optical telescopes. Like a photograph taken through an optical telescope, a VLA picture shows the relative brightness of the source. But unlike a camera, the VLA measures wavelengths of energy that we cannot see. The result may be either a contour map of the object or a plot that resembles a photograph.

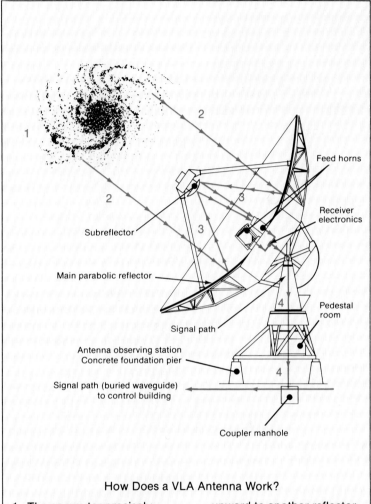

Feed horns

Receiver electronics

Subreflector

Main parabolic reflector

Signal path

Pedestal room

Antenna observing station
Concrete foundation pier

Signal path (buried waveguide) to control building

Coupler manhole

How Does a VLA Antenna Work?

1. The computer precisely aims the antenna at the distant radio source and commands the antenna to begin observing.
2. Invisible radio waves travel vast distances through space and strike the antenna's main reflector.
3. The signals are bounced upward to another reflector and back onto a feed horn.
4. The feed horn picks up the signals and routes them to the receiver electronics, which amplify the radio waves over 1,000,000 times. These signals are then sent to the computers for processing.

Chapter 18

18-13 How does a microwave oven cook food?

Microwaves

The frequencies used for radio astronomy merge into the next region of the electromagnetic spectrum, **microwaves**. The frequencies for microwaves range from about 10^9 Hz to 10^{11} Hz. Wavelengths range from approximately 0.3 cm to 30 cm. Microwaves can be generated electronically, in much the same way radio waves are generated.

Microwave ovens use these same waves to cook food. Microwaves set up within the oven a changing electric field, which affects water molecules in the food. Water has polar molecules with positive and negative ends. The changing electric field causes the water molecules to turn first one way, then the other. As the molecules turn, they collide with other molecules, giving off energy in the form of heat. Thus, the inside of the food is heated almost as quickly as the surface. Cooking time is greatly reduced because it is not necessary to wait for the heat to move from the surface to the interior of the food as in a standard oven.

Microwaves are also used in **radar** (RAY dar) (*radio detection and ranging*). They can be reflected by relatively small objects such as automobiles, airplanes, and ships, and large objects such as storm systems and land masses. Transmitters beam powerful microwave pulses at the object being studied. The returning scattered radiation is picked up by an antenna, and the time interval between transmission and reception is measured. This time interval reveals the distance from the transmitter to the object. By aiming a radar pulse at a car, a policeman can determine its speed.

18-14 How radar works.

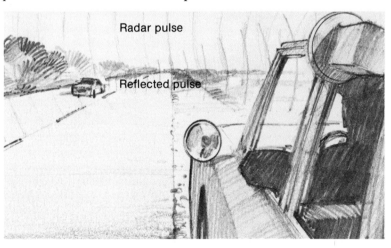

Radar pulse

Reflected pulse

Infrared waves

Moving up the spectrum to still higher frequencies and higher energies, we come to heat, or **infrared** (IN fruh RED) **waves**. The prefix "infra" means *below*. The frequency of this type of energy is just *below* red visible light.

Sir William Herschel (HUR shul) (1738-1822), an English astronomer, discovered infrared radiation. He refracted rays from the sun through a prism to separate the different colors. Herschel placed a thermometer in the regions of each of the colors and recorded their temperatures. Then he placed the thermometer in the region just below the red color. The temperature he recorded in this infrared region was greater than in any other part of the spectrum. He called the energy he uncovered "rays of heat."

An **incandescent** (IN kun DES unt) object (one heated to glowing) is a good source of both infrared and visible light energy. You have probably noticed that incandescent lights give off considerably more heat than fluorescent lights. Because fluorescent lights waste less energy as heat, they are more economical to operate. Another example of an incandescent object is the burner of an electric stove. After a stove burner has warmed up for a time, it emits an orange glow. It radiates both visible and infrared energy. Can you predict what will happen when the burner is turned off? The color will disappear, but the burner will still emit infrared energy. You can readily detect this energy by holding your hand near the burner. Human skin contains sensitive infrared receptors (detectors) that are plentiful in certain locations, such as on the face and the back of the hand. Manmade devices for detecting infrared energy include thermometers, thermostats, and infrared-sensitive film.

Visible light

Visible light extends in frequency from 4.3×10^{14} Hz (red light) to 7.5×10^{14} Hz (violet light). Its waves are exceedingly small, having lengths ranging from 4×10^{-5} cm (violet) to 7×10^{-5} cm (red). Visible light is thought to be generated by the outer electrons of atoms when they are given extra energy. The additional energy vibrates them and raises them to higher orbitals, whereupon they fall back to their normal levels, giving off light in the process.

FACETS
OF BASIC SCIENCE

The photograph at right was taken with the special color infrared Earth Terrain Camera aboard Skylab. It shows portions of Connecticut, New York, and New Jersey. Can you guess which area of the photograph is a major city?

Southern Louisiana was also captured on film by the Skylab camera. The Mississippi River meanders southward through the photograph below from Baton Rouge at the top to the suburbs of New Orleans at the bottom. The large, dark-blue lake in the corner is Lake Pontchartrain. The smaller body of water, Lake Maurepas, is connected to Lake Pontchartrain by a canal. Can you find the canal?

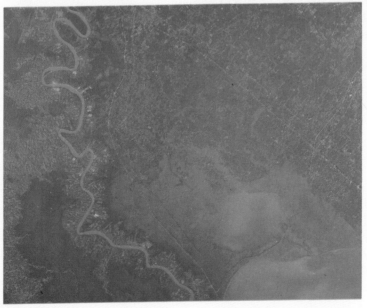

Infrared Photography

Sir William Herschel's "rays of heat" have become increasingly useful to modern man. Although we cannot see infrared light, almost everything gives it off. Therefore infrared light can give us information about things invisible in shorter wavelengths of light.

One property that makes infrared light such a valuable source of information is its ability to affect infrared film just as ordinary light affects ordinary film. Medical science, for example, has used infrared photography to diagnose disease by making "thermal maps" of the temperatures on human body

Mount Etna, the highest volcano in Europe, was caught in action by the Skylab camera. If you look carefully, you can see a thin plume of smoke coming from the volcano's crest. More recent lava flows appear black in contrast to the older, cooler flows and debris which appear red. The small cone-shaped areas on the flanks of the volcano are sites of previous eruptions.

The photograph below is a composite of infrared-, red-, and green-light images taken by Earth Resources Technology Satellite-1. The completely black area is the Dead Sea. Vegetation appears bright red. What is the name of the country in this picture? What kind of climate does it appear to have?

surfaces. Scientists have used the same technology to make "portraits" of the earth—portraits that may help man plan how he will manage its resources in the future.

As we have become aware that our supplies of food, energy, and mineral wealth have limits, management of the earth's resources has become more and more important. In the early 1970s, an "energy crisis" prompted NASA scientists to form the Earth Resources Laboratory, a program for locating and recording the earth's remaining resources, and for studying how they are used. The researchers found that normal-light satellite photographs could not give them all the information they needed. They developed special cameralike sensors that could detect different wavelengths of light—especially infrared—and launched them into orbit.

The images collected by these sensors have given scientists an entirely new way of looking at the earth's surface. By reading these heat images, they have been able to identify pollution of air and water; to discover areas that might yield oil, natural gas, or other minerals; and to study changes in ecology caused by forest fires, floods, earthquakes, and strip mining.

Ultraviolet light

The prefix *ultra* means "beyond." **Ultraviolet** (UL truh VY uh lit) **light** is just beyond violet light in frequency. Its vibrations are too fast for the human eye to detect. The frequency range for ultraviolet light is about 10^{15} to 10^{17} Hz. Because it cannot be seen, it is sometimes referred to as "black light."

Ultraviolet radiation was discovered by J.S. Ritter (1776-1810) and W.H. Wollaston (W*OOL* uh stun) (1766-1828). They found that the energy adjacent to the violet region in sunlight passing through a prism had the ability to darken certain silver compounds. The compounds decomposed to form dark-colored metallic silver. The researchers reasoned that the ultraviolet light was the energy that caused this reaction.

X-rays

W.K. Roentgen (RENT gun) (1845-1923), the first winner of the Nobel prize, discovered **x-rays** in 1895 while studying cathode rays (streams of electrons). X-rays have frequencies ranging from about 10^{17} to 10^{21} Hz. They are generated when high-energy electrons are rapidly decelerated (slowed down) by striking a solid target.

The best-known property of x-rays is their ability to penetrate matter. This has made them useful in medical work for viewing internal structures of the body. X-rays are used in industry to inspect metal objects for internal defects. X-rays have also been used to determine whether or not a painting is genuine.

18-15 These doctors are studying x-rays of a fractured hand to determine how the bone should be set.

Prolonged exposure to x-rays can cause burns, cancer, and even death. X-rays are capable of destroying body cells and causing mutations in genetic material. However, since x-rays destroy unhealthy cells more easily than healthy cells, they can be used in the treatment of certain types of cancer.

FACETS OF BASIC SCIENCE

Black Lights

Ultraviolet radiation is thought to be produced in much the same way as visible light, but by electrons close to the nucleus rather than by the outer electrons. Incandescent objects give off ultraviolet energy when they are heated to a high enough temperature. The sun, whose surface is approximately 5800° C, is a strong radiator of ultraviolet energy. This energy would threaten life on earth if it were not for the *ozone layer* in the atmosphere.

Ozone (the O_3 form of oxygen) effectively filters ultraviolet radiation. The ozone layer, a region extending from 20 km to 50 km above the earth's surface, is clear-cut evidence of an intelligent design by a benevolent Creator. It has posed an embarrassing problem for evolutionists. In attempting to explain how the oxygen in the atmosphere could develop by natural processes, they suggest that it was produced by simple plants such as algae in the oceans. However, there would be no ozone layer unless oxygen were first present in the atmosphere, and without the ozone layer the plants would quickly be killed by the ultraviolet rays. Then plants would obviously be unable to produce the oxygen with which the ozone layer was supposedly formed. The only successful way to form such a closely interdependent system would be to set it up all at one time as Scripture records!

In spite of the ozone layer, a small amount of the ultraviolet energy from the sun does get through to the earth's surface. In this amount it has a beneficial effect: it stimulates the manufacture of vitamin D in the skin. Vitamin D is needed for healthy bone structure. The vitamin-D content of certain foods such as milk can be increased by exposing them to ultraviolet light.

It is important to avoid *over*exposure to the ultraviolet energy in sunlight. Ultraviolet waves are a high-energy form of radiation. They can remove electrons from the atoms and molecules in skin cells, causing sunburn, nausea, fever, and skin cancer. You can protect yourself from ultraviolet rays by applying large amounts of oils or creams to your skin. These coatings effectively stop the short wavelengths of ultraviolet rays.

Because ultraviolet radiation can kill bacteria, it is used to sterilize objects and preserve foods. Ultraviolet light also causes certain minerals to fluoresce (give off visible light) in characteristic colors that are often different from their colors in ordinary light. Not only is this property useful for identifying these minerals, but it also allows special markings to "glow in the dark." In the darkened cockpits of military aircraft, ultraviolet lights make visible the mineral-coated markings on the instrument panel. Laundry marks written with invisible ink made from such minerals can also be read in ultraviolet light.

X-ray astronomy (observing astronomical objects using x-rays instead of visible light) is a recently developed area of science. X-ray telescopes have been placed in satellites to gather information concerning x-ray emissions from the sun and other astronomical bodies. X-rays are produced by gases at very high temperatures, such as those that exist in the atmosphere of stars. Thousands of x-ray sources in space have now been catalogued, among them the famous Cygnus X-1 object, thought by some to contain a "black hole."

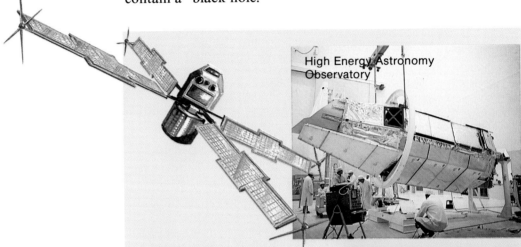

High Energy Astronomy Observatory

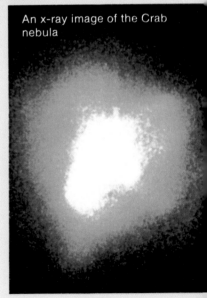

An x-ray image of the Crab nebula

18-16 In 1962 scientists discovered that they could detect x-rays from far galaxies as well as from our own sun. X-ray astronomy has become an important tool for testing theories of physics and for expanding man's view of God's universe. The "Uhuru" **(above)**, an early orbiting x-ray observatory, found more than 300 x-ray sources. A recent x-ray satellite **(above right)** discovered the most distant galaxies yet seen and recorded images of x-ray sources outside our own Milky Way galaxy. Some of the stars studied by x-ray have plasma so hot that many of the elements in them have ionized, becoming invisible to optical observatories.

Gamma rays

Gamma rays are very similar to x-rays but originate from the nuclei of atoms rather than from electrons. Their frequencies overlap with those of x-rays but extend even higher, ranging from 10^{20} Hz upward. Gamma rays are the most energetic form of electromagnetic radiation known to man. Their wavelengths are the shortest known, ranging from 10^{-9} cm downward. This is a mind-boggling *billionth* of a centimeter, and most gamma rays have wavelengths even shorter than this.

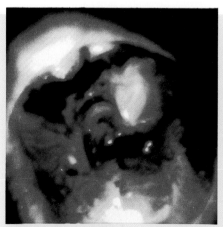

An x-ray photo of our sun **(above left)**. An optical view of the Great Nebula in Andromeda **(top right)** and a detailed x-ray image from the same galaxy **(lower right).** The quasars (bright areas) in the image below are 10 billion light-years away.

Gamma rays have many of the same uses as x-rays. In medicine, gamma radiation is used to treat cancer. In non-destructive testing, gamma rays are sometimes used in place of x-rays to test thicker objects.

Scientifically Speaking

waves
mechanical waves
electromagnetic waves
crests
troughs
amplitude
cycle
wavelength
frequency
hertz
transverse wave

longitudinal wave
pulse
reflection
refraction
interference
constructive interference
destructive interference
radio waves
transmitter
radio astronomy

microwaves
radar
infrared waves
incandescent
visible light
ultraviolet light
x-rays
ozone
x-ray astronomy
gamma rays

Questions to Talk Over

1. In a certain experiment, a wave is generated on a tightly stretched spring. A string has been tied to one of the coils of the spring and hangs freely from the spring. Describe the motion the string will have if the wave on the spring is a transverse wave. How will the string move if the spring wave is a longitudinal wave?

2. When a rock is dropped into a pool of still water, waves begin to spread out in all directions from the rock. What happens to the wavelengths of these waves as they move out from the rock? Does the amplitude of these waves change as they travel?

3. What do sonar, radar, mirror images, and echoes have in common? How can you explain these phenomena as the result of a property of waves?

4. Bob told his sister Jenny that the "light" of the visible spectrum is only a very small portion of a broader classification of energy called the electromagnetic spectrum. He told her that in the electromagnetic spectrum, the ultraviolet region lies just above the visible spectrum, and that the infrared region lies just below the visible spectrum. Jenny refused to believe Bob because she could not "see" any of this energy. How could Bob demonstrate to Jenny that these two regions exist?

CHAPTER
19

During World War I the fate of the British nation hung on a simple underwater listening device. By late 1917, German submarines, called U-boats, had sunk over 3000 Allied ships. At one point it seemed that Germany would be able to cut off Britain's food supply and starve the island nation into submission.

When submerged, the German U-boats were invisible, but fortunately for the British they were also very noisy. Detecting the sounds of U-boats became the Allies' only way of escaping this hidden threat.

In 1917 underwater listening devices were very crude. Most were simply T-shaped tubes capped with rubber membranes. When the captain of a ship suspected that he was sailing through

19-1 Sonar uses sound waves to detect submerged objects.

19-2 Sound waves are made up of alternating compressions and rarefactions of the molecules of the medium through which they are traveling.

submarine-infested waters, he would stop the ship's engines, allowing the ship to drift silently through the water. An operator would then listen with a stethoscope at the inboard end of the partially submerged tube. These crude but effective devices helped the British stem the U-boat threat.

The detection of sound during World War I depended almost entirely on passive listening devices. But the postwar science of sound gave birth to sensitive underwater microphones and high-frequency echoing devices. Modern listening devices are called **sonar** (SO nar) (for *s*ound *n*avigation *a*nd *r*anging). The sonar on modern ships is so sensitive that it produces detailed images of underwater objects on screens.

Sound Waves

Sound is the form of energy detected by our ears. To produce sound, some object must be rubbed, struck, dropped, or by some other means made to vibrate. These vibrations in turn send waves coursing through the medium in which the object is vibrating. These waves are *longitudinal* (LAHN ji TOO duh nul) *waves*. They vibrate in the same direction as they travel. You can picture a sound wave traveling through air as a series of alternating **compressions** (kum PRESH unz) and **rarefactions** (REHR uh FAK shunz). A compression is a region where the air molecules are pushed closer together than normal; a rarefaction is a region where the air molecules are spread out.

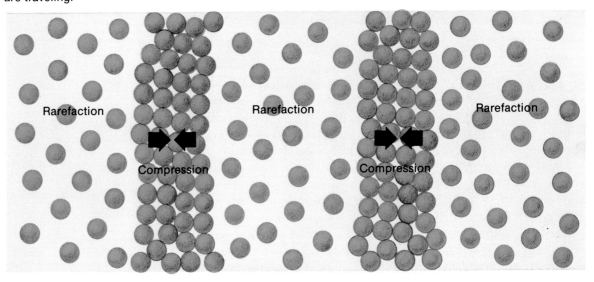

Rarefaction

Rarefaction

Rarefaction

Compression

Compression

Mediums of sound waves

Robert Boyle, who formulated one of the gas laws, conducted an experiment that clarified the true nature of sound. In 1660 Boyle suspended "a watch with a good alarm" from a thread in a glass jar and pumped all the air out of the jar. With his assistants, he "silently expected the time when the alarm should begin to ring," but the time passed and the experimenters did not hear the alarm.

To confirm his experiment, Boyle opened a valve and allowed air to enter the jar. As the air rushed in, the alarm grew louder and louder. Boyle had demonstrated that sound needs a medium—in this case, air.

Will sound vibrate through mediums other than air? Swimmers know that sound travels clearly through water. If you put your ear against an oak table, you can hear sound travel through wood. Sound travels exceptionally well through metals. Train robbers in the old West put their ears to the iron rails to learn whether or not a train was approaching. Indians are said to have used a variation of this trick; Indian hunters would listen with an ear to the ground to locate the thundering herds of buffalo.

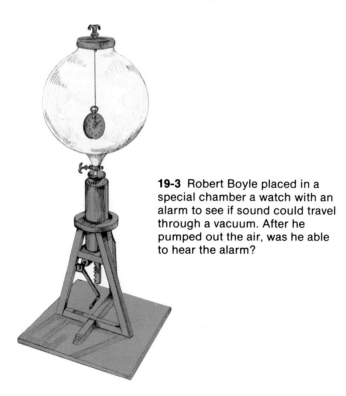

19-3 Robert Boyle placed in a special chamber a watch with an alarm to see if sound could travel through a vacuum. After he pumped out the air, was he able to hear the alarm?

The speed of sound waves

How fast does sound travel through air? In 1708 William Derham of England calculated the speed of sound through air. Stationing an observer some distance away, Derham fired a cannon into the air. Using the length of time between when the observer saw the cannon flash and when he heard its boom, Derham calculated the speed of sound. He averaged the results of several trials and came up with a value that was surprisingly accurate. Since Derham's time, scientists have measured the speed of sound through air with precise instruments. Today, the accepted value is 332 m/s at 0°C.

The speed at which sound travels through a medium is affected by the temperature of that medium. The molecules in a cold medium move slowly, reducing the speed at which the vibration of sound can be transmitted. Sound travels through air at 0°C at 332 m/s; yet in air at 100°C, sound travels at 386 m/s.

The speed at which sound travels through a medium also depends on the density of the medium. The denser the medium, the faster sound travels. Thus sound travels faster in liquids than in gases, and (generally) faster in solids than in liquids.

19-4 William Derham used cannons to measure the speed of sound. How did he determine the speed of sound from the difference in time between the cannon's flash and the cannon's boom?

Table 19-5

The Speed of Sound in Various Mediums	
Medium	**Representative Speed**
air	332 m/s
water	1450 m/s
wood	3830 m/s
iron	5100 m/s

The characteristics of sound waves

Have you ever wondered how we distinguish one sound from another? We identify sounds on the basis of three important characteristics: *pitch, loudness,* and *quality.*

Pitch is how high or how low a tone sounds to our ears. Pitch is directly related to frequency: the higher a sound's frequency, the higher its pitch. You may have heard a steam whistle demonstrate this relationship. When some steam whistles begin to blow, their pitch is relatively low but builds rapidly until the whistle is in full shriek. At first, the pressure of the steam is relatively low and produces vibrations of low frequency in the whistle; therefore, the pitch of the whistle starts low. As the steam pressure builds, the whistle vibrates faster and faster, giving a higher and higher pitch until it reaches its peak.

Recall from Chapter 18 that frequency is measured in hertz (Hz); a frequency of one vibration per second is designated as 1 Hz. Young children can hear pitches ranging from about 20 to 20,000 Hz. As a person grows older, his eardrums become less elastic and the upper limit of the frequencies he can hear is reduced.

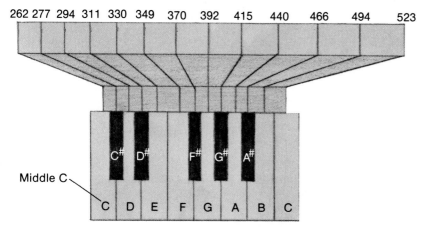

19-6 The frequencies of the notes on a piano.

FACETS
OF BASIC SCIENCE

Nature's Loudest Sound

What would you guess is the loudest sound ever produced in nature? The roar of a mighty waterfall? The rumble of a devastating avalanche? The clap of an 80,000-ampere stroke of lightning? These events are indeed loud, but the world's record for sheer sound intensity in nature is held by *volcanoes*. Volcanoes are the earth's safety valves. Steam pressure generated by rock-forming reactions inside the earth occasionally builds up to a level where "something has to give." Sometimes this pressure escapes gradually in a series of small volcanic eruptions. At other times it is stored over many years and suddenly unleashed in a single violent upheaval.

One of the most violent volcanic eruptions ever recorded took place in 1883 on the island of Krakatoa (KRAH kuh TO uh) between Java and Sumatra. Two-thirds of the island was instantly demolished. The column of dust, ashes, and pumice that blasted into the upper

atmosphere took more than two years to settle to the ground. The force of the blast blew out windows up to 160 km away! The monumental explosion was heard clearly in the Philippines 2240 km away, in Ceylon (today's Sri Lanka) 3200 km away, and on Rodrigues Island

4800 km across the Indian Ocean. Pressure changes recorded on barometers indicated that the sound waves actually traveled around the world—not once, but four times!

Archeologists and volcanologists working together have deduced that an even more destructive eruption occurred in ancient times on the island of Thera (THIR uh) (now called Santorini) in the Aegean Sea. Thera's crater is several times as large as Krakatoa's, indicating that four or five times as much material was ejected. What was originally a sizeable, round island is now a thin crescent of land with a 300-m cliff facing the center of the submerged crater. The bottom of the crater lies another 300 m beneath the surface of the water! Monstrous sea waves and heavy falls of volcanic ash from the eruption are now known to have inflicted heavy damage on the nearby island of Crete. Interestingly, the inhabitants of Thera itself, warned of the danger by severe earthquakes, successfully fled the island in ships.

Volcanoes are awe-inspiring spectacles. They speak to us of God's power and wrath. "Who hath hardened himself against him, and hath prospered? Which removeth the mountains, and they know not: which overturneth them in his anger. Which shaketh the earth out of her place, and the pillars thereof tremble." (Job 9:4b-6)

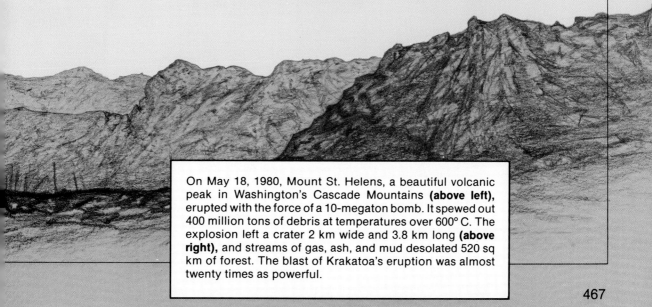

On May 18, 1980, Mount St. Helens, a beautiful volcanic peak in Washington's Cascade Mountains **(above left)**, erupted with the force of a 10-megaton bomb. It spewed out 400 million tons of debris at temperatures over 600° C. The explosion left a crater 2 km wide and 3.8 km long **(above right)**, and streams of gas, ash, and mud desolated 520 sq km of forest. The blast of Krakatoa's eruption was almost twenty times as powerful.

Loudness is the response of your ear to the intensity of a sound wave. Loudness is related to the power of sound energy hitting a surface. It was first measured in units called *bels* (after Alexander Graham Bell), but it is commonly expressed in units of one-tenth of a bel, called **decibels (db)** (DEH suh belz). One decibel is the smallest difference between the loudness of two sounds that the human ear is capable of detecting.

The very softest sound level that can be heard is called the **threshold of hearing**. If the threshold of hearing is considered to be the "zero" point of the decibel scale, the level of a whisper is about 20 db; normal conversation is about 60 db; and the noise of a vacuum cleaner is about 80 db. At 120 db sound becomes painfully loud.

What about extremely loud noises? One of the dangers of extremely loud rock music in cars, restaurants, and stores is the potential loss of hearing! Rock music is often played at a sound level of 125 decibels. Permanent loss of hearing has occurred from such exposure. Noise at 125 decibels is over the threshold of pain!

Table 19-7

Representative Noise Levels

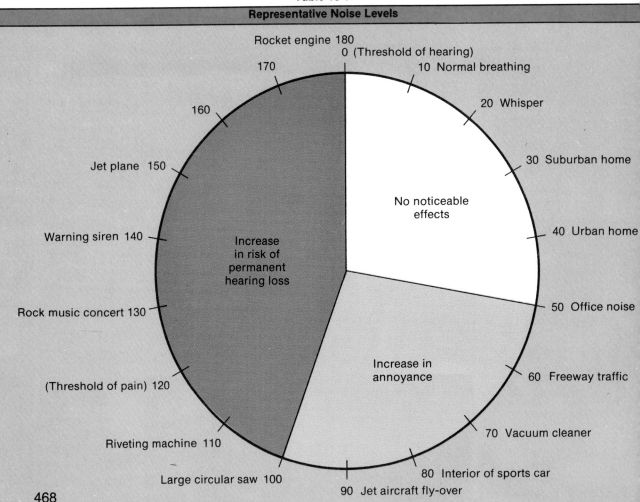

468

The **quality** of a sound depends on the particular mixture of overtones present in its waves. In turn, the presence of overtones depends on how the sound generator is vibrating. The lowest tone a vibrating object produces is called the **fundamental** of the sound produced by that object. Multiples of this frequency, called **overtones,** are also present in the sound waves produced by most sound generators. Overtones enable us to distinguish one musical instrument from another. Each instrument has its own "vibration recipe," or mixture of overtones. A clarinet, for example, has strong odd-numbered multiples of the fundamental and weak even-numbered multiples. A trumpet, on the other hand, has strong overtones, both odd and even, all the way up to sixteen times the fundamental. This difference in overtones should help us understand why the trumpet is the louder of the two instruments. In summary, a musical tone is a combination of a fundamental and several overtones. The frequency of the fundamental determines the pitch of the sound, and the number and intensities of the overtones determine the quality of the tone.

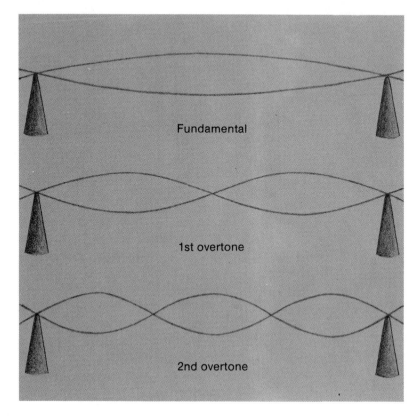

Fundamental

1st overtone

2nd overtone

19-8 This diagram shows a fundamental and two of its overtones. Actually the fundamental and overtones occur at the same time on the same string, but they were separated here to help you see them more clearly.

469

19-9 Many architectural features of the Sydney Opera House in Sydney, Australia, were designed with sound phenomena in mind. These features help make sure that every listener has a good seat.

Sound Phenomena

The statuary hall of the United States Capitol building is sometimes called the Whispering Gallery. The architect of the Capitol building unintentionally designed the elliptical room so that its hard plaster walls reflect sound from one end of the room to the other. Although no one in the center of the room would notice, a person at one end of the hall could easily hear the hushed conversation of persons at the other end. This is one of the many interesting sound phenomena that we will discuss in this section.

Acoustics

When we speak of a building's **acoustics** (uh KOO stiks), we mean the building's effect on sounds. Any type of enclosure will reflect sounds. How well it reflects sounds is another matter. The *science* of acoustics is the study of controlling the sounds that reach our ears. Using this science, architects can build auditoriums with good acoustics. In a poorly designed auditorium, listeners in the front seats may be able to hear well, while those in other seats cannot. Sounds may be uncomfortably loud in one section, and muffled in an adjacent section. **Reverberations** (rih

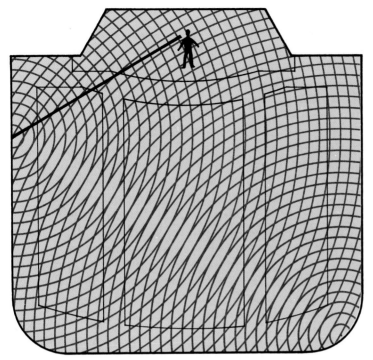

19-10 An interference pattern formed by constructive and destructive addition of sound waves can be set up when the speaker's voice meets its own reflection from a wall. The dark bands indicate areas where the sound will be deadened by the interference. Acoustical engineers design auditorium interiors to reduce these troublesome echoes. One way to do this is to use special acoustical tiles.

vur buh RAY shunz)—multiple echoes of sounds— may distract listeners seated behind the platform.

Years ago, before public-address systems became available, hard, concave surfaces were placed behind speakers' podiums to reflect the sound of speakers' voices. Today, the walls of many auditoriums and stages are designed to put the principles of sound reflection to good use.

Often the sides of a stage are equipped with slanted surfaces (called "splays") that reflect sound outward to the audience. Other auditoriums utilize convex (curved outward) wall surfaces along the seating area to reflect sound to various points in order to achieve a more even distribution of sound.

In general, materials with hard surfaces are used where good sound reflection is desired. However, if sound is reflected back too strongly, reverberations may occur. These repeated echoes can be prevented by covering walls and ceilings with materials that absorb some of the sound energy from each sound wave that strikes them. Soft, porous materials make good sound absorbers. A large number of small holes or openings greatly improve the sound-muffling qualities of almost any material. Acoustical tiles are designed with many such holes to trap sound energy.

Resonance

If two strings of a violin are tuned to the same pitch, plucking one of the strings will cause the other to vibrate. This phenomenon, called **resonance** (REZ uh nunce), will not occur when the strings are tuned to different pitches. (There is one exception to this statement: resonance will occur when two strings are tuned to pitches one octave apart.)

Why does resonance occur? In general, resonance exists when sound energy from a vibrating object is transferred to another object with the same natural frequency. The photograph below shows two tuning forks with the same natural frequency mounted on identical wooden boxes and placed several inches apart. When one of the tuning forks is struck with a rubber mallet, both it and the other tuning fork begin to vibrate. If the first tuning fork is suddenly grasped with a hand, the other tuning fork will still be heard. Resonance has taken place as energy from one tuning fork (the transmitter) has been transferred to the other (the receiver).

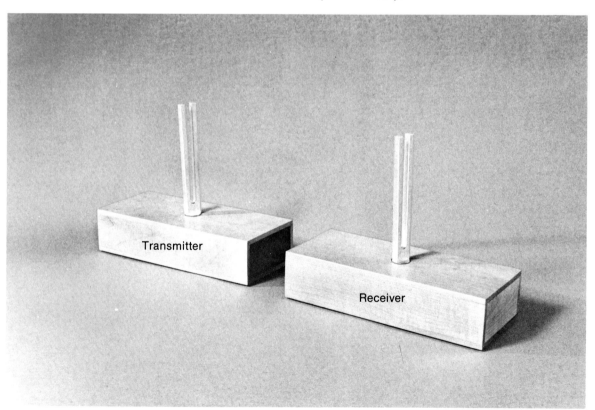

Resonance plays a number of important roles in our daily lives. Resonance in your sinuses (the hollow spaces in the bones of your skull) amplifies the sounds of your voice. The resonant air column housed in the auditory canal of your ear amplifies incoming sounds in the middle range of the audible spectrum. The sound boxes of stringed instruments also function as resonant chambers.

Have you ever blown across the opening of a bottle to produce a hooting noise? The air rushing over the opening at the proper angle creates vibrations that resonate in the bottle. Can wind cause larger objects to resonate?

On November 7, 1940, the Tacoma Bridge in Washington was destroyed when a strong wind caused it to vibrate like a fiddle string. As the winds continued, the vibrations resonated throughout the center span, getting larger and larger. The internal stresses became so great that the huge suspension bridge literally fell apart.

Could marching soldiers destroy a bridge with vibrations? Apparently the United States Army believes that they could! When American troops cross a bridge, they are required to break step. If they marched across a bridge in regular cadence, the frequency of their steps could match the frequency at which the bridge would naturally vibrate. If the bridge began to resonate with the soldiers' marching, the resulting vibrations could weaken the structure of the bridge, causing it to come crashing down.

19-11 The Tacoma Bridge resonating with the wind **(left)** and afterwards, showing the effects of the resonance **(right)**.

FACETS
OF BASIC SCIENCE

Quiet, Please, I'm Working!

The office of twenty years ago was a noisy place. Typewriters clanking, telephones ringing, people chattering, and a dozen other sounds filled offices with an almost unbearable level of noise. By contrast, today's office buildings are relatively quiet. What has changed?

Much of the comparative silence of today's offices can be attributed to acoustical ceiling tiles, thick carpeting, and specially designed dividers that absorb sound. But perhaps the most significant factor in silenc-

ing office noise is the constant "sssss" of **white sound**.

In a sense, white sound serves the same purpose as the music that covers the clatter of glassware and dishes in restaurants. To our ears, white sound resembles the soft rush of escaping steam. In reality, it is a

blend of a wide range of audible frequencies. In many offices, devices designed by acoustical engineers produce just the right level of white sound to mask distracting noises. The "quiet" of these offices is actually the result of the muting effect of white sound.

Beats

When waves pass through each other, they cause an interesting effect. Scientists call this phenomenon *interference*. If two sound waves having slightly different frequencies and about the same amplitude meet, they interfere with each other in such a way that the intensity of the sound rises and falls regularly. These regular changes in intensity are called **beats** (not to be confused with the units of musical rhythm or the percussive strokes used to punctuate music).

Exactly how do beats develop? When two waves, differing only slightly in frequency, interfere, they produce a high amplitude and a loud sound at some times, and a low amplitude and almost no sound at other times. Thus the sound builds up and dies down periodically. Each separate cycle from the smallest combined amplitude through the maximum combined amplitude and back to the smallest amplitude is referred to as a "beat."

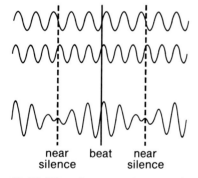

near   beat   near
silence   silence

19-12 When two sound waves of similar frequencies occur at the same time, the constructive addition of their waves creates "beats." The destructive addition causes the near silence between the beats.

Beats are sometimes used to tune musical instruments. As the frequencies of two sounds are brought closer and closer (for example, the sounds of a piano string and a tuning fork), the time between beats decreases until the beats disappear. The two sounds then have exactly the same pitch.

The Doppler effect

The pitch of a sound reaching your ear will vary if either you or the source of the sound is moving. If you are standing at the side of a road and a car approaches with its horn blowing, you hear a certain pitch. As the car passes and leaves you, the pitch of the sound decreases. This phenomenon, called the **Doppler** (DAH plur) **effect**, is named in honor of the Austrian physicist Christian Doppler, who offered a correct mathematical description for it in 1842.

The Doppler effect is the result of relative motion between a sound source and a listener; either the source or the listener or both may be in motion. If the two are coming closer together, extra waves arrive at the ear of the listener each second, and the pitch seems higher. If the motion is such that the two are moving farther apart, fewer waves than normal arrive at the ear of the listener each second, and the pitch seems lower.

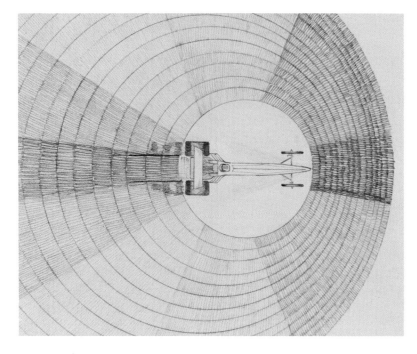

19-13 As a race car travels forward, the sound waves are produced closer together in front of the car than they are behind the car. Would you hear a higher pitch as the car approached you or as it passed you?

FACETS
OF BASIC SCIENCE

The Ear

The human ear is an amazing organ. Man has never duplicated its complex anatomy and physiology by a working model. To the objective observer, the ear is clear evidence of an intelligent Designer.

Sound enters the ear through the *external ear* and the *external auditory* (AW di TAWR ee) *canal.* The external ear helps us determine the direction of a sound source by blocking sounds coming from behind. The external auditory canal serves as a resonating chamber, amplifying many different frequencies throughout the middle range of the audible spectrum.

The inner end of the auditory canal is formed by the *tympanic* (tim PAN ik) *membrane,* or *eardrum,* which separates the outer ear from the middle ear. This thin, flexible membrane vibrates in response to extremely tiny movements of air in the auditory canal. A normal eardrum responds to pressure changes that move it as little as a billionth of a centimeter. This distance is only one-tenth the diameter of a hydrogen atom! Ordinary sounds move the eardrum about a millionth of a centimeter.

Before sound impulses in the ear can be converted into nerve impulses and sent to the brain, they must enter the liquid that contacts the nerve endings in the inner ear. Transmitting sound from air to a liquid presents a challenging problem. Have you ever sat in a boat and tried to talk to someone swimming underwater? Since most of the sound energy would simply bounce back from the water's surface, you may not be heard underwater at all. This problem is solved very neatly by the mechanism of the middle ear.

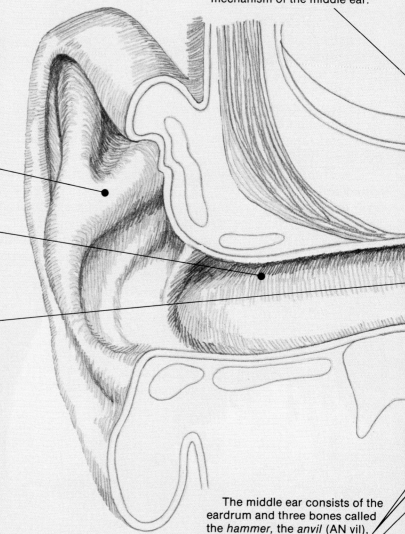

The middle ear consists of the eardrum and three bones called the *hammer,* the *anvil* (AN vil), and the *stirrup* (STUR up). Suspended by ligaments, these bones function as little levers. The hammer transmits vibrations from the eardrum to the anvil.

The anvil in turn passes the vibrations along to the stirrup. The footplate of the stirrup covers the *oval window,* the entrance to the fluid-filled inner ear. The fulcrums of the three bones are positioned in such a way that the force of their vibrations increases about 1.5 times

action and pressure amplification in the middle ear increase the force of vibrations about thirty-seven times.

Several structures in the middle ear protect it from injury. Two tiny muscles, controlled by the brain, restrict the vibration of the eardrum and the stirrup as a safeguard against uncomfortably

air pressure on both sides of the eardrum. If your ears "pop" as you ascend rapidly in an elevator or airplane, you know that your Eustachian tubes are doing their job. The sound is caused when you yawn or swallow, opening your Eustachian tubes, and the eardrum, which has been pushed outward by the unequal pressure, snaps back into place.

The inner ear is the most intricate and least understood part of the ear. It contains two fluid-filled organs: the *semicircular canals* (the organs of balance) and the *cochlea* (KAHK lee uh), the snail-shaped tube where sound is converted into nerve impulses.

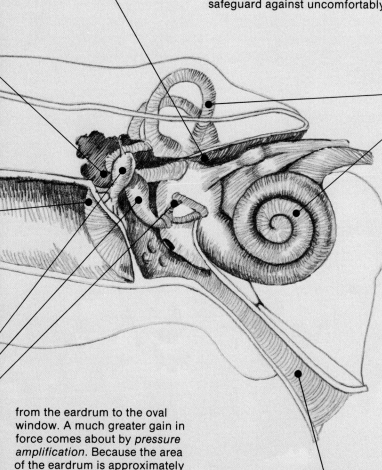

Imagine that the cochlea can be unrolled. Running almost the entire length of the cochlea is a delicate partition that divides it into two fluid-filled parts. At the oval window, the stirrup transfers sound vibrations to the fluid of the cochlea. The vibrations travel through the fluid to the *organ of Corti* (KAWR tee), which runs the length of the partition and contains thousands of sensory cells and nerve endings. In some unknown way, sensory cells in the organ of Corti relay to the auditory nerve thousands of separate signals that indicate the pitch, loudness, and quality of a sound. The auditory nerve conducts these signals to the brain, which interprets them as sound.

from the eardrum to the oval window. A much greater gain in force comes about by *pressure amplification.* Because the area of the eardrum is approximately twenty-five times the area of the oval window, the pressure of a vibration is increased twenty-five times as it is transmitted to the oval window. Together, the lever

loud sounds. The *Eustachian* (yoo STAY shun) *tube* connects the middle ear cavity with the throat and helps to equalize the

Musical Instruments

19-14 The singers in an opera use the human voice to communicate a story.

One of the most complex of all musical instruments is the human voice. The larynx, (LEHR ingks), or voice box, located inside your windpipe produces the musical (and sometimes unmusical) sounds of your voice by means of two flexible vocal cords. When you direct air across these cords, they vibrate and produce sound. You tighten your vocal cords to produce high tones and relax them to produce low tones. More complicated sounds are produced by varying the shape and position of your lips, tongue, and teeth. The flexibility of the human voice is amazing. The Russian bass Ivan Ribroff has the ability to sing tones over a four-octave range.

19-15 A symphony orchestra can produce a wide variety of sounds by combining many different instruments. On the next few pages we will take a look at the instruments that make up an orchestra.

Stringed Instruments

Since there are hundreds of different stringed instruments in various parts of the world, we will limit our discussion to the instruments usually present in the string sections of symphony orchestras. This division of the string family includes the *violin*, the *viola*, the *cello*, and the *string bass* or *double bass*. All these instruments produce sound through vibrations of four tightly stretched strings. The bridge, one of the wooden supports for the strings, conducts vibrations from the strings to the front plate of the instrument. This plate forms one side of a hollow sound box, which greatly amplifies the sound through resonance. The lower the instrument's range, the larger its sound box must be. A double bass, which is tuned considerably lower than a violin, has more than 100 times as much air space in its sound box as the violin.

The pitch of a vibrating string depends on three factors—the string's length, tension, and mass per unit length. The player adjusts the length of the strings as he fingers them with his left hand. The tension of each string is regulated by tuning pegs. The mass per unit length of each string depends on the material and the thickness of the material. On any given instrument the lower-pitched strings are noticeably thicker and heavier than the higher-pitched strings.

19-16 The stringed instruments in the orchestra include the double bass, the cello, the viola, and the violin.

Brass instruments

The brass family, including *trumpets, trombones, baritones, tubas,* and *French horns,* is named for the metal from which these instruments are usually made. Brass instruments produce sound by means of a vibrating air column. These air columns have one thing in common with the strings of stringed instruments: the greater their length, the lower their pitch. You can easily see how the length of the air column in a trombone is varied. When the slide is extended, the air column is lengthened and the pitch is lowered. Most other brass instruments have valves or keys by which players can change the lengths of the air columns.

The air column in a brass instrument is set in motion by the vibration of the player's lips against the mouthpiece. By controlling the tension in his lips, the player can regulate their rate of vibration and thus produce several different pitches at each length of the air column. Because there is no way to change the length of the air column in a bugle, bugle players must produce all the different pitches by changing the tension in their lips.

Because of their strong overtones, the brasses are the loudest instruments in bands and orchestras. Their easily audible tones have made them popular among military leaders for signaling instructions to troops.

19-17 The brass instruments in an orchestra include tubas, baritones, French horns, trombones, and trumpets.

481

19-18 Bagpipes, recorders, and ocarinas are not usually found in modern orchestras. The woodwind members of the orchestra are bassoons, oboes, saxophones, clarinets, and flutes.

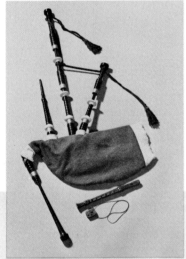

Woodwind instruments

The woodwinds are instruments whose pitch is varied by opening or closing various holes in the side of a vibrating air column. In most band and orchestra woodwinds, such as the *clarinet, saxophone, oboe, English horn, bassoon, flute,* and *piccolo*, flaps controlled by keys cover or uncover the holes. In other woodwinds, such as the *bagpipe,* the *ocarina*, and the *recorder*, the player's fingers open and close the instrument's holes.

The air columns in woodwinds are made to vibrate in several different ways. Clarinets and saxophones use a single vibrating reed to set their air columns in motion. English horns, oboes, and bassoons use double reeds. The Scottish bagpipe produces sound through a combination of three single reeds and one double reed. Flutes and piccolos use no reeds at all. Their air columns vibrate when a player blows across an opening at one end of the column.

Percussion instruments

Percussion instruments generate tone when they are struck. Included in the percussion family are *drums, cymbals, tambourines, triangles, bells, chimes, xylophones, castanets,* and *wood blocks.* The *piano* is classified as a percussion instrument because its strings vibrate and produce sound when they are struck with hammers.

As in other instruments, physical size is important in determining the pitch of percussion instruments. The small snare drum has a much higher pitch than the large bass drum. The bars of a xylophone are longest at the low-pitched end of the scale and shortest at the high-pitched end.

19-19 A variety of percussion instruments are found in the orchestra. A piano, a xylophone, and a kettle drum are pictured here.

19-20 **(below)** Stringed instruments mentioned in the Bible; **(opposite)** a modern organ and a harp.

The harp and organ

By the eighth generation of man, the musical arts had been highly developed. The Bible first refers to musical instruments in Genesis 4:21: "Jubal . . . was the father of all such as handle the *harp* and *organ*." The ancient harp had only a few strings, each tuned to a different fixed pitch. Other early instruments similar to the harp included the lyre, the sackbut, and the psaltery. The modern harp is much larger than any of these ancient instruments. Its forty-six strings are graduated in length from a few centimeters to almost 2 m.

The organ mentioned in Scripture was a graduated series of pipes played by blowing over the tops of the air columns. Modern organs are, of course, far more complex. Two or more keyboards and a row of foot pedals activate many separate sets of graduated pipes in most modern pipe organs. Pressing one of these keys or pedals completes an electrical circuit, thereby admitting air to the base of a pipe. As air enters the pipe, the air column vibrates and gives off sound. Any number of pipes can be activated simultaneously by pressing any number of pedals or keys at the same time. Different sets of pipes with different tonal qualities may be selected by the player through switches called *stops*. In recent years, technological advances have made it possible to generate the sounds of a pipe organ electronically.

Scientifically Speaking

sonar	fundamental
sound	overtones
compressions	acoustics
rarefactions	reverberations
pitch	resonance
loudness	white sound
decibels (db)	beats
threshold of hearing	Doppler effect
quality	

Questions to Talk Over

1. Icebergs make crackling noises as they melt. These noises are often picked up by sonar on ships and submarines. Sonar operators refer to this sound as "bergy-seltzer." Why does melting ice produce this sound?
2. We identify sounds on the basis of pitch, loudness, and quality. How do these three characteristics differ, and which is most important in determining the difference between noise and music?
3. Plays are presented at an outdoor amphitheater in a state park on summer afternoons. No sound-amplification system is available because of the remote location of the rustic amphitheater. How can the state park department improve the acoustics of this amphitheater?
4. What would happen if an entire class on a field trip walked across a rope bridge in perfect step?
5. Why does the pitch of any given note on a wind instrument become higher as an orchestra warms up while the pitch of any given note on a string instrument becomes lower?

LIGHT

CHAPTER
20

Blackout—July 13, 1977

On a midsummer evening in the city of New York, the light from brightly illuminated skyscrapers, dazzling streetlights, and multicolored advertising signs blended to a dull glow in the haze above the giant metropolis. Tourists jammed restaurants, theaters, and concert halls in Manhattan. Crowds at Coney Island sought relief from the heat on the fast-moving rides of the amusement park. Baseball fans at Shea Stadium cheered the Mets as they battled a 2-to-1 Chicago Cubs lead. People in their homes fanned themselves listlessly and watched reruns on television. Suddenly and without warning, at 9:34 P.M., the lights flickered and went out. In a single moment, as if someone had thrown a gigantic switch, nine million people were plunged into darkness.

At first most New Yorkers carried on, assuming that power would soon be restored. After all, the great blackout of 1965 had taught the power companies how to deal with such emergencies. The mayor of the city, who had been addressing a political gathering, quipped, "See, this is what you get for not paying your bills." Neither he nor anyone else realized then that the lights would be out for the rest of the night! Flashlights were pressed into service wherever they could be found. Diners in restaurants finished their meals by candlelight. Sightseers stranded on the observation deck of the Empire State Building chose to stay overnight rather than to walk down the eighty-six flights of unlighted stairs and out into the darkened streets.

The worst part of the disaster was the looting and vandalism that took place as soon as people realized that the lights were out to stay. Thousands of looters in roving bands broke into stores and removed everything they could carry—jewelry, clothing, food, liquor, drugs, TV sets, and furniture. Fifty new cars were stolen from a Pontiac dealer in the Bronx. Arsonists started over 1000 fires. Some of the firemen battling the blazes were attacked and injured by jeering rioters.

Power was finally restored on the evening of the fourteenth, twenty-five hours after the outage began. By the morning of the fifteenth, over 3500 people had been arrested. Property loss totaled more than a billion dollars. The loss in human endeavor was equally staggering. Many merchants, too discouraged to continue, gave up businesses that had taken a lifetime to build. Their employees lost their jobs. Some of those injured in accidents or violence would carry with them marks of the blackout for the rest of their lives.

The entire tragedy would have been averted if the lights had stayed on!

Identifying Light

Both light and sound travel in the form of waves. Both have characteristic ranges of frequencies and wavelengths. Yet, despite their many similarities, the two are different in several important ways. For instance, light can travel through a vacuum; sound cannot.

All you need to do to confirm this difference is to look at the sky on a clear day. The fiercely glowing plasma of the sun dominates your view. It is clearly visible even though over 150 million km of space separate it from the earth. If you have ever heard a *roaring* fire, you can imagine the tremendous sound that the astronomical furnace we call the sun must produce. But who has ever heard the sun?

The sun is the primary source of radiant energy in our solar system. Other sources include flames, heater coils, and incandescent lamps. Each of these sources releases radiant energy that stimulates the retina of our eyes. We call the portion of radiant energy that we can see **visible light.** The rest of the radiant energy—in fact, the majority of the radiant energy—emitted by these sources cannot be sensed by our eyes. Together, both visible and invisible radiant energy make up the broad range of frequencies and wavelengths known as the electromagnetic spectrum.

20-1 The colors of the visible spectrum, in order, are red, orange, yellow, green, blue, indigo, and violet. They are easy to remember if you use this simple device: the first letters of the names sound like a man's name—Roy G. Biv.

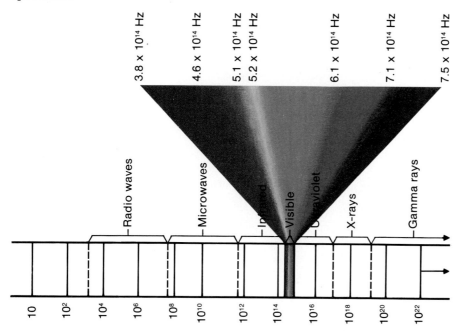

FACETS
OF BASIC SCIENCE

Solar Sails

Yacht races in space? No, but solar sailing may soon become an important scientific tool. Huge solar sails, pushed along by sunlight and perhaps as large as a kilometer across, may move between planets or space stations. They may transport equipment, supplies, and even the products of space industry. Billions of tons of rich ores mined from asteroids, delicate electronic parts manufactured in the weightless environment of space—all could be towed to earth without using a gram of earth's fuel!

Solar sailing is not a new idea. Fridrikh Tsander, a Russian scientist, was probably the first to propose it. In 1924 he suggested using large mirrors in a propulsion system powered by the pressure of sunlight. Tsander based his work on a long history of theory and experiment. James Clerk Maxwell had laid the foundations for this research when he theorized that light, if it were indeed electromagnetic energy, must exert pressure. Johannes Kepler had expressed a similar idea when he suggested that the tails of comets streamed out because they were pushed by sunlight. It was not until about 1900 that scientists found experimental evidence that light could actually exert force.

For decades Tsander's ideas were largely ignored by everyone but writers of science fiction, who made very good use of "light sails" in their stories. In 1950, the scientific community started to take a serious look at solar sails. Finally, in 1976, NASA's Jet Propulsion Laboratory (JPL) began a solar sail research project.

Scientists at JPL were trying to design a spacecraft that could track Halley's comet on its 1985 pass through our solar system. They needed a method of propulsion that could keep going for long periods of time. The solar sail seemed to be the answer. Chemical propulsion systems, such as conventional rockets, use up their heavy loads of fuel quickly in short blasts of power. Solar sails, on the other hand, would steadily build up speed from the constant push of sunlight. And because they require no fuel, solar sails could theoretically "sail" through space indefinitely.

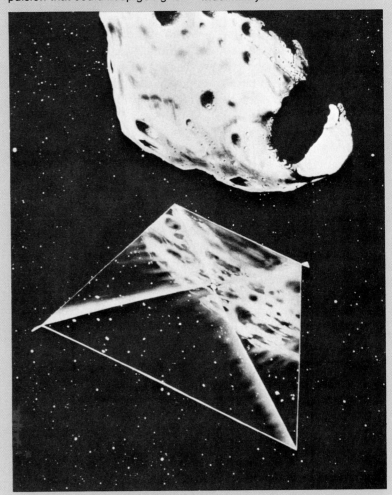

When JPL was forced to abandon the Halley's Comet project because of government budget cuts, a group of JPL scientists who believed in the potential of the solar sail decided to continue the work on their own. They gathered private support and founded the World Space Foundation, a private, nonprofit organization for space research. If all goes according to plan, the Foundation will soon send an experimental solar sail into orbit around the earth.

How could sunlight push a spacecraft? Actually, sunlight pushes everything it touches. Tiny photons (energy packets) of sunlight impart a small amount of momentum to everything they strike. You cannot feel photons striking you because you are surrounded by air. The effect of photons is very tiny compared to the pressure of the air molecules that bombard your body. Scientists believe that in the near-vacuum of space, the force of these photons could propel a solar sail and payload through space. (*Payload* is space talk for men, materials, and instruments that are moved by a spacecraft.)

What would a solar sail be like? It must have two primary features: a large surface area (to catch as many photons as possible), and a very small mass (so that the momentum of the photons can overcome the inertia of the sail itself). The designs for solar sails vary widely. Some look like a number of helicopter blades projecting from a central pod. Most, however, consist of a single sheet of special metallized plastic film just a few molecules thick. This delicate sail would be unfurled in space to its full size— a kilometer or more across. Attached to the sail like a sky-diver to his parachute, the payload would move steadily on, traveling hundreds of thousands of miles under the force of light.

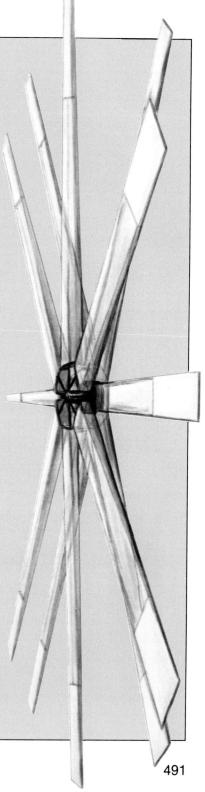

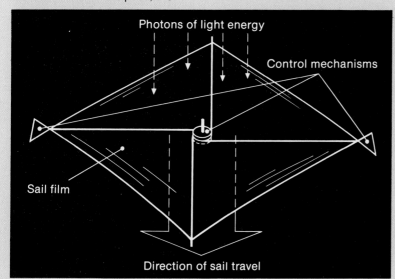

Photons of light energy

Control mechanisms

Sail film

Direction of sail travel

The visible spectrum

Visible light consists of waves of electromagnetic radiation of various wavelengths. These wavelengths make up only a narrow slice of the complete spectrum of *electromagnetic radiation*. We call this slice the visible spectrum.

We see light as **colors**. Even sunlight, which appears to have no color, is really the sum of light of all colors. Sunlight reveals its secret in the majesty of a rainbow. We see individual colors when specific wavelengths of light stimulate certain responses in our eyes. Our minds convert these responses into our perception of specific colors. Because color is the mind's interpretation of a stimulus, different people sense colors in different ways. What seems to you to be a definite bluish green may appear to another person to be what you call pure green.

Scientists define colors by a less subjective method. They define each color by a specific frequency and wavelength.

20-2 The colors that we see are caused by different wavelengths of light.

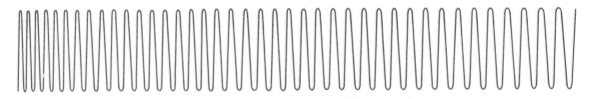

Frequency in hertz

7.5×10^{14} 4.3×10^{14}

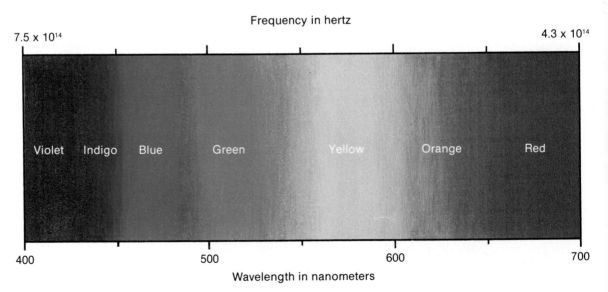

| Violet | Indigo | Blue | Green | Yellow | Orange | Red |

400   500   600   700

Wavelength in nanometers

A *luminous* (LOO muh nuss) object *emits* light waves. Some luminous objects produce white light. White light contains almost all the colors of the spectrum. Our sun produces white light.

Some luminous objects, such as a laser, produce a single color of light. These luminous objects are *monochromatic* (MAHN uh kro MAT ik) (from the Greek *monos*, meaning "single"; and *chroma*, meaning "color"). All the waves emitted by a monochromatic source have the same frequency and the same wavelength. A fluorescent light contains many monochromatic sources, giving what is called a **line spectrum**. The many lines of this spectrum represent the different colors produced by the different glowing gases in a fluorescent tube. The individual colors from a fluorescent tube combine to give the overall effect of white light.

20-3 A line spectrum shows the various monochromatic waves that combine to form the light emitted from a particular source.

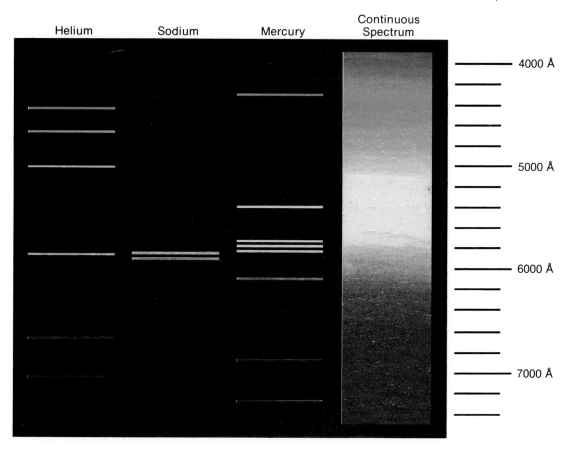

An *illuminated* object *reflects* light waves. While the sun is a luminous object, the moon is an illuminated object. It reflects the light of the sun. Many illuminated objects appear to have different colors. For example, three cars in the same sunlight may appear three different colors. Why is this true? Why, for instance, does a red car look red? The paint on a red car absorbs all light except light with the wavelength which we see as red. Red light waves are reflected from the paint and then sensed by your eyes. What colors would blue paint absorb? What color would it reflect?

The colors of illuminated objects help to shape our moods and alter our tastes. Could you eat a sandwich made with green ham on blue rye with bright orange cheese? Psychologists who study our responses to color have uncovered information that helps us design not only soothingly colored work places, but also better warning systems. One recent color study has proposed that fire trucks be painted a bright orange-yellow. The study found that orange-yellow trucks are far more noticeable than the traditional red fire engines.

The speed of light

The first accurate measurement of the **speed of light** was made in the 1920s by an American scientist named Albert Michelson (MY kul sun). Michelson measured the time it took for a beam of light to pass between Mount Wilson and Mount San Antonio in California. He obtained a value of approximately 300,000,000 m/s (3×10^8 m/s). Scientists code this value with a small letter c.

The speed of light depends on what it is traveling through. Light travels fastest in a vacuum. The chart below reveals that light moves more slowly in denser mediums. Can you think of a reason for this decrease in the speed of light?

Table 20-4

The Speed of Light in Various Mediums	
Medium	**Approximate speed**
air	300,000,000 m/s
water	223,000,000 m/s
glass	200,000,000 m/s

At 3×10^8 m/s, light should travel about 18 million km per minute. Since the sun is 150 million km away, its light takes approximately 8.3 minutes to get to the earth. We could say that the sun is about 8.3 *light-minutes* away, defining the light-minute as the distance light travels in a minute. Sunlight takes over five hours to reach the planet Pluto. We could, therefore, say that Pluto is more than five *light-hours* from the sun.

In discussing distances to stars, astronomers use a larger unit, the **light-year (ly)**. The light-year is defined as the distance light travels in a year (approximately 10 trillion km). The nearest stars, Alpha Centauri (sen TOR ee) and its two neighbors, are about 4.3 light-years away.

20-5 The Crab nebula is 615 light-years away.

The intensity of light

Intensity is a measure of how bright the light from a light source is. To tell exactly how bright a light is, we must be able to compare it to a known standard. Years ago, scientists used a specific type of candle as a standard of intensity. Candles, however, could not be made with exact uniformity, and even a single candle does not burn with a perfectly steady light. Therefore, scientists developed a more accurate unit of intensity called the **candela (cd)** (kan DEL uh). This unit is based on the intensity of light from a standard incandescent source operating at a specific temperature. Since the candela is an exact standard, it can be reproduced in laboratories around the world. Interestingly, ordinary incandescent light bulbs produce about one candela of light energy for each watt of electrical power they use. A 25-W bulb produces 21 cd; a 50-W bulb, 55 cd; and a 100-W bulb, 125 cd. (Notice that the higher-wattage incandescent bulbs are more efficient than the smaller-wattage bulbs.) Fluorescent tubes are considerably more efficient than all incandescent bulbs; fluorescent lights produce about 4 cd per watt.

When you read a book indoors, the amount of light, or illumination, you receive on the printed page depends on two factors—the intensity of the light source and the distance of the light source from the page. Common sense indicates that the illumination you receive is directly proportional to the brightness of the light source. In other words, a lamp that produces 100 cd will illuminate the page twice as much as a 50 cd lamp the same distance away; a 200 cd lamp will provide twice as much light as the 100 cd lamp; and so on. However, it comes as a surprise to most students to learn that moving twice as far from a lamp

20-6 High-intensity lighting is used to illuminate a large stage. Altering the color and intensity of the light can create visual moods that influence the way the audience perceives the performance.

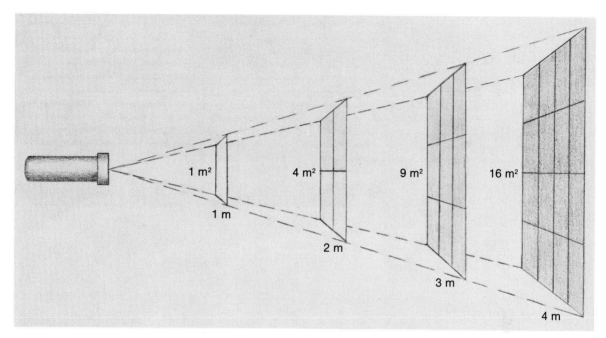

1 m² 4 m² 9 m² 16 m²

1 m

2 m

3 m

4 m

reduces the illumination they receive from the lamp to *one-fourth* the original amount. Moving three times as far from the lamp cuts the illumination to a mere *one-ninth* the original amount. Distance from the light source, therefore, is a far more critical factor in illumination than you might ordinarily think.

Illumination is *inversely* proportional to the *square* of the distance from the light source. (Remember, squaring a number makes its influence much greater.) This type of relationship is called an **inverse square law**, a situation frequently encountered in the world of physics.

Photographers use **light meters** to measure the exact amount of illumination on their subjects. Inside a light meter is a photoelectric cell, which changes light energy into an electric current. The brighter the illumination, the more electric current is put out by the photoelectric cell. This current is used to deflect a needle across a scale that is calibrated in units of illumination. Using the reading from this scale, the photographer adjusts the lens opening and shutter speed of his camera to fit the illumination on his subject.

The human eye can detect an amazing range of intensities. Although it can function in bright sunlight, it can also adjust to operate in nearly total darkness—light only one-billionth the intensity of sunlight!

20-7 The inverse square law states that illumination is inversely proportional to the distance from the light source. This diagram illustrates why. The same cone of light must spread out to illuminate larger and larger areas.

20-8 A photographer's light meter.

FACETS
OF BASIC SCIENCE

L.A.S.E.R.

Laser (LAY zur) stands for *l*ight *a*mplification by the *s*timu-lated *e*mission of *r*adiation. A laser produces a coherent, con-centrated, monochromatic beam of light. An ordinary lamp pro-duces *incoherent* (IN ko HIHR unt), or uncoordinated, light. The waves of this light are of many different lengths, and even those of the same length are not in step with one another. Inco-herent light spreads out as it travels; the light beam becomes wider and less intense with distance.

In a beam of *coherent* (ko HIHR unt) light, every wave is the same length and is synchro-nized in lock-step formation with every other wave. Coherent light does not spread out and become diffuse. This unique behavior of coherent light is the key to the usefulness of lasers.

The straightness of laser beams has made them useful tools for measuring distances. If a scientist knows the time it takes for a laser beam to cover a distance, he can use the speed of light to calculate the distance. For instance, after Apollo 11 astronauts placed a laser reflec-tor on the moon, NASA scien-tists directed a laser beam toward it. By timing the trans-mission of the laser, NASA scientists were able to measure very accurately the distance between the earth and the moon. Surveyors use lasers to measure distances on the earth, and geologists use lasers to measure the movement of the earth's crust along fault lines.

Pulsing laser beams are used to carry large amounts of infor-mation, such as audio (sound), video (television images), and computer data, across long dis-tances. Certain types of laser beams generate a tremendous amount of heat at whatever point they strike. These lasers are used in industry to weld sheet metal and to fuse sections of glass or plastic. The medical applications of lasers include reattaching detached or torn ret-inas, and other forms of micro-surgery. Laser beams can also be used to transmit power from one place to another. In the future, laser beams may transmit power from giant solar-energy-collecting stations in space.

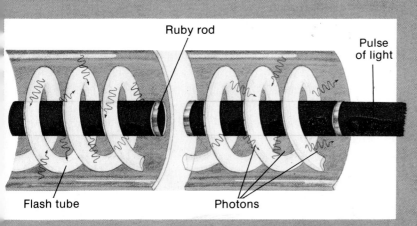

Ruby rod

Pulse of light

Flash tube

Photons

A pulsed laser produces short bursts of coherent light **(left)**. The action starts when a flash tube fires and supplies photons of light energy to the ruby rod. The electrons of the ruby rod absorb this energy and release it in the form of new photons. These photons are produced in a very orderly pattern: pulses of coherent light.

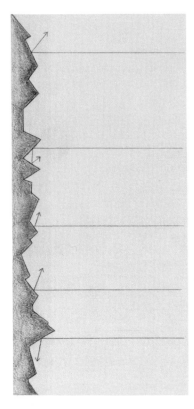

20-9 Light is diffused from a rough surface because the beams of light are reflected in many directions.

Using Light

Have you ever watched dust particles dance through a sunbeam? Have you ever sliced through darkness with a beam of light from a flashlight? Have you ever noticed the beam of light from a slide projector? All these observations tell us that light travels in straight lines.

A **beam** of light consists of a very large number of individual light waves traveling together in a straight line. Scientists use the fact that light waves travel in straight lines to help describe the behavior of light. They represent the directions of light waves by straight lines called **rays**. The study of the movement of light in straight lines is called *ray optics*.

Reflection

Pitch-black darkness surrounds you. The windows of your room have been sealed so that no light can enter. The lights have been turned off. Can you see anything? You are probably thinking that this is a silly question, but it provides us with an observation that will help us answer the question, "How do we see things?" You cannot see in the dark because you see things by sensing the light that is reflected by or emitted from them.

Different objects reflect light differently, depending on the shape of their surface and the angle at which light strikes them. When a beam of light is reflected from a flat surface, a simple relationship holds true: the angle at which incoming rays strike the reflecting surface is equal to the angle at which the reflected rays leave the same surface. Scientists normally measure angles of incoming and reflected rays from a line drawn perpendicular to the reflecting surface at the point where the ray strikes it. This line is called the **normal**. An incoming ray is called an **incident** (IN sih dunt) **ray**. An outgoing ray is called a **reflected ray.** The angle between an incident ray and the normal is called the **angle of incidence**. The angle between a reflected ray and the normal is the **angle of reflection.** The **law of reflection** states that the angle of incidence is equal to the angle of reflection.

The image formed by a **plane mirror** (flat mirror) is the result of many separate light rays, each obeying the law of reflection. This reflected image appears to be exactly the same distance behind the mirror as the actual object is in front of the mirror. Thus, if you stand one meter from a plane mirror, your image

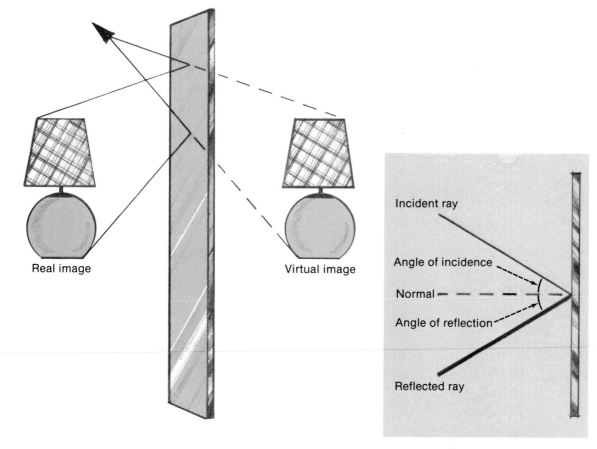

Real image

Virtual image

Incident ray

Angle of incidence

Normal

Angle of reflection

Reflected ray

20-10 Reflection in a plane mirror.

will appear to stand 1 m behind the mirror—2 m away from you. If you stand 5 m from the mirror, your image will appear to stand 10 m from you. The farther you are from your image, the smaller it appears. Plane mirror images are also reversed left to right. When you see yourself in a mirror, you do not see yourself as others see you; instead, you see yourself exactly reversed.

Are there really images behind mirrors? No, rays of light only appear to be originating behind mirrors. Scientists call the images we see in plane mirrors **virtual** (VUR choo ul) **images** (rather than real images), because the rays of light that form the image are not actually behind the mirror where the image appears to be.

Concave mirrors (mirrors that "cave in") also obey the law of reflection. Figure 20-11 shows parallel rays approaching a concave mirror. When a separate normal is drawn at the point where each ray strikes the surface of the mirror, the angle of reflection equals the angle of incidence for each ray. Notice that the incident rays are also parallel to the line which is perpendicular to the center of the mirror. This line is called the *principal axis*. If a concave mirror is well designed, the reflected rays all pass through a definite point on the principal axis called the **principal focus.**

20-11 Reflection in a concave mirror.

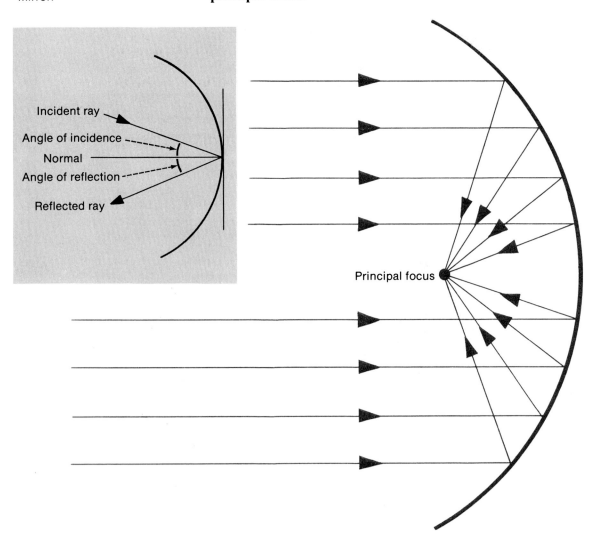

Have you ever looked into a spoon? Your reflection is upside-down. The light that strikes this concave mirror is not all parallel to the principal axis. Figure 20-12 shows a dog and its image reflected from a concave mirror. Light rays from each point on the dog are reflected from the mirror to a single point. Together, all these points make up a complete focused image of the dog. Because the light rays actually pass through this image,

20-12 A concave mirror produces an inverted image smaller than the original.

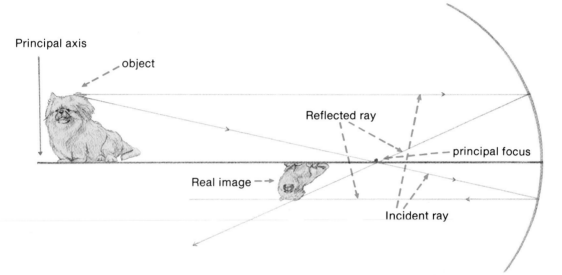

Principal axis

object

Reflected ray

principal focus

Real image

Incident ray

scientists call it a **real image**. A real image could be projected onto a screen. Could a virtual image be projected onto a screen?

Notice that each ray of light reflected from a concave mirror is reflected onto the opposite side of the principal axis from its starting point. Thus, the image formed by a concave mirror is upside-down, or *inverted.* In Figure 20-12 the image of the dog is smaller than the actual dog. Concave mirrors can also be made to produce larger-than-actual images.

Concave mirrors are used in *reflecting telescopes* to bring parallel rays of light from a star to a focus at the principal focus of the telescope. From this point the light can be reflected sideways to an eyepiece lens by means of a small plane mirror. Concave mirrors may also be used in the reverse direction. When a light is placed at the focal point, it sends light rays fanning out in many directions. When these rays reach the concave mirror, they are reflected as parallel rays. This arrangement is used to produce concentrated beams of light in flashlights, spotlights, searchlights, and automobile headlights.

20-13 This reflecting telescope uses a mirror that is over a meter in diameter.

FACETS
OF BASIC SCIENCE

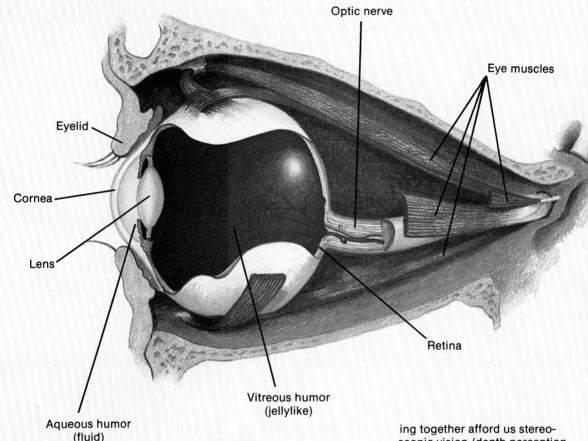

Optic nerve

Eye muscles

Eyelid

Cornea

Lens

Retina

Vitreous humor
(jellylike)

Aqueous humor
(fluid)

The Eye

We have all seen advertisements for cameras that focus an image, expose the film, and develop a picture in seconds. These cameras are the products of impressive technology. Yet we are blessed with eyes that have automatic aiming, automatic focusing, and automatic aperture adjustment. The "film" on which they record is instantly developing and self-renewing. The focusing ability in the normal eye is so good that it can clearly distinguish an object only 0.05 mm across—the diameter of a fine human hair. Our two eyes work-ing together afford us stereo-scopic vision (depth perception by the use of two different vantage points). On a typical day our eyes make some 100,000 separate motions. Functioning up to sixteen or more hours with seldom a complaint, our eyes carry on their own maintenance work during the few hours we are asleep.

At the front of the eye is a lens whose magnifying power can be varied by a change in its thickness. No one has yet been able to build such a lens. The lens of the human eye, working in conjunction with the rest of the optical system, accounts for the eye's remarkable miniaturization. The eyeball is only about 2½ cm in diameter—smaller than a ping-pong ball! Compare this with the dimensions of a high-quality camera, which in spite of its much greater size is capable of far less performance. A photographer focuses a camera by moving its lens forward and backward, varying the distance from the lens to the film. Think how inconvenient it would be if our eyes focused in this way. How strange we would look when we focused on a close object with our lenses all the way out! Yet this type of focusing is the closest modern science has come to a working imitation of the focusing mechanism of the lens in an eye!

Light entering the eye passes in order through the cornea, the aqueous humor, the lens, and the vitreous humor before striking the retina. All these parts of the eye are optically transparent and help to form a sharp image on the retina by refracting each ray the proper amount. The retina corresponds to the film of a camera. It is here that the little-understood photoelectric conversion takes place: light energy is changed to electrical impulses, which are carried by means of the optic nerve to the brain. How the brain interprets these impulses is even less understood than the photoelectric action of the retina.

Each eye is equipped with six powerful muscles, which serve to aim it at the objects being viewed. These muscles are synchronized with the six muscles of the other eye by nerve impulses from the brain. Another pair of muscles controls the opening and closing of each eyelid. Tiny muscles inside each eyeball adjust the focusing of the lens and the size of the pupil. The outside of the eye is provided with an eyelid, a "windshield-wiper" mechanism that keeps the exposed surface moist and dust free.

In view of the phenomenal way these amazing mechanisms work together to produce human vision, it is difficult to understand how some people can believe that the human eye came about through a trial-and-error process. The eye is a wonderful testimony to the omnipotent hand of our Creator. Yet some scientists believe that the eye evolved as an adaptation to our environment. Let us take the time to think this idea through.

At one time, these scientists tell us, none of the organisms on earth possessed eyes. Sunlight flooded the earth, but the eyeless creatures swimming about in the "primitive oceans" were insensitive to this portion of the electromagnetic spectrum. (Note carefully that no person was there to *observe* this imaginative picture.) How did this blind world develop vision? Most of the evolutionary theorizers are strangely silent on this point. Light rays striking the skin of the primitive marine organisms would in some way have had to stimulate the formation of primitive eyes, if indeed the eye is an adaptation to the environment. But how could light stimulate the formation of an eye? Light rays striking skin never stimulate the formation of eyes in any creature today.

Even if such an event *could* and *did* happen, the newly formed eyes could not be passed on to the next generation. It is a well-established fact of biology that acquired characteristics, such as these eyes would be, cannot be inherited. In order for a new trait to be passed on to an organism's offspring, there must be a change *in the reproductive genes* of the organism. Yet these genes are *inside* the organism, totally unaffected by the light on the outside. Light has no way of stimulating an organism's reproductive genes to direct the building of an eye.

Suppose, just for the sake of argument, that an imperfectly formed eye did appear in some creature. According to evolutionists, such an eye would be a very crude organ, capable only of distinguishing between light and darkness. We are now asked to believe that this eye will better itself over the course of many generations. Will it? Again, the genes receive no stimuli to improve the eye. Some evolutionists place their faith in random mutations as the source of these supposed improvements. But mutations have never been observed to carry out even one minor step toward improving a structure such as an eye. Evolution fails completely as a scientific explanation for the eye. Creation is the only alternative. We can say with the psalmist, "I will praise thee; for I am fearfully and wonderfully made" (Ps. 139:14).

Refraction

When a ray of light passes from one medium to another, its speed changes as the going gets easier or harder. As a result of this speed change, light that enters a new medium at an angle is bent. To see why this is true, look at the diagram of soldiers marching in formation (Figure 20-14). The soldiers are marching at an angle from land into a swamp containing waist-deep water. The entire formation is bent because the men who arrive at the water earlier are slowed down for a longer period of time than the men who arrive later. Light waves can be thought of as behaving in the same way. The bending of light as it enters a new medium is called **refraction**.

In Figure 20-16, a beam of light passing through the air strikes a block of glass at an angle. The normal is perpendicular to the surface of the block. Notice that the beam of light bends *toward* the normal as it enters the glass, a *denser* medium. Inside the new medium, the ray again follows a straight line. Examine

20-14 The line of soldiers bends as the men walk into the swamp. How is this effect like refraction?

the beam as it leaves the glass. Since the ray is now entering a *less dense* medium (air), it bends *away from* the normal.

The refraction of light as it enters water causes many illusions. Have you ever tried to net a fish in an aquarium? When you lowered the net into the water, did you find that you had "overshot" the fish? Refraction of light fools you by making the fish seem farther away than it really is.

Another interesting effect of refraction is the bending of the sun's rays that is evident when the sun is just below the horizon. The refraction that takes place as the sunlight enters the atmosphere from space causes us to see sunrises a little earlier than we otherwise would, and sunsets a little later than we otherwise would. Thus refraction slightly lengthens the period of daylight each day. On the equinoxes (approximately March 21 and September 21), when you would expect days and nights of exactly equal length, refraction actually causes the days to be a bit longer than the nights.

20-15 Is the meter stick really bent? No, the bend is an optical illusion caused by the refraction of light in water.

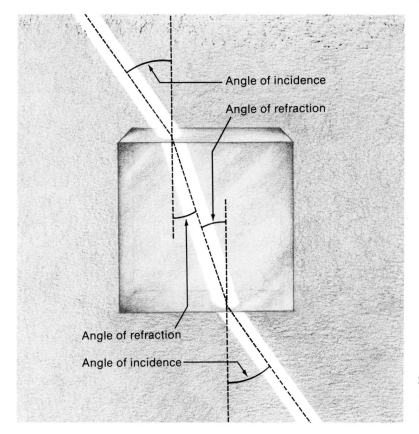

Angle of incidence

Angle of refraction

Angle of refraction

Angle of incidence

20-16 Follow the path of the light as it enters and leaves the block of glass. Why does it bend?

FACETS
OF BASIC SCIENCE

Bending Light

Lenses are specially formed pieces of glass that bend light to form enlarged or miniaturized images. Lenses refract light in two different ways: converging lenses direct light rays toward one another; diverging lenses spread light rays apart.

Convex (KAHN veks) lenses are converging lenses. They are thick in the center and thin at the edges. When light rays traveling parallel to the principal axis of a convex lens pass through the lens, they are bent so that they all pass through a single point, the principal focus. The distance from the lens to the principal focus is called the focal length of the lens.

If an object is *farther* from a convex lens than twice the focal length, the light rays from the image are bent by the lens to form an upside-down and smaller-than-life-size image.

In Figure A, representative light rays from two different points on a candle are shown passing through a convex lens. Notice that as the light rays leave the points they are moving apart. The lens refracts the light rays, bending them back toward each other. Where the light rays from each point meet, they form an image of that point. Since light passes through the lens from every point on the candle, a complete image of the candle is formed where the light is focused by the lens. This image is inverted because the light from each point on the candle is focused on the opposite side of the principal axis from the actual point.

If an object is *closer* to a convex lens than the lens's focal length, a viewer on the opposite side of the lens sees a magnified image.

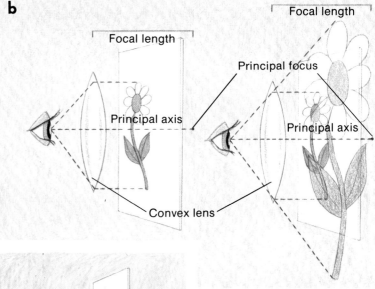

b

Focal length

Focal length

Principal focus

Principal axis

Principal axis

Convex lens

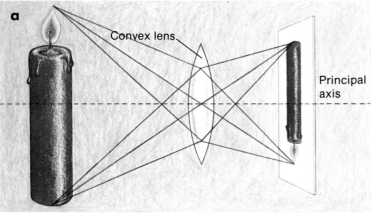

a

Convex lens

Principal axis

As light rays from each point on the flower travel through the convex lens, they are bent toward each other. When these converging light rays reach our eye, our eye "assumes" that the rays have been traveling at the same angle since they left the flower. If this were actually the case, the flower would have to be the size of the larger flower in Figure B. Because our eyes see the flower as though the light rays had always been converging, the flower appears larger. Is this magnified image a real image? No. The large flower that you think you see does not have light rays passing through it or coming from it. Therefore, this magnified image is a virtual image.

Concave lenses are diverging lenses. Thin in the middle and thick on the edges, concave lenses spread light apart. Figure C shows light from two representative points on a candle passing through a concave lens. Notice that the light rays from any one point on the candle never meet at a focused point on the opposite side of the lens. Thus a concave lens cannot form a real, focused image. However, when you view the candle through the concave lens (as shown in Figure C), at least one of the light rays from each point still reaches your eye. To your eye, it appears that the rays have been traveling in the same direction ever since they left the candle. Therefore the candle appears to your eye to be the size of the smaller candle shown in the figure. The image you see as you view an object through a concave lens is always right-side up and smaller than the actual object.

The lenses our eyes use to focus are convex lenses. They produce an inverted and reduced image on the retina. In some people's eyes, the distance from the lens to the retina is too short; the person is then far-sighted. In others it is too long; the person is then nearsighted.

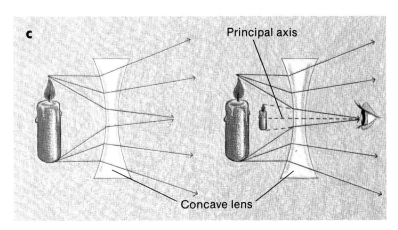

c Principal axis

Concave lens

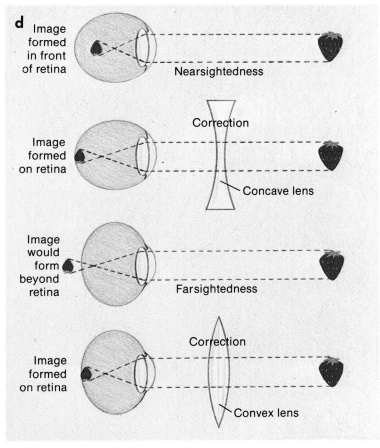

d Image formed in front of retina

Nearsightedness

Correction

Image formed on retina

Concave lens

Image would form beyond retina

Farsightedness

Correction

Image formed on retina

Convex lens

On hot days, the refraction of light causes illusions called *mirages* (mih RAHZH ez). If a layer of hot, less dense air is located next to the ground beneath a layer of cooler, denser air, the density difference between the two layers will cause light rays to bend gradually upward. This refraction of light often fools people in the scorching heat of a desert into thinking that they see pools of water ahead. Similarly, as you drive along in a car on a hot day, the highway may appear wet in the distance. These mirages are due to refraction.

" NICE DIVE . . . "

Lenses use the properties of refracted light to magnify or reduce images. When parallel rays enter a lens, each ray is bent the right amount so that all the rays meet at a single point. This point, like the focused point produced by a concave mirror, is called the principal focus. The distance from a lens to its principal focus is called the **focal length** of the lens.

Some of the most useful applications of refraction are made possible by putting two or more lenses together. In a *refractor telescope*, a large lens, called an *objective*, focuses light from distant objects, while a smaller lens, called the *eyepiece,* magnifies the focused image. In a compound microscope, multiple lenses make magnifications of more than 1000 times possible. For example, if the lower lens (objective) has a magnification of 100X, and the upper lens (eyepiece) has a magnification of 15X, the overall magnification of the microscope will be the product of the two, or 1500X.

20-17 The arrangement of lenses in **(a)** a microscope, **(b)** a camera, and **(c)** a telescope.

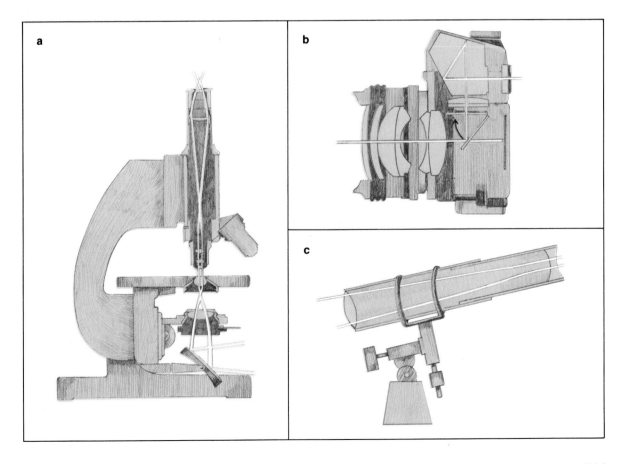

Dispersion

The electromagnetic waves that make up the various colors contained in sunlight all travel at the same speed in empty space. Entering a medium such as glass or water reduces the speed of the waves. The amount each wave is slowed depends upon its wavelength. In a medium like glass or water, red light travels fastest and violet light travels slowest. Waves of other colors assume speeds ranging between these extremes. If white light passes through a prism (a block of glass, usually triangular in shape), the unequal speeds of the various light waves inside the glass cause each color to bend at a different angle and separate from the other colors. The separation of white light into its differently colored light waves is called **dispersion** (dih SPUR zhun).

A *rainbow* is the result of dispersion. As sunlight shines through rain, each raindrop acts both as a prism and as a concave mirror. Therefore, the sunlight is both divided into its colors and reflected to observers on the ground. What you see reflected from the raindrops depends on where you are standing. No two people see the same rainbow because the dispersed rays come to each person from different raindrops.

20-18 A rainbow is caused by the dispersion of light through water droplets in the atmosphere. Could you ever find the end of a rainbow?

Scientifically Speaking

visible light
colors
line spectrum
speed of light
light-year (ly)
intensity
candela (cd)
inverse square law
light meters
laser
beam
rays
normal
incident ray

reflected ray
angle of incidence
angle of reflection
law of reflection
plane mirror
virtual images
concave mirrors
principal focus
real image
refraction
lenses
focal length
dispersion

Questions to Talk Over

1. Galileo is said to have tried to measure the speed of light by quickly uncovering a lantern and measuring how long it took for the light to reflect back to him from a mirror 1.5 km away. How long would light take to travel from Galileo to the mirror and back? Why did Galileo's experiment fail?

2. The curved mirrors at amusement parks can make you appear fat, or skinny, or wavy. How do these mirrors create these images?

3. If you place a ruler in a glass of water and observe it from above the glass, the ruler appears to be normal. But if you observe the ruler from the side, it appears to be bent. Why is this true?

4. A meteorologist was trying to determine the exact location of a weather balloon that had floated into the upper atmosphere. Would the fact that the upper atmosphere is less dense than the lower atmosphere affect where the meteorologist will see the balloon through a telescope?

5. God placed the rainbow in the clouds as a symbol of His promise that He would never again destroy the entire earth by a flood. If the rainbow is caused by the refraction of light by water droplets in the air, why was there no rainbow before the Flood?

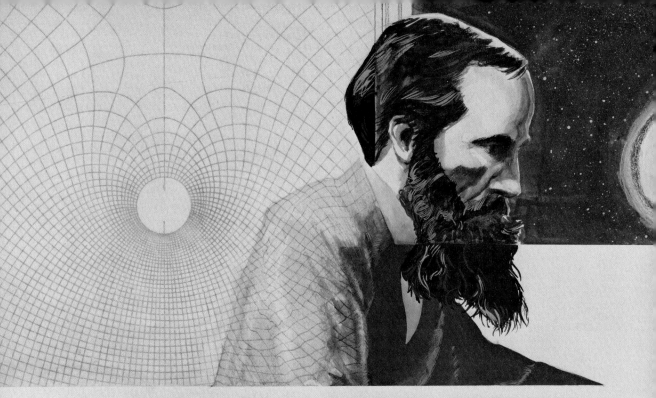

JAMES CLERK MAXWELL
SCOTTISH PHYSICIST (1831-1879)

James Clerk (KLARK) Maxwell was undoubtedly one of the greatest geniuses in the history of science. His mathematical equations predicted the existence of radio waves many years before their discovery and served to unite the separate sciences of optics, electricity, and magnetism in a single comprehensive framework. Albert Einstein called this achievement "the most profound and fruitful that physics has experienced since the time of Newton." At the same time, Maxwell was a humble and devout man of God.

Maxwell was born in Edinburgh, Scotland, in 1831. His mother, a dedicated Christian, took charge of his education

until her death in 1839. She continually urged him to "look up through nature to nature's God." By the time he was eight years old, he had memorized Psalm 119 completely. Maxwell received his formal education at Edinburgh Academy, the University of Edinburgh, and Trinity College, Cambridge. At first he did not do outstanding work in his studies. Poor health often prevented him from attending classes. But by the time he graduated from the academy (high school), he ranked first in his class in mathematics and English. From this time on his instructors expected something unusual of him.

His brilliant career included teaching at three different institutions of higher learning. Two years after he had accepted his

first teaching position at Marischal College in Aberdeen, Scotland, he married Katherine Mary Dewar (DOO ur), who proved to be a lifelong source of strength and encouragement. In 1860 he became professor of physics and astronomy at King's College in London, and in 1871 he took over the newly formed chair of experimental physics at Cambridge University. In connection with this position he was selected to supervise the planning and construction of the famous Cavendish Laboratory.

Maxwell's spiritual life set an example for all around him. Those who knew him best described him as humble, sincere, tenderhearted, devoted, and fearless in promoting the truth. His beliefs were biblical, and his

scientific research consistently strengthened his conservative stand. He strongly disliked the preaching of morality without the gospel remedy. Through constant study he developed a thorough knowledge of the Scriptures, and regularly shared that knowledge with the sick and shut-in persons in the community. He also served as an elder in the Corsock Church at Glenaire, Scotland, a church that had been founded and built through his spiritual leadership and financial assistance.

Maxwell viewed science as a God-ordained means of subduing the earth. He wrote in his notes: "Almighty God, Who hast created man in Thine own image, and made him a living soul that he might seek after Thee, and have dominion over Thy creatures, teach us to study the works of Thy hands, that we may subdue the earth to our use, and strengthen the reason for Thy service; so to receive Thy blessed Word, that we may believe on Him Whom Thou hast sent, to give us the knowledge of salvation and the remission of our sins. All of which we ask in the name of the same Jesus Christ, our Lord."

One of Maxwell's most important works was disproving Laplace's nebular hypothesis. In 1796, the French atheist Laplace (luh PLAHSS) proposed a theory that the solar system had "evolved" from a large cloud. The cloud, Laplace claimed, contracted over a period of millions of years and gradually produced the solar system as we know it today. Many who had an anti-religious turn of mind accepted this idea without question. Maxwell, however, analyzed it mathematically and found two major flaws in the theory: (1) The material would never condense into planets; (2) There would be no way to slow the rapidly spinning mass in the center to form our present slowly rotating sun. The theory was discarded, and to this day it has never been replaced with one that is truly workable.

Some of Maxwell's other contributions to science include experiments in color vision and optics, original extensions of pure geometry, a mathematical analysis of Saturn's rings, and investigations of elastic solids, mechanics, and molecular physics. He extended Faraday's work, particularly by giving a solid mathematical basis for the concept of "lines of force." He invented both the optic bench and the opthalmoscope, the instrument doctors use to see inside the eye. The bell-shaped curve used in statistics is called a *Maxwellian distribution* in his honor. He was also memorialized in the name of the physical unit of magnetic flux, the maxwell.

Maxwell died of cancer at the age of forty-eight. During the following three years, two of his friends, Lewis Campbell and William Garnett, collected his letters and papers and penned his biography, entitled *The Life of James Clerk Maxwell.* Included in the book is a statement by one of his intimate colleagues, G.W.H. Tayler, Vicar of Trinity Church, Carlisle: "Maxwell has indeed left us a very bright memory and example. We, his contemporaries at college, have seen in him high powers of mind and great capacity and original views, conjoined with deep humility before his God, reverent submission to His Will, and hearty belief in the love and atonement of that Divine Saviour Who was his portion and comforter in trouble and sickness, and his exceeding great reward" (London: Macmillan, 1882, p. 174).

EIGHT

SOME MATTERS OF TECHNOLOGY

ENGINEERING

CHAPTER
21

The sun shone brightly as students gathered around the edge of the school's baseball field. Their eyes followed a helicopter moving slowly into position. As they watched, the pilot dropped several dozen specially designed boxes, each containing a single uncooked egg. Was this a new version of Humpty Dumpty for modern times?

No, the students in the school's ninth-grade science classes had been given the following assignment: Design a protective package that will allow a raw egg to survive a 250-m fall. The package may not exceed 20 cm in any dimension. No wings or flaps are permitted; however, small vanes that come within the 20-cm limitation are permissible. After the package has been dropped from a height of 250 m, your teacher will examine your egg to see whether it is intact. If so, he will break the egg to verify that it is uncooked.

The students combined their knowledge of physics with plenty of imagination. For packing materials they tried plastic foam, popped corn, rubber bands, shredded paper, and even liquids. One student encased his egg in a small package that was suspended by elastic bands within a larger package. Some students made their packages very heavy, thinking that the egg should be only a small fraction of the total weight. Others used loosely packed plastic foam pellets to keep their packages as light as possible.

In the test the lighter packages, which hit the ground with less force, survived the fall much better than the heavier ones. The most successful were very lightweight, rounded packages equipped with small vanes that caused them to rotate. These spinning packages struck the ground with a glancing impact rather than a dead thud, then continued to roll along the ground.

The students in this egg-dropping competition faced an **engineering** (EN juh NIHR ing) problem. Engineering is the process of using scientific knowledge in practical ways. These students tried to apply their knowledge of gravity, momentum, and impact to protect an egg.

Engineers are problem solvers. They apply the theories and principles of science and mathematics to technical problems. They develop new products and processes. They may be involved in producing, testing, selling, installing, operating, and maintaining their inventions. Engineers develop space shuttles and shuttle buses, automobiles and automated robots. They help us to control the amount of waste products we produce and to turn our wastes into useful raw materials.

Most engineers have a specialty. *Mechanical engineers* design new and more efficient machines. *Civil engineers* develop plans for roads, bridges, dams, and canals. *Chemical, electrical, electronic, aeronautical, aerospace, biomedical, metallurgical,* and *environmental engineers* keep other aspects of industry and society running.

An engineer is a planner. His plans begin as a design on a drawing board. Here he figures out how certain materials and combinations of materials will work. As he develops an idea, he may try it out by building a model. Models are often subjected to demanding tests. Aeronautical engineers simulate flight by testing models of their designs in wind tunnels. Biomedical engineers test their models of artificial organs in animals such as calves.

21-1 An aeronautical engineer uses a wind tunnel to test the design of an aircraft.

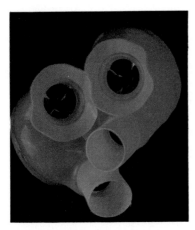

21-2 In designing the first artificial heart to be used successfully, biomedical engineers had to select materials that would stand up to the constantly changing pressure of the circulatory system.

21-3 The architectural engineers who designed the World Trade Center in New York City had to consider the tremendous stress that the wind would place on the 110-story structures, as well as the weight of the structures themselves.

Tests are important because they may point out flaws in the design. The engineer can then adjust his design to correct problems.

The engineer must make sure that his machine, process, or structure works well. Often he must also think about how well it will sell. He must decide how big it will be, how much it will weigh, how much it will cost, what it will look like, and how easy it will be to take care of. If any of these features is not satisfactory, he must go "back to the drawing board" to fix it.

Structural Engineering

In solving any problem, the engineer must first ask, "Will the material be strong enough for what it needs to do?" To answer this question, he must decide how much **stress** the material will receive. Stress is any force that tends to change a material's size or shape. It can be applied in different ways. *Compressive* (kum PRESS iv) *stress,* or *compression* (kum PRESH un), squeezes the material together. *Tensile* (TEN sul) *stress,* or *tension* (TEN shun), tends to stretch the material apart. Almost every material used in any structure is affected by one of these forces.

Stress will change slightly the size or shape of any material. The amount of distortion is called the **strain** on the material. Strain can be a change in length, a change in thickness or width, or a twisting or bending of the material. Stress always produces *some* strain because no object is completely rigid. The chains supporting a swing stretch a little when someone swings on it. The heel of your shoe squeezes down a bit when you step on it. Even the steel and concrete of a skyscraper bend and sway slightly. The twin towers of the World Trade Center in New York City are 110 stories tall; they sway as much as 3½ m in a strong wind.

Materials that *flex* (bend) under pressure are **flexible.** Materials that return to their original shape and size after stresses are removed from them are **elastic** (ih LASS tik). When metals are flexed repeatedly, they show signs of **fatigue** (fuh TEEG), or weakness. If the fatigue continues, the metal will eventually break apart. You have probably broken a wire coat hanger by bending it back and forth until it cracked. What if the metal used in skyscrapers were brittle? Would their swaying in the wind cause a disaster? Part of the engineer's job is to choose materials and designs that will make the structure strong enough to endure the stresses it will meet.

21-4 In the ancient world, rows of columns were used to support heavy stone ceilings. These columns were beautiful as well as functional.

Weight support by columns

Roll a sheet of notebook paper into a cylinder about 4 cm in diameter, and secure the roll with tape. Stand the paper cylinder on end, and set a paperback book on top of the cylinder. It should support the book easily. Now place this textbook on top of the first book. You have now probably exceeded the cylinder's buckling point (the limit of the weight it can support). A *column* must have a certain amount of strength to support a given weight. Engineers either add material or select a better material to increase the strength of a column and to allow it to support a greater weight.

You know, for instance, that the taller and heavier a tree is, the greater the diameter of the trunk is. The more weight the column must support, the greater its cross-sectional area must be. This principle holds true whether the column is a ship's mast, a flagpole, or one of your bones! In your backbone the vertebrae near the base of the column are wide and massive; those near the top of the column are slender and light. Each vertebra provides the exact amount of support needed at its position in the back. God has designed your bones with wonderful efficiency.

A hollow column is much stronger than a solid column with the same cross-sectional area. That is one reason that your bones are hollow. This design feature makes your skeleton strong but not too heavy! Your thigh bones, for instance, would need 22 per cent more material to support your body if they were solid instead of hollow.

The use of hollow columns to conserve material is especially important in the bones of birds. The lighter a bird's skeleton is, the less energy the bird must expend in flight. The wing bones of birds are columnar structures with remarkably thin walls, braced internally by bony struts. This design keeps the total bone material in the wing of a bird at a bare minimum.

Weight support by beams

A log is long compared to its diameter. If it is laid across a stream to serve as a bridge, it may sag noticeably when a person stands at its center.

Compressive stress

Tensile stress

21-5 Most of the stress on a beam affects the top and bottom surfaces.

The sagging caused by placing a weight on a beam produces compression along the top of the beam and tension along the bottom. The center of the beam is neither stretched nor compressed. The unstressed center of the beam does not contribute to its strength.

By locating the stress points in beams, engineers have been able to design a beam that uses as little material as possible to provide as much support as possible. This beam is called an I-beam. Most of the material of an I-beam is located along its top and bottom to counteract the compression and tension produced by a load. Very little material is located in the central, unstressed area. Most steel supports used in construction are I-beams.

Although it makes an excellent support, steel is often expensive to use in construction. Because concrete is much cheaper, engineers have designed beams built of concrete. Concrete can withstand very strong compression, but under tension concrete tends to crack and pull apart. If an I-beam were made solely of concrete, the top would perform well, but the bottom would crack. These cracks would extend upward, and the beam would soon fail. To counteract this effect of tension, concrete beams are reinforced from within by steel rods. If the steel is firmly anchored in the concrete, the excellent tensile strength of the steel keeps the concrete from cracking under tension. Fortunately, since steel and concrete have almost exactly the same rate of thermal expansion, they work well together over a wide range of temperature.

Construction crews make reinforced concrete by pouring wet concrete into a mold containing carefully positioned steel rods. To keep the rods closely bound to the concrete and to prevent them from slipping as the concrete bends under its load, the ends of the steel rods are hooked. The surfaces of the rods are ridged and grooved to increase their friction against the concrete.

Prestressing gives reinforced concrete even more strength. Engineers have found that stretching the steel rods when they are placed in the concrete makes the building material much stronger for the amount of steel used. The stretched steel rods compress the concrete so that it can endure much more tension before cracking. A bridge built with prestressed reinforced concrete requires only one-half as much concrete and one-third as much steel as a bridge built with ordinary reinforced concrete.

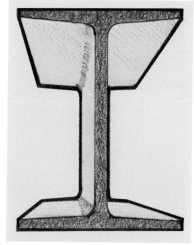

21-6 An I-beam is designed to spread stress over a large area of the beam.

21-7 When concrete has been reinforced and prestressed, it can withstand the stress of supporting a tall building. Many builders now use prestressed concrete as an economical alternative to steel.

21-8 (right) The ruins of Roman aqueducts can still be found in the countryside near Rome. They were used to transport water to the city during the time of Christ. **(left)** The weight of an arch is distributed evenly over the two springers of the arch.

Weight support by arches

An **arch** is a curved structure built to support weight above an open space. Many ancient civilizations used arches. The Romans built great triumphal arches to honor their emperors. They also used a series of rounded arches called **arcades** (ar KAYDZ) to support waterways called *aqueducts* (AK wih DUKTS) and to build the Coliseum in Rome. By the twelfth century A.D., pointed arches began to gain popularity in medieval Europe. These *Gothic* (GAHTH ik) arches are frequently seen today in bridges and ornamental structures.

The simple stone archway shown in the figure above is made up of a semicircle of wedge-shaped stones. Though each of the stones is equally important in supporting the weight of the arch, the stones at the top and bottom of the arch have been given special names. The center stone at the top of the arch is called the **keystone** (KEE stone). The stones at the bases of the arch are called *springers*. The horizontal distance from one springer to the other is called the *span* of the arch. The vertical distance from the springers to the keystone is termed the *rise* of the arch.

Weight placed on an arch tends to push the sides of the arch outward. This outward force, or *thrust,* is greatest about one-third of the way up the sides of the arch.

To keep an arch from crumbling, a **buttress** (BUT riss) must be used to support the sides of the arch. Buttresses often consist of massive amounts of stone or concrete positioned alongside an arch. In Gothic architecture the **flying buttress,** a slanted brace anchored in a large pier, was used to support arches. In an arcade each arch forms a buttress for the arch next to it. Additional buttresses are necessary only at the ends of the arcade. Mountains often formed natural buttresses for at least one end of the arcades that supported the Roman aqueducts.

Arches also support certain parts of the human body. The arched soles of your feet support your body's weight very efficiently. The bones that form the arches of your feet actually consist of a series of smaller arches. Because of their arches, your feet can support your weight without being extremely large. The arch formed by your hip bones and thigh bones distributes the weight of your upper body equally on your two legs.

The basic arch structure can be expanded to form a **vault** (VAWLT), a curved ceiling that can enclose a large area. A barrel vault and an intersecting vault are shown below.

21-9 (above) The builders of the cathedral in Bourges, France used flying buttresses to support the center spans of the cathedral's arches. **(below left)** The Arch of Triumph in Paris is a large barrel vault. **(below right)** These arches intersect at a single column to support the roof of a medieval sanctuary.

21-10 Domed structures.

The Taj Mahal in Agra, India—
one of the most beautiful domed
buildings in the world.

The Silverdome, an inflated
dome in Pontiac, Michigan.

The Dome of the Rock, a
mosque in Jerusalem.

The United States Capitol in
Washington, D.C.

Weight support by domes

The three-dimensional version of the arch is the **dome.** A dome is shaped like an upside-down bowl. Domes can support much larger loads than arches because they distribute weight in many different directions. You can test the strength of the dome structure by pushing in on the two ends of an egg. You probably cannot break it because an eggshell is two domes placed base to base. Another dome makes you "hardheaded." Your dome-shaped skull is ideally suited to protecting your brain.

Domes are used for support in all types of architecture. Igloos and mud huts are simple dome structures. The Capitol Building in Washington, D.C.; the Pantheon in Rome; the Taj Mahal in India; and the Dome of the Rock in Jerusalem are more elaborate domes. Architects now enclose even huge stadiums with domed roofs. The Astrodome in Houston, Texas, towers 63 m above the playing field and spans a distance of 196 m between supports. The Astrodome is called a *geodesic* (GEE uh DES ik) *dome* because it is strengthened by a network of steel triangles.

Inflated domes are supported merely by air, which is forced into the dome by powerful fans. One of the largest encloses the Silverdome in Pontiac, Michigan. Inflated domes also make ideal shelters for satellite-tracking stations. The synthetic fabric of the dome protects the station's equipment and workers from rain, snow, wind, and subfreezing temperatures. Yet it allows the station to transmit and receive radio waves, which a reinforced-concrete dome would block.

The house of the future may be a dome. Engineers can now produce a very inexpensive permanent dome by spraying a polymer foam over an inflated dome. When the polymer hardens, the inner dome is deflated, and a free-standing structure of polymer foam remains. This rapid and inexpensive construction method may one day replace traditional wood-frame methods of construction.

Weight support by trusses

Arches are closely related to *triangles*. If you were to straighten the two sides of an arch, you would produce a triangular structure. Triangular supports are often more practical than arched supports because building materials (such as wooden timbers and steel beams) usually come in straight pieces. Because triangles provide excellent support, many roofs have an

FACETS
OF BASIC SCIENCE

Aeronautical Engineering

As fighter Red-Dog 5 streaked into enemy territory, a white cloud burst from the hillside below. Almost immediately, the plane's radar picked up a potentially deadly antiaircraft missile. Fighter Red-Dog 5 was in danger. Her pilot knew that with the missile's infrared tracking system zeroing in on the heat from his engines, the missile could chase him down at speeds up to 1800 kilometers per hour—one and a half times the speed of sound. Wherever he went, the missile was sure to follow. Could he outrun it? Could he outmaneuver it? That was up to his plane.

Almost automatically, the pilot banked his plane into a steep, climbing turn. The missile faithfully copied him. At an altitude of 3000 m, the fighter banked again, this time into a screaming dive. The missile did the same. The pilot throttled the plane to top speed and barreled straight at the missile launch pad! At the last moment, he pulled his plane out of the dive. The fighter shuddered under the tremendous forces of inertia; the wings almost ripped from the body, and the pilot was slammed into his seat. The force of the maneuver made it impossible to breathe for several seconds. The plane barely skimmed over the top of the hill. The missile, however, did not. Its guidance system did not respond to the sudden maneuver in time, and it smashed into its own launch pad. The plane had beaten the missile.

Fighter Red-Dog 5 had been designed to undergo severe and sudden stress. Her airframe and engines were engineered to survive the pilot's defiance of inertial forces. Aeronautical engineers had spent years designing the fighter so that she would not fail her pilot. Aeronautical engineers are constantly designing faster, more maneuverable planes to keep up with missile engineers' new and better missile designs.

Aeronautical advances require creative ideas, careful calculations, and testing—lots of testing. Testing, however, poses some problems. First of all, it is expensive. Prototypes (working models) of airplanes cost much more than the mass-produced finished products. Each new aeronautical idea requires a new multimillion-dollar prototype. Secondly, testing is dangerous. Engineers need to find each prototype's performance limits, but pushing a test plane too far can easily kill the test pilot. Pilots' lives cannot be endangered just to test a new idea. True, engineers can do some testing in wind tunnels, but the results are sometimes different from the results of real flights.

In 1982, NASA and the U.S. Air Force began a unique testing program that overcame many of these difficulties. The HiMAT (Highly Maneuverable Aircraft Technology) program started out just like any other test program—on the drawing boards. Here, engineers fleshed out their ideas with specifications and fed them into computers for analysis. Next, they built small models, tested them in wind tunnels, and finally constructed an in-flight research plane.

The HiMAT program conquered the safety problems of aeronautical testing. HiMAT "pilots" flew the test plane from the ground by remote control. They forced the plane through extremely sharp turns at top speed in complete safety. HiMAT also saved money. By building the test plane half-size, HiMAT engineers reduced construction costs and made wind tunnel tests possible. The HiMAT plane also had the unique feature of interchangeable parts. Its engine nozzles, air inlets, and wings could all be easily enlarged, reduced, or converted into different shapes. Consequently, one prototype could be used to test many different ideas.

Through the HiMAT program, engineers have learned more about maneuvering at transonic (faster than sound) speeds. Planes developed from HiMAT research may be able to bend into different shapes to perform particular maneuvers. The data from the HiMAT program will help engineers design fighters to beat the missiles of the 1990s.

21-11 Chicago is famous as the "Windy City." To help resist the added stress these winds place on a tall structure, the designers of the John Hancock Building added trusses to their building design.

overall triangular cross section. Most tables, shelves, bridges, skyscrapers, and airplane wings also depend on triangular bracing.

Combining two or more triangles increases the strength of the structure even more. **Trusses** use this principle. A truss is an architectural support made of beams, bars, or other straight objects arranged to form triangles. A truss is strong because the lower beam can bend downward only if the other parts of the truss bend as well. It takes much more force to deform the entire truss than it does to deform the lower beam alone.

Mechanical Engineering

Mechanical engineering may seem like something that only a trained professional could do, but you have probably done some mechanical engineering yourself! Have you ever built a ramp for a wheelbarrow, rigged a set of pulleys to lift a heavy load, waxed the bottom of your skis to speed you down a snowy slope, or greased a doorknob as a practical joke? If so, you have used mechanical principles to solve practical problems. Two of the most common types of mechanical engineering problems involve altering motion and reducing friction.

Altering motion

The motion produced by a motor or engine may have to be sped up, slowed down, changed in direction, or even changed to a different type of motion before it can be useful in a machine. Engineers have invented a wide variety of mechanisms to transform the motion produced by engines and motors.

Gears, for instance, transfer turning motion from one object to another. Gears are toothed wheels that mesh with one or more similar wheels. When one gear turns another, the direction of rotation is reversed. If, for example, the first gear rotates clockwise, the gear it turns will rotate counterclockwise.

In a machine the gear connected to the motor or engine is called the *drive gear.* The teeth of this gear mesh with the teeth of the *working gear.* When the working gear turns, it propels the moving parts of the machine.

Changing the speed of motion If the working gear in a machine is smaller than the drive gear, it will rotate faster than the drive gear, and the moving parts of the machine will turn faster than the engine. If the working gear is larger, it will turn more slowly than the drive gear, and the machine will work more slowly than the engine. If the two gears are the same size, they will turn at the same speed.

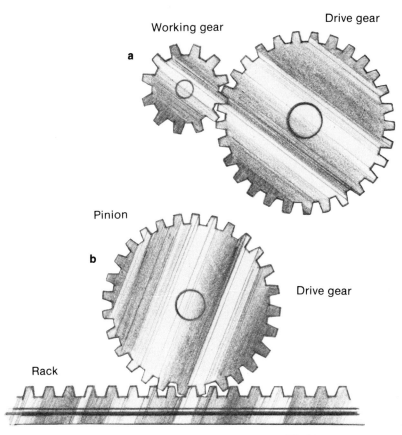

21-12 **(a)** When the drive gear is larger than the working gear, the gears are used to slow down the motion. **(b)** The gears in a rack-and-pinion steering mechanism change the circular motion of the steering column into the straight-line motion that turns the wheels.

Changing rotational motion to straight-line motion Often a machine that uses straight-line motion is powered by a motor or engine that produces rotating motion. How do engineers change turning motion to straight-line motion? Often they use either a *windlass* (WIND luss) or a *rack and pinion* (PIN yun). In a windlass a rope or cable is wound onto a rotating drum. Anything attached to the cable is pulled in a straight line. A rack and pinion is a modified pair of gears. The drive gear, called the pinion, is a typical round gear. But the working gear, called the rack, is a straight bar with teeth that mesh with the teeth on the pinion. The steering mechanisms in most sports cars use a rack-and-pinion arrangement.

Changing the direction of motion The direction of motion can be changed as much as 90° by the use of *bevel gears.* Bevel gears have slanted teeth that meet at an angle, so that the working gear turns at a different angle than the drive gear. You have probably watched bevel gears operate in a hand drill or rotary (hand) beaters.

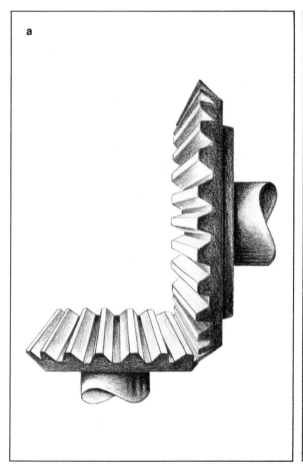

a

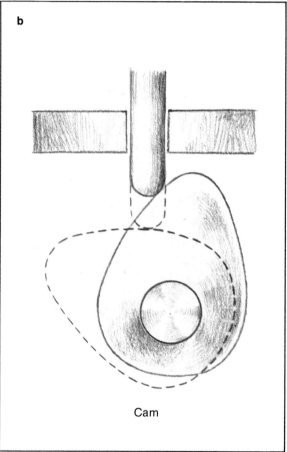

b

Cam

21-13 (a) Bevel gears can change the direction of motion by as much as 90°. **(b)** Cams like those used in sewing machines turn circular motion into back-and-forth (or up-and-down) motion.

Changing rotational motion to oscillatory motion A **cam** is a humped or oddly shaped wheel that is mounted on a rotating shaft. As the cam rotates with the shaft, its "humps" periodically apply pressure to another part of the machine, causing that part to oscillate (move back and forth). The cams in a sewing machine produce the motions that make not only straight stitches and zigzag stitches, but also buttonholes and even stitches shaped like leaves and geometric figures.

FACETS
OF BASIC SCIENCE

Biomedical Engineering

"I recognize that . . . a mechanical heart will be placed within my chest in the space formerly occupied by my own natural heart, and that this mechanical device will require my body to be attached to an air-driving system by two plastic six-foot-long air tubes to pump my blood through my mechanical heart and circulate it through my body."

On November 29, 1982, at the University of Utah Medical Center, a retired dentist named Barney Clark signed the eleven-page consent form that contains this statement. Three days later Barney Clark received his artificial heart, and it extended his life 125 days.

The Jarvik 7 artificial heart that Mr. Clark received is just one example of technology's growing store of "spare parts" for the human body. Biomedical engineers are developing replacements for the parts of our bodies that most often fail: limbs, kidneys, lungs, eyes, bladder, pancreas, and several joints and bones.

(a) The artificial arm that this woman is wearing has allowed her to return to a productive home life after losing her arm.
(b) Artificial joints restore mobility to damaged joints. This computer diagram shows the placement of an artificial elbow.

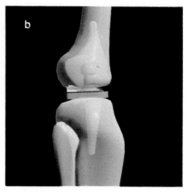

(c) Barney Clark after his historic operation.
(d) Dr. DeVries, the surgeon who implanted the Jarvik 7, with the artificial heart.

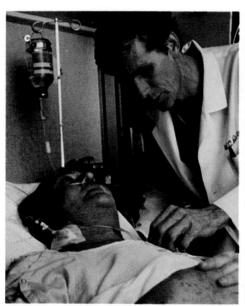

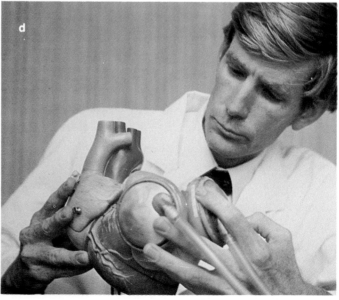

Changing oscillatory motion to rotating motion Your family's car has a combustion engine, which produces motion by a series of small explosions. Each explosion pushes a **piston** (a solid cylinder that slides within another cylinder), producing oscillatory motion. How does this up-and-down motion make the wheels on the car go around? When the fuel explodes inside a cylinder, it pushes a piston outward. A rod attached to the piston then pushes against a "crank" on a shaft. The crank is pressed down, turning the shaft and producing rotational motion. There are usually several pistons attached to a single shaft. Their explosions are timed to keep the shaft rotating—and the wheels on your car rolling!

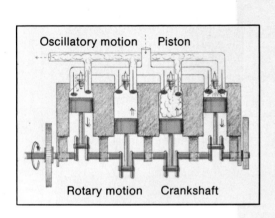

Oscillatory motion   Piston

Rotary motion   Crankshaft

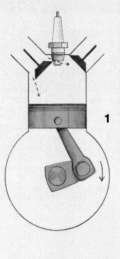
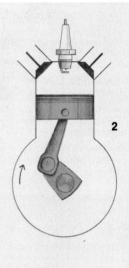

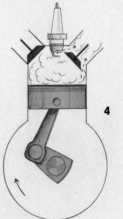

21-14 How do the pistons of an engine produce the rotary motion that turns the wheels of a car? The process begins when a valve is opened and a gasoline-air mixture is sucked into the cylinder **(1)**. Next the piston swings upward in a compression stroke **(2)**. At the point of maximum compression, a spark plug fires to ignite the mixture **(3)**. The exploding gases push the piston downward **(4)**, and the cycle starts over again. This piston motion is converted into rotary motion by the "humps" in the crankshaft, and is transferred through the drive gears and drive shaft to the axle.

Reducing friction

Friction presents one of the engineer's most challenging problems. Friction wastes mechanical energy by converting it to heat and sound. It can also reduce motion and cause wear on moving parts. Since all of these effects make machines less efficient, engineers and scientists have found many ways to overcome them.

Engineers have studied the friction between various surfaces and have discovered that the right combinations of materials can greatly reduce friction. For example, engineers know how to build ball-and-socket joints like the human hip joint. But making both the ball and the socket of steel does not work well. Steel rubbing against steel produces too much friction. Instead the engineers sometimes build the ball of steel and the socket of *Teflon,* a synthetic material which produces very little friction when it rubs against steel. Teflon-and-steel joints produce so little friction that they can be used to replace human ball-and-socket joints.

Bearings work on the principle that two surfaces rolling along each other produce far less friction than two surfaces sliding across each other. Ball bearings, like the "ball" in a ball-point pen, and roller bearings, such as those in automobile wheels, reduce friction in precision instruments, machine tools, household appliances, turbine engines, airplanes, trains, and many other machines.

If you have ever oiled a squeaky hinge or a stiff lock, you have used a *lubricant.* Lubricants, such as oil, grease, and graphite, reduce friction by forming a thin film between two moving surfaces and keeping them slightly separated. Besides reducing friction and wear, some lubricants also absorb heat and prevent corrosion. Engineers are still trying to match the smooth, almost frictionless movement of human joints.

21-15 (above) The ball bearings sealed between the two rings reduce friction. Ball bearings are essential to precision machinery. **(below)** Roller bearings are similar to ball bearings, but their design allows the inner ring to turn.

An Engineering Career

Have you ever considered engineering as a career? If you are interested in science and math, and you do well in these subjects, the Lord may wish to use you in the field of engineering.

If you are to be effective in any ministry, you should apply yourself consistently and begin your preparation early. In other words, start now and work hard so that you will be fitted for service. For engineering, preparation includes four years of math and four years of science in high school, and an introductory course in computers if possible. (Some computer stores offer courses in computer programming.) Of course, other courses should not be neglected. An engineer, like anyone else, needs to be a well-rounded individual. He must understand the social sciences so that he can comprehend the world around him—and the technical problems that he must solve for it. He also needs a firm grasp of English skills so that he can communicate effectively. And he must be willing to study on his own; an engineer's education must go on constantly if he is to keep up with advancing technology.

If engineering interests you, begin praying for the Lord's guidance and preparing for the work. There is a growing need for engineers in our technology-oriented world, and if the Lord leads you in that direction, you will have plenty of work to do!

Scientifically Speaking

engineering	arcades	trusses
stress	keystone	gears
strain	buttress	cam
flexible	flying buttress	piston
elastic	vault	bearings
fatigue	dome	
arch		

Questions to Talk Over

1. If your school planned a "Great Egg Drop," how would you package your egg to protect it in a 250-m fall?
2. Engineers face a special problem when they design tall buildings for cities on the west coast of the United States. Their problem? The high risk of earthquakes. Tall buildings must be able to sway back and forth with the tremors—without crumbling. What stresses would these buildings undergo? What materials should *not* be used in building them? Why?
3. Sometimes an object's shape is as important as the material used to construct it. Suppose that you were asked to design a plastic chair. What shapes would you use to make the chair strong?
4. Design a building that uses a circle of arches to support a large dome. Compare your design with others in your class. Which one would probably work best? Why?
5. How do you think engineers change the circular motion of an electric motor into the back-and-forth motion of a windshield wiper?

ELECTRONICS

CHAPTER
22

The morning begins much like any other morning. At six o'clock your AM-FM clock radio blares rudely to wake you up. After rolling slowly out of bed, you slip on your digital watch and stumble across the room to the television. Flipping the dial, you tune in to the latest weather report, complete with color radar. The clock now reads exactly one minute past six and you have already used three different electronic devices!

What do we mean by an "electronic device"? How does an electronic device differ from an ordinary *electrical* device? *Electronic* devices contain components (parts) that control the conduction of electrons through vacuums, gases, or semiconducting materials. *Electrical* devices generally use only conducting wires to form circuits.

22-1 The first computers used hundreds of vacuum-tube circuits. These early models were hot and noisy, and they had very limited functions. Many were nothing more than giant calculators—far less powerful than the microcomputers of today.

Vacuum-Tube Electronics

The huge machine continued its loud clanking in spite of all that the scurrying technicians could do. The fierce heat grew more intense as the water cooling system suddenly failed. Large boards strung with mazes of wires seemed constantly to require corrections—unplug this wire, insert that connection, change circuit AA73, replace that vacuum tube, and so on. The machine was a computer, one of the earliest ever invented, and most of its shortcomings could be traced to its primary components—*vacuum tubes*. At least one vacuum tube burned out and had to be replaced every seven minutes the computer was in operation. The heat the tubes produced was stifling, and their ability to be programmed was severely limited. Because of these disadvantages, more advanced electronic components have largely replaced vacuum tubes in computers and other electronic devices. Although today's applications of vacuum tubes are limited primarily to radio and television broadcasting, the story of vacuum-tube electronics lays an important foundation for the study of modern electronics.

Thermionic emission

At one point during his research on carbon-filament light bulbs, Thomas Edison (ED ih sun) sealed a metal plate into a light bulb. Then he connected the plate and the filament of the light bulb to opposite terminals of a battery. Interestingly, he found that when he connected the positive terminal of the battery to the plate and the negative terminal to the filament, a small current flowed through the arrangement. This observation surprised Edison, for the air inside the bulb had been removed. How could a vacuum conduct a current? The problem became even more complicated when he reversed the battery terminals and found that the current no longer flowed through the bulb.

The explanation for the *"Edison effect,"* as Edison's observation is now called, came in 1897 when J.J. Thomson identified the electron. At that time scientists realized that the current carriers in most electrical circuits are electrons—the lightweight, negatively charged particles in atoms. The hot filament in Edison's bulb was "boiling off" electrons. **Thermionic** (THUR mye AHN ik) **emission**, the release of electrons from a heated conducting material, is strictly a heating effect—not an electrical effect. Ordinarily, the electrons emitted by a hot filament remain around the filament as a thin, invisible cloud. However, when

Edison placed a positively charged plate into his light bulb, some of the electrons that "boiled off" the bulb's hot filament were attracted to the oppositely charged plate. As these electrons jumped across the intervening space to the plate, they completed the electrical circuit in the bulb, and a sensitive meter indicated the flow. When Edison gave the filament a positive charge and the plate a negative charge, the filament remained hot and still emitted electrons. However, the meter indicated no current because the emitted electrons were repelled by the negatively charged plate.

Rectification

In 1904 Sir John Ambrose Fleming, an English electrical engineer, carried Edison's experiment to a useful conclusion. Fleming placed a filament and a metal plate in a glass bulb, ran wires from the plate and filament to the outside of the bulb, pumped the air from the bulb, and sealed it. Today this apparatus is known as a **vacuum tube**. Fleming observed that when he connected an alternating current source between the wires leading to the plate and filament, a pulsating direct current flowed through the vacuum tube from the filament to the plate. The current pulsated because it flowed from the filament to the plate only when the alternating current gave the filament a negative charge and the plate a positive charge. When the filament was positive and the plate was negative, no current flowed at all.

22-2 Thomas Edison's experiments with filaments led to his discovery of thermionic emission.

22-3 John Ambrose Fleming developed the first vacuum tubes.

Fleming's invention performed the important function of **rectification** (REK tuh fuh KAY shun)—the changing of alternating current to direct current. Because it produced an intermittent flow of current, Fleming compared his device to a *valve*, a term still used in England for vacuum tubes. Scientists commonly call the Fleming valve a **diode** (DY ODE), because it contains two elements (the filament and the metal plate). Vacuum tube diodes are still used today as rectifiers in electronic power sources and high-power radio transmitters, but for most purposes they have been supplanted by more efficient semiconductor diodes.

Amplification

By today's standards the vacuum tube diode had a very limited range of applications. It could change AC to pulsating DC, but that was essentially the extent of its usefulness. Fleming had hopes that his diode would be able to detect radio waves, but its operation in this role proved disappointing. A modification was necessary to make the vacuum tube versatile.

In 1906 the American inventor Lee DeForest (dih FOR ist) added a third element, a *grid*, to a vacuum tube diode. In doing

22-4 Diodes such as these from a high-powered transmitter are still in use today.

so he invented the **triode** (TRY ODE). By suspending the grid between the filament and the plate, DeForest forced electrons traveling through the tube to pass through the openings between the grid's finely meshed wires. DeForest found that by placing a charge on the grid, he could exert a tremendous influence on the number of electrons flowing through the vacuum tube. When he made the grid positive, the electron flow greatly increased. When he made it negative, the electron flow greatly diminished. If sufficiently negative, the grid could stop the flow of electrons completely. The high sensitivity of the triode enabled a very small change in the charge of the grid to change the current in the filament-plate circuit by a sizable amount.

The charge on a triode grid may be produced by connecting the grid to a power source. Changes in the voltage of the power source produce changes in the charge on the grid. Small changes in the grid charge produce very large changes in the current flowing from the filament to the plate. This effect is called **amplification** (AM pluh fih KAY shun). You may benefit from amplification each time you listen to a radio, a television, or a public-address system. In each of these devices, sound is converted to a varying-voltage electric current, which is then amplified electronically and converted back to sound.

Diodes

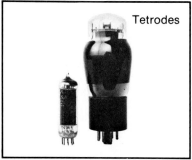

Tetrodes

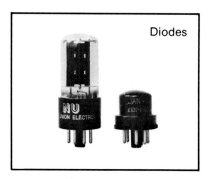

Triodes

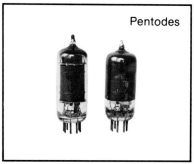

Pentodes

Oscillation

Oscillation (AHS uh LAY shun) is a back-and-forth motion of electrons in a circuit. Oscillators are used in producing and receiving radio and television signals. Television stations broadcasting over Channel 13, for instance, send out signals with more than 216 million oscillations per second. A broadcaster can change the frequency and amplitude of an oscillation by adjusting a circuit.

A microphone converts sound energy into oscillations and transmits the signal to an amplifier. The amplifier in turn makes the signals strong enough to operate a loudspeaker. Sometimes the oscillations from the loudspeakers of a public-address system are picked up by the microphone and reamplified in the amplifier. We call the resulting effect **feedback**—additional, undesirable oscillations that we hear as howling or squealing in the loudspeakers. Although most feedback oscillations are annoying, controlled feedback can be extremely useful and has a wide variety of applications in electronics.

Improvements in the vacuum tube

DeForest's vacuum-tube triode has been called the single most important invention in the history of electronics. As versa-

22-5 How feedback occurs.

1. Sound waves enter the microphone, are converted into electrical impulses, and travel to the amplifier.
2. The amplifier signal is played through the speakers, which produce sound waves of high amplitude.
3. Some of the amplified sound waves are picked up by the microphone.
4. When these are amplified again, they become the high-amplitude screech we call feedback.

tile as it was, however, the triode was not the "final word" in vacuum tubes. In the years that followed, researchers found a way to produce more efficient thermionic emission. Experiments revealed that an externally heated negative electrode emitted more electrons than an internally heated light-bulb-type filament.

Most modern vacuum tubes contain an externally heated negative electrode, called a filament or a *cathode* (KATH ODE). Cathodes are hollow metal cylinders coated with special oxides. Inside each cathode an insulated resistance wire, called a *heater*, gives off heat when it carries current. As the surrounding cathode absorbs this heat, it emits large numbers of electrons. Notice how the cathode-heater arrangements differ between the triode and the pentode shown below.

Another innovation in the vacuum tube involved adding a second grid to the triode. This grid, placed between the first grid and the plate, possessed a positive charge to help attract electrons to the plate. To distinguish between the two grids, the first was called the *control grid,* and the second, the *screen grid.* A vacuum tube with two grids is called a **tetrode** (TET RODE) because it has four electrodes—filament (or cathode), control grid, screen grid, and plate.

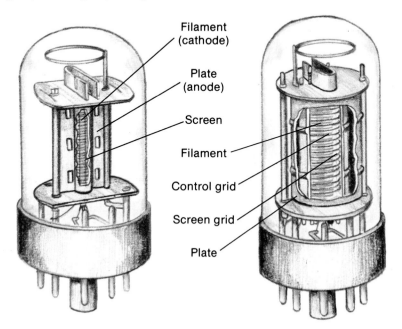

Filament
(cathode)

Plate
(anode)

Screen

Filament

Control grid

Screen grid

Plate

22-6 (a) A diagram of a triode. **(b)** A tetrode.

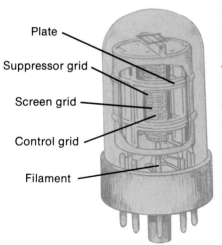

Plate

Suppressor grid

Screen grid

Control grid

Filament

22-7 A pentode.

The screen grid worked well. In fact, it accelerated electrons toward the plate so effectively that many of the electrons hit the plate and bounced back toward the screen grid. To combat this problem, a third grid, called the *suppressor* (suh PRESS ur) *grid,* was added between the screen grid and the plate. The suppressor grid slowed the electrons down as they approached the plate and repelled them back to the plate if they bounced off. The five-element tube formed by adding a suppressor grid to a tetrode is a **pentode** (PEN TODE).

Further refinements in vacuum tubes included reducing their physical size and combining two or more tubes into a single glass or metal envelope. The resulting multiunit tubes were twin diodes, twin triodes, diode-triodes, triode-pentodes, and so on.

Solid-State Electronics

Modern electronics is sweeping our society forward faster than anyone could have dared to predict. Futuristic devices such as watch radios, watch televisions, and cordless telephones have become possible. Today's hand-held calculator easily eclipses the performance of the room-size computer of yesteryear. Fiber-optic cables only 2 cm thick transmit telephone messages as beams of laser light, surpassing the carrying capacity of outdated 15 cm copper cables. Army commanders can detect the enemy even at night by using infrared-sensing cameras. What has caused this avalanche of electronic advancement? The discovery and development of **solid-state electronic components.**

Semiconductors

Most solid-state electronic components are made of *semiconducting* materials—usually silicon or germanium. Like most semiconductors, silicon and germanium are metalloids, elements listed near the middle of the periodic chart. The primary characteristic of semiconductors is their mediocre electrical conductivity; they conduct currents better than insulators but not so well as conductors.

Solid-state electronics utilizes two different types of semiconducting materials—*N-type* (negative type) and *P-type* (positive type). These materials perform much the same functions as the positively and negatively charged grids, plates, and cathodes in vacuum tubes. What are the N-type and P-type materials?

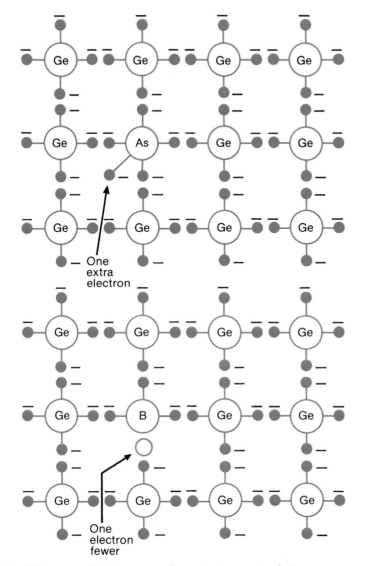

22-8 A comparison of negative-type and positive-type semiconductors.

In an N-type semiconductor, the semiconductor crystal is "doped" with atoms of elements that have "extra" electrons. Germanium, which has 4 valence electrons, can be doped with arsenic. Arsenic atoms have 5 valence electrons, which result in an "excess" of electrons in the crystal.

In a P-type semiconductor, the crystal is doped with atoms of elements that have fewer valence electrons than the semiconductor crystal. Germanium could be doped with boron to produce the crystal of a P-type semiconductor. The boron atoms have only 3 valence electrons each and form positive "holes" (spots with fewer electrons) in the crystal.

Both N-type and P-type semiconductor materials are germanium or silicon with impurities added. N-type materials contain impurities such as arsenic and phosphorus. These substances possess *more* valence electrons than germanium or silicon do. Aluminum, gallium, and boron—impurites usually added to form P-type materials—contain *fewer* valence electrons than the semiconductors do. In electronic components, N-type materials behave somewhat like the negatively charged cathodes and grids of vacuum tubes; P-type materials behave like the positively charged plates and grids.

22-9 Semiconductor diodes and transistors are much smaller than the tubes that they replaced.

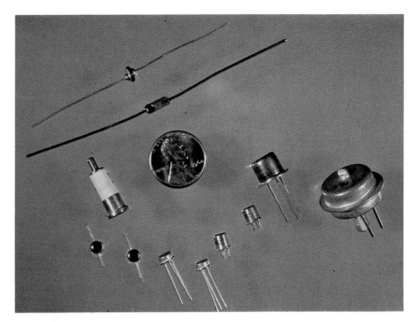

Rectification

The simplest solid-state electronic component, the *semiconductor diode,* consists of a section of P-type material next to a section of N-type material. When the positive terminal of a battery is connected to the P-type side of the diode, and the negative terminal to the N-type, current flows through the diode. Reversing the terminals produces almost no current flow through the diode. When an alternating current source is connected to a semiconductor, pulsating current flows only one way through the diode—from the P-type material to the N-type material. Thus, like the vacuum-tube diode, the semiconductor diode acts as a valve and rectifies current.

Semiconductor diodes rectify current in many common devices and appliances. *Silicon diodes* have proved especially useful as rectifiers. They work better than vacuum tubes in this role because they require no filaments or cathode-heaters, which periodically burn out. They also produce far less heat than vacuum tubes produce, thus minimizing the danger to nearby heat-sensitive components. Because semiconductor diodes develop a very small internal voltage drop, they also conserve energy. You probably own a silicon diode. The adapters that allow battery-powered calculators to operate from alternating current sources contain silicon diodes in connection with a step-down transformer.

Amplification and Oscillation

For many years scientists worked to develop a semiconductor component that would amplify. The desired breakthrough came in 1948, when two American scientists, John Bardeen and Walter Brattain (BRAT un), developed the world's first solid-state amplifier—the **transistor** (tran ZISS tur). This transistor contained a point-contact arrangement, consisting of a germanium crystal with two thin wires, or *cat whiskers,* touching its surface. By 1951 this original transistor had already become obsolete. Another American, William Shockley (SHAHK lee), had developed the more effective *junction transistor.* The junction transistor has formed the basis for most subsequent solid-state transistors. In recognition of their research on transistors, Bardeen, Brattain, and Shockley shared the Nobel prize in physics in 1956.

The junction transistor is basically a sandwich of semiconductor materials. Sandwiching a layer of P-type material between two pieces of N-type material forms an *NPN transistor.* Placing a slice of N-type material between two pieces of P-type material yields a *PNP transistor.* PNP and NPN transistors must be wired to power sources differently, as shown by the figures below.

22-10 NPN and PNP transistors are made by layering the different types of semiconductors.

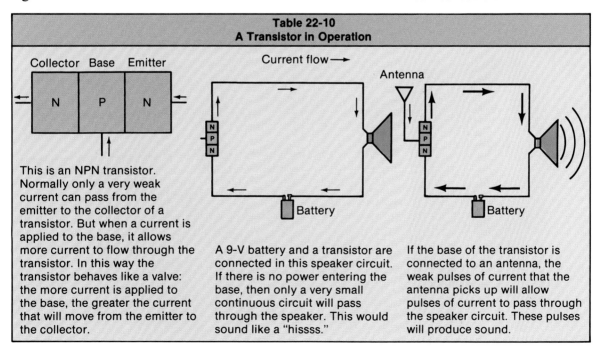

Table 22-10
A Transistor in Operation

Collector   Base   Emitter

Current flow →

Antenna

This is an NPN transistor. Normally only a very weak current can pass from the emitter to the collector of a transistor. But when a current is applied to the base, it allows more current to flow through the transistor. In this way the transistor behaves like a valve: the more current is applied to the base, the greater the current that will move from the emitter to the collector.

A 9-V battery and a transistor are connected in this speaker circuit. If there is no power entering the base, then only a very small continuous circuit will pass through the speaker. This would sound like a "hissss."

If the base of the transistor is connected to an antenna, the weak pulses of current that the antenna picks up will allow pulses of current to pass through the speaker circuit. These pulses will produce sound.

Transistors act like vacuum-tube triodes. The center layer of a transistor, called the *base*, corresponds to the grid of the vacuum-tube triode. The two outer sections of the transistor, called the *emitter* and the *collector*, act like the cathode and plate of the triode. Two different currents are made to flow through a transistor. For instance, in an NPN transistor the current that is to be amplified flows through the emitter and into the base, where it gives the base a charge. The other current flows from the emitter through the base to the collector. In vacuum tubes tiny changes in a grid charge could produce huge changes in the filament-plate current. Likewise, in a transistor, a small variation in emitter-base current can produce a variation 50 to 150 times as large in the emitter-collector current. Thus the transistor amplifies changes in currents. Transistors can also be used in much the same way as vacuum-tube triodes for oscillation.

Transistors have replaced vacuum tubes in most applications because they do not contain filaments or heaters, and because they operate at very low voltages and currents. One of their most common uses is in transistor radios. Portable radios originally required two fairly heavy batteries to produce current for the filaments, plates, and screen grids of their vacuum tubes. Today, transistor portables can be designed to operate on a single small, lightweight battery.

22-11 Transistors have allowed us to reduce the size of a radio from this cabinet model to one that can fit in the palm of a hand.

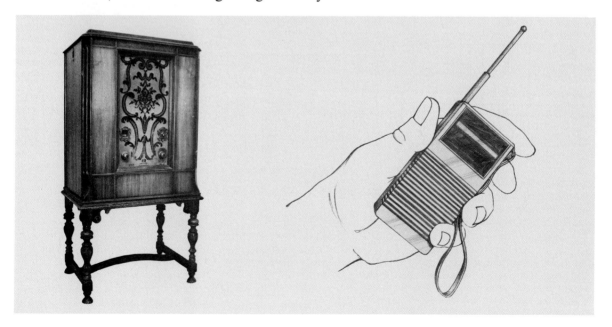

Improvements in solid-state components

One advanced form of the semiconductor diode is the **light-emitting diode (LED).** In most diodes, the conducting electrons give off heat when current flows through the diode. In LEDs certain compounds of gallium are substituted for the usual silicon or germanium compounds, and the conducting electrons give off light as well as heat. LEDs make up the lighted digits widely used for calculator and computer readouts. These digits consist of seven line-shaped LEDs arranged in the shape of a square-cornered figure eight. When current passes through different combinations of LEDs, any digit from zero to nine can be displayed. Any number of digits can be displayed by placing the required number of seven-segment units in a row.

22-12 Light-emitting diodes (LEDs) are used in the read-out displays of calculators, clocks, stereos, and many types of scientific equipment.

The year 1957 brought the invention of semiconductor **integrated** (IN tih GRATE id) **circuits**, called **ICs**. An integrated circuit (chip) is a combination of two or more semiconductor components in one unit. Though the transistor and the diode had always been small, the invention of the chip brought incredible miniaturization to the electronics industry. Not only could several semiconductor diodes and transistors be combined into the same unit, but resistors and capacitors could be included as well. Today, a thin square chip measuring 0.5 cm on a side may contain as many as 200,000 components. Remarkably, it is far more economical to mass-produce chips than to mass-produce the separate components they contain. Integrated circuit technology has made possible the pocket calculator, electronic games, and microcomputers (computers having their entire central processing units on a single chip).

22-13 This microprocessor chip contains over 100,000 transistors. It serves as the "brain" of a microcomputer. It replaces a roomful of vacuum tubes or a boxful of transistors, and it occupies less space than a dime.

Applications of Electronics

The electronic advances of the twentieth century have brought about a modern-day industrial revolution. Studies predict that half of the jobs existing in industry today will be eliminated during the next twenty-five years. Why? Because electronic equipment will accomplish the functions now accomplished by the ones who hold those jobs.

What has caused this revolution? The tremendous increase in the efficiency of electronic components and the accompanying surge in electronic technology. The electronic calculator of twenty years ago occupied an entire room. Today, an equivalent calculator will fit in the palm of your hand! And its cost has plummeted from half a million dollars to a mere five dollars! In addition, the modern calculator consumes only a fraction of the energy consumed by the old, generates far less heat, and completes computations much faster than its predecessor. Although applications of electronic advances touch every aspect of our lives, we will consider only three major electronic achievements—radio, television, and computers.

22-14 Guglielmo Marconi, the inventor of the crystal set, listening to his invention. The listener needed earphones to use this early radio.

Radio

In 1856 the Scottish physicist James Clerk Maxwell became aware of the theoretical possibility of *radio waves*. He predicted that radio waves would have electromagnetic properties like light and would travel at the speed of light, but would differ from light in wavelength and frequency. Eventually all three of his predictions proved to be correct. In 1888, thirty-two years after Maxwell's prediction, the German physicist Heinrich Hertz first generated and detected radio waves. He produced the radio waves by means of an induction coil (step-up transformer), an oscillating circuit, and a spark gap. He received the waves a short distance away by using a loop of wire and a second spark gap. Hertz found that, like light waves, the radio waves could be reflected and focused.

In 1895 Guglielmo Marconi (mar CO nee), an Italian engineer, built the first "wireless telegraph," as early radio transmitters were called. Using a spark transmitter similar to Hertz's, he sent Morse-code signals by rapidly turning the spark on and off to form the long and short characters. The technique of **modulation**—impressing sound or patterns of light on the transmitted wave—had not yet been developed. Many physicists said that the human voice could never be carried by radio waves.

They believed that it was too delicate and intricately structured to be taken apart at the transmitter, sent over the air, and accurately put back together again at the receiver. Yet the human voice had been transmitted by Alexander Bell's telephone (invented in 1876), and some physicists held that the modulation of radio waves was possible as well.

During the first decade of the 1900s, two Americans, Lee DeForest and Reginald Fessenden (FESS un dun), labored independently to impress sound waves on radio waves. Both men succeeded, and though DeForest is now known as the "father of radio," Fessenden received wider recognition at the time. On Christmas Eve, 1906, Fessenden transmitted what is generally regarded as the world's first radio broadcast, from Brant Rock, Massachusetts. Speech and classical music (Handel's "Largo") were clearly received by many ship and coastal radio-station operators who had previously tuned in only Morse-code transmissions. With this stimulus, interest in radio transmission and reception skyrocketed. Scientists focused their efforts on radio research. Many amateurs began experimenting in their attics, basements, and garages. Small private stations sprang up all over the country. By 1920 the first commercial broadcasting station, KDKA in Pittsburgh, went on the air, followed in rapid succession by stations in other key cities.

For a time, transmitter technology outstripped receiver technology. Though many of the radio transmitters of the early 1920s were relatively strong and clear, listeners were forced to receive radio programs on **crystal sets**—simple receivers that required outdoor antennas, had difficulty separating stations, and could not amplify signals.

Most crystal sets received signals by means of one or more capacitors and one or more coils of wire. The combination of these components provided a tuned circuit that could select specific stations. The radio waves received from the desired station were passed on to the crystal, which extracted the audible component from the radio wave and directed it to the headphones.

The heart of a crystal set is the crystal itself—a specially prepared mineral or combination of minerals that has been provided with two metal contacts. Crystals have changed considerably from the pioneer days of radio to the present. In early radios a mineral such as galena (lead sulfide) was embedded in a small metal cup, leaving one surface exposed. Current from the

22-15 In less than seventy years, radio receivers have progressed from the crude crystal set with its headphones to the modern receiver. The crystal set had only tuning controls. The modern receiver has volume, bass, and treble controls; special filters; automatic fine tuning; and an ever-increasing array of computer-controlled options.

FACETS
OF BASIC SCIENCE

Understanding AM and FM

When we wish to send information from one place to another, we usually use a vehicle, or carrier. For example, when we send a written message, a piece of paper is the carrier. Radio-broadcasting stations also convey their messages by carriers. These carriers are electromagnetic waves having frequencies measured in kilohertz or megahertz. Carrier waves travel outward from a radio station's antenna at the speed of light. Amazingly, if a message can be successfully impressed on the carrier (made to *modulate* the carrier), the message will "hitch a ride" and will be carried along at the same speed—300,000 km/s. At this speed, if they followed the curve of the earth, radio waves would circle the globe 7½ times in a single second!

Each radio station in a broadcasting area is assigned a carrier wave of a different frequency. If a station were to send just its carrier with no sound impressed upon it, the effect would be the same as sending a blank piece of paper. An *unmodulated,* or "open," carrier, as it is called, creates a blank spot on the dial of any radio receiver that tunes it in. Aside from very faint background sounds caused by distant stations on the same frequency, it carries no sound.

The oscillations of an unmodulated carrier show how the strength of its electric field

increases and decreases thousands of times per second.

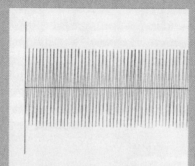

We would need to impress it on the unmodulated carrier wave. We can do this by first using a microphone to convert the sound to oscillations of electrons in an electric current. Then we must amplify the current in a powerful amplifier and conduct the amplified current to the transmitter that generates the carrier wave. In the transmitter the two waves combine into the waveform broadcast by the antenna. The *amplitude* of the transmitted wave (the distance of the wave above and below the center line) changes as the *amplitude* of the sound wave changes. Consequently, we call this type of modulation **amplitude modulation,** or **AM** for

short. It was the first means of voice modulation to be discovered and is the easiest type of modulation to decipher at the receiver. Stations on the standard AM-broadcast band (540 to 1600 kHz) and many short-wave broadcasting stations also use amplitude modulation.

Notice the amplitude modulation in the combination of the carrier wave and the sound wave:

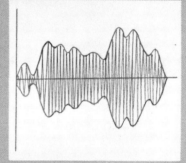

Other radio stations combine sound waves and carrier waves by the system called **frequency modulation (FM).** First, microphones convert sound to varying oscillations in an electric current. Then this current is amplified and combined with the carrier wave to produce changes in the *frequency* of the wave. These changes correspond to changes in the tone, volume, and quality of the original sound.

The amplitudes of all the waves are the same, but their frequency (spacing) varies. Stations transmitting on the FM-broadcast band (88 to 108 MHz) use frequency modulation. FM signals usually require more sophisticated receiving equipment than AM signals.

tuned circuit entered the crystal through a thin wire (the cat whisker), which touched the exposed surface lightly. Current leaving the crystal passed through the metal cup and then to the headphones. The operator of the set adjusted the cat whisker to the spot on the crystal that gave him the loudest sounds in the headphones. In time, preadjusted crystals with enclosed, preset cat whiskers sealed in wax became available. Today, such an arrangement is called a *point-contact diode.* Modern radios contain solid-state electronic components. Semiconductor diodes have taken the place of the early crystals, and transistors amplify the currents entering and leaving the diode.

Computers

What is a computer? How is it different from a calculator? Many people confuse these two types of electronic machines. A *calculator* is a device designed specifically for doing mathematical operations. A **computer**, however, is a general-purpose machine that can manipulate numbers, letters, or any other kind of data. Computers can even be programmed to play games such as chess and checkers. The best chess computers can beat all human challengers who play on less than a grand-master level!

Although computers come in an unending variety of sizes, shapes, and capabilities, most have three basic parts in common: the **central processing unit (CPU),** the **main memory**, and the *input/output unit.* The *central processing unit* is the heart of the computer. Here the instructions fed into the computer are actually accomplished.

The *main memory* stores information for both present and future use by the computer. The *program,* the series of instructions that tells the computer what to do with the data it receives, is stored in the main memory of the computer during a given assignment.

When they are not in use, programs are usually stored on disks. During use, the information from one or more disks is stored in the **RAM**, or **random-access memory**, a section of the computer's main memory. The RAM also stores new information generated by the computer as it operates. This information is often recalled by the central processing unit of the computer and used to perform a later step of the same assignment. The main memories of most computers also contain a small permanent bank of information, called the **ROM**, or **read-only mem-**

ory. ROMs usually contain only the information a computer needs to be able to process programs that are fed into its RAM.

The input/output unit (I/O) is the communications center of a computer. Here the computer receives **input** (information from the outside world) through keyboards, sound or light sensors, or even touch-sensitive screens. Here the computer also displays its **output**—the result of its assignments. A computer's output usually consists of such things as printed materials, sounds, mechanical actions, or graphic displays on video terminals.

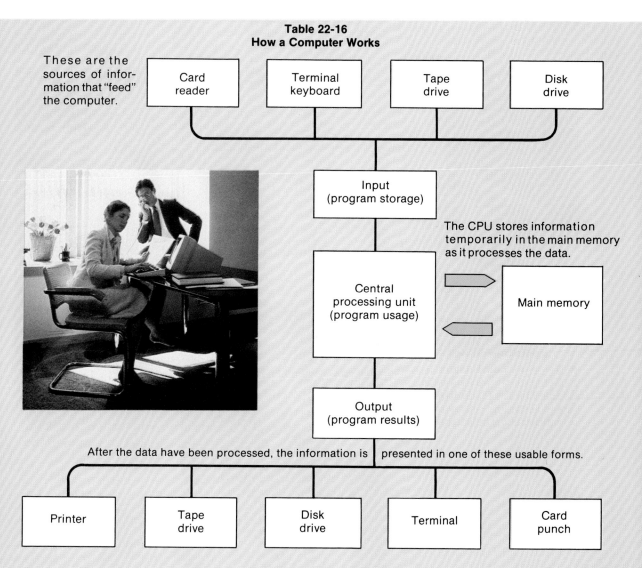

Table 22-16
How a Computer Works

These are the sources of information that "feed" the computer.

Card reader	Terminal keyboard	Tape drive	Disk drive

Input
(program storage)

The CPU stores information temporarily in the main memory as it processes the data.

Central processing unit (program usage)

Main memory

Output
(program results)

After the data have been processed, the information is presented in one of these usable forms.

Printer	Tape drive	Disk drive	Terminal	Card punch

555

FACETS
OF BASIC SCIENCE

Computer Vistas

The uses for computers are almost endless. The following list of computer applications only touches on the major fields now being computerized.

Word processing ▶
Computers called word processors can greatly reduce the workload of secretaries, writers, and editors by checking letters and manuscripts for spelling and grammatical errors. Word processors can be programmed to rearrange sentences or paragraphs on command. Word processors can also index for ready access all the key terms in letters, articles, books, or legal documents.

◀ Numerical computation
Computers have long been noted for their incredible speed and accuracy in carrying out mathematical calculations.

Accounting ▶
Many businesses use computers to facilitate their payroll, book-keeping, and billing operations.

Communications

Computers now automatically record long-distance telephone calls and switch telephone circuits to make the most efficient use of available lines.

Factory operations ▶

Computers can efficiently guide routine assembly-line operations and quality-control testing, thus freeing employees for more creative work.

◀ Simulation of problems

By simulating battle conditions on computers, military leaders can gain valuable information to help them in making strategic decisions. Creationists have used computers to simulate the conditions of the Genesis Flood and to discredit certain evolutionary ideas in astronomy.

◀ Transportation

Airlines, railroads, and busing companies use computers to keep track of their rates, reservations, and itineraries.

◀ Space research

NASA relies on computers to calculate the trajectories and orbits of space-going vehicles. The successes of the U.S. space program would have been impossible without both on-board and ground-based computers.

557

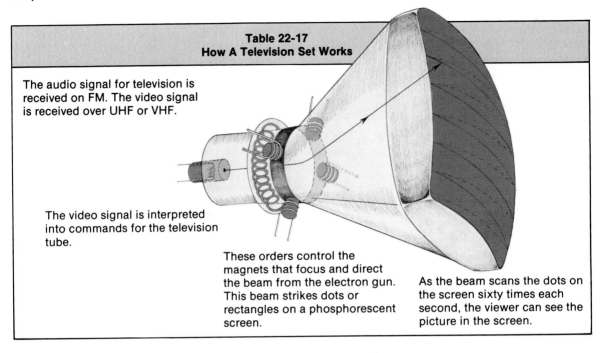

Table 22-17
How A Television Set Works

The audio signal for television is received on FM. The video signal is received over UHF or VHF.

The video signal is interpreted into commands for the television tube.

These orders control the magnets that focus and direct the beam from the electron gun. This beam strikes dots or rectangles on a phosphorescent screen.

As the beam scans the dots on the screen sixty times each second, the viewer can see the picture in the screen.

22-18 A modern television tube.

Television

Television must be rated as one of the major achievements of the electronic age. Though it is often misused, television plays an invaluable role as a communication device in space probes, weather satellites, underwater probes, surveillance monitors, and teaching aids.

The primary component of modern television cameras is an advanced vacuum tube called an **image orthicon** (OR thih KAHN) **tube**. Light reflected from the scene to be televised is focused by the lens of the camera onto a transparent signal plate in the orthicon tube. The surface of this plate has a photo-sensitive metallic coating that gives up electrons wherever it is struck by light. The brighter the light, the more electrons the coating gives off. The liberated electrons, guided by the attracting force from a positively charged plate lining the tube, hit a second plate, called the iconoscope target. Here they knock off other electrons, leaving a pattern of positively charged points on the plate. This pattern carries picture information and changes rapidly to keep up with the action being televised.

The cathode of the orthicon tube produces a continuous beam of electrons that scans the positive pattern on the target plate. Because electrons are so mobile, the electron beam can scan the plate very rapidly. Guided by *deflection coils,* the electron beam moves across the picture from left to right many times each second, with each scan line positioned slightly lower than the one before it. When the electron beam reaches the bottom of the target plate, the picture is complete and the beam starts over at the top of the plate. The beam scans the plate from top to bottom sixty times each second—thirty times for the 525 even-numbered lines and thirty times for the 525 odd-numbered lines.

As the electron beam scans the target plate, it neutralizes each positively charged point on the plate. Since the neutralizing process removes electrons from the beam, the number of electrons remaining in the reflected beam accurately indicates the amount of light existing at each point in the picture. This information is amplified and passed on to the television transmitter as a *video signal.* At the same time, synchronizing information from the deflection coils of the orthicon is sent to the transmitter to tell the receiving television sets how to reproduce the picture. This synchronizing information is superimposed onto the video signal and sent out on the carrier wave. The audio signal, which originates from microphones at the television studio, is transmitted on a second carrier wave, slightly higher in frequency than the video carrier.

This simplified description of television transmission applies to black-and-white television systems. Color television systems function in much the same way, except that filters in color television cameras divide the incoming light into the three primary colors (red, blue, and green). These colors are then scanned separately in three different orthicons or in a single three-color orthicon.

The electromagnetic waves used as carriers for television signals have high frequencies and very short wavelengths. The VHF (very-high-frequency) channels (channels 2 through 13) occupy frequencies between 54 and 218 MHz. UHF (ultra-high-frequency) channels occupy still higher-frequency carrier waves. Both VHF and UHF waves have wavelengths too short to follow the earth's curvature; moreover, they do not bounce back from the ionosphere as short-wave radio waves do. Because television waves follow essentially line-of-sight paths, engineers design television transmitting antennas to be placed as high as possible above the terrain they serve. Cables, relay stations, or satellites must be used to carry television signals over long distances.

Television signal reception begins when the receiving antenna intercepts the television carrier wave from the air. Electrical impulses travel through the antenna to the television set, where the video and audio signals are separated. Transistors or vacuum-tube triodes amplify the audio current and send it to the speaker, which converts the electrical impulses to sound. After the video signal is amplified, it is fed to the **picture tube,** or **kinescope** (KIN ih SKOPE), where it produces an electron beam. Synchronizing signals extracted from the video signal direct this

FACETS
OF BASIC SCIENCE

Amateur Radio

Perhaps you know a radio amateur who relays messages for missionaries, provides communications in time of emergencies, or simply talks to his friends on the shortwave bands. Radio amateurs, or "hams," are different from CB (citizen's band) operators, who generally use less powerful equipment and who are not held to the same standards of technical knowledge and operating skill as hams. The term *amateur* refers to the fact that the radio amateur receives no pay for his broadcasting but pursues short-wave radio strictly as a hobby.

If you wished to be a ham, you would be required to take an examination given by the Federal Communications Commission (FCC). The examination would cover the technical aspects of radio, rules and regulations, and Morse-code sending and receiving. According to which examination you passed, you would receive a license designated Novice, Technician, General, Advanced, or Extra. If you

received a license in one of the higher classes, you would be allowed to broadcast either voice or code over transmitters with up to 1 kW of power. You would also be assigned a set of call letters, such as W4CNR or K2VDC.

Most radio amateurs broadcast over manufactured transceivers—units that combine the transmitter and receiver in a single cabinet. Hams usually transmit by Single Sideband (SSB), a system several times more efficient than either FM or AM. To achieve a good signal, hams almost always use outdoor antennas; these range from simple horizontal wires strung between insulators to rotating beam antennas perched atop tall towers.

Once they receive their broadcast license, most radio amateurs set broadcasting goals. Some aim for at least one contact in each of the fifty United States. Others choose to see how many of the world's approximately 300 countries they can log. Many enjoy simply transmitting "CQ," a general call to anyone who wants to chat. Some amateurs have regularly scheduled contacts with friends or relatives on specific frequencies. A large number of hams may form

a "network," meeting regularly on a particular shortwave frequency for a specific purpose.

Just listening to the amateur bands with a short-wave receiver does not require a license. Many people make a hobby of listening not only to radio amateurs, but also to the short-wave broadcasting services of other countries. Short-wave listeners are called "SWLs" if they are interested mainly in program content, or "DXers" if they are interested mainly in achieving distance. Many radio amateurs, SWLs, and DXers eventually apply their experience in short-wave radio to research in electronics, employment with commercial radio stations, or teaching in related sciences.

electron beam to scan the face of the picture tube in the same way that the electron beam in the orthicon scanned the target plate. The material lining the television screen (the face of the kinescope) glows when electrons strike it. Thus the kinescope accurately reproduces the picture transmitted from the television station. Reception of color television signals involves extracting additional information from the received wave and using it to control three separate electron beams.

Scientifically Speaking

thermionic emission
vacuum tube
rectification
diode
triode
amplification
oscillation
feedback
tetrode
pentode
solid-state electronic components
transistor
light-emitting diode (LED)
integrated circuits (ICs)

modulation
crystal sets
computer
central processing unit (CPU)
main memory
random-access memory (RAM)
read-only memory (ROM)
input
output
image orthicon tube
picture tube
kinescope
amplitude modulation (AM)
frequency modulation (FM)

Questions to Talk Over

1. Make a list of ten devices in your home that depend on solid-state electronics. What would happen to the size, shape, and availability of these items if electronic devices still depended on vacuum tubes?
2. Look up the word *amplify* in a dictionary. How can an electronic device "amplify" a signal without violating the first law of thermodynamics (the law of energy conservation)?
3. How has "wireless" transmission (including radio and television) changed the way we think about people in other countries?
4. The computer is invading! Describe the home of the future as it may be in 1999.

JOHN AMBROSE FLEMING
ENGLISH ELECTRICAL ENGINEER (1849-1945)

It is hard to pinpoint the beginning of the electronic age, but it is certain that Sir John Ambrose Fleming's invention of the vacuum tube in 1904 was an important turning point in the science of electricity. The "Fleming valve," as the first tube was called, opened up a whole new world of possibilities—radio, sound recording, television, and finally even the space program. Few people realize that Fleming, known as the inventor of the

vacuum tube, was an ardent, Bible-believing Christian. Fleming contended earnestly for the Faith in his writings, pointing out the errors of all scientific theories that disagree with the Bible.

John Ambrose Fleming was born in Lancaster, England, on November 29, 1849. Ambrose, as he was called, was the eldest child of a Congregational minister. When he was four years old, his family moved to London, where his father had been called

to pastor a new church. London was an exciting place for a budding young scientist to grow up, especially for one who was interested in electricity and magnetism. Michael Faraday, the famous Christian inventor, was giving lectures at the Royal Institution in downtown London. By this time Faraday had already invented the motor, the generator, and the transformer. Young Fleming was impressed with Faraday's work, and he became

562

unalterably convinced that electrical engineering was the field he should study. He attended University College in London and graduated with high honors in 1870. Later, at Cambridge, he was privileged to study under another famous Christian, James Clerk Maxwell. After earning his doctoral degree, Fleming became a professor at his alma mater, University College in London, where he taught electrical engineering for forty-one years.

While he was teaching, Fleming carried out many experiments on the sending and receiving of radio waves. By now Marconi (mahr KO nee) had already transmitted Morse code messages over more than a mile in Italy. Since nobody in that country seemed to be interested in the invention, Marconi moved to England in 1896. Here he had no trouble obtaining a patent for his invention and soon set up a company to demonstrate it. Marconi gave the first public demonstration of broadcasting messages without wires between two buildings in London.

Marconi began tests to improve his invention. He soon succeeded in signaling across the English Channel, and even sent a signal from a ship at sea to the English coast, a distance of about 120 km.

The next goal was an extremely ambitious one—to span the Atlantic! At this point, Marconi brought in Professor Fleming as scientific adviser to his company. It was Fleming's responsibility to design the English station. The installation had to be a hundred times more powerful than anything that had been built before. The task was a formidable one, but in Fleming's know-how and a capable supporting crew, Marconi had found a winning combination. Success came late in 1901, when signals were transmitted from Cornwall, England, to St. Johns, Newfoundland.

But the work for which Fleming is best remembered came in 1904. His invention, the "Fleming valve," was the element needed to further improve the wireless. The device looked like a glorified light bulb. It *was* in fact a light bulb, with one important addition—a metal plate with

a wire connected to it had been placed inside the bulb. This strange-looking contrivance was awarded English Patent No. 24850. It was called a "valve" because it allowed an electric current to pass through it in one direction, but not the other. When Fleming was knighted for this invention in 1929, King George V praised him for his "valuable service in science and industry." Many other honors were bestowed on him, both in England and the United States.

In his later years Fleming became increasingly intent in his study of the Scriptures. It was during this period of his life that he wrote two important books— *Evolution or Creation?* and *The Origin of Mankind.* In these he discussed some mistaken views of the origin of the universe. He showed that the record of Creation that God has given us in the Bible is completely reliable, and that all theories of evolution are false. He showed that man is a fallen creature in need of salvation, and that Christ is the only answer to the problem of sin in the human heart. Fleming lived to the age of ninety-five. His was a full and productive life, and, most important, he lived his life in a way that glorified God.

APPENDIXES

Appendix A

Units of Measure: Common Conversions

For Units of	When You Know the Number of		Multiply by	To Find the Number of
Length	millimeters	X	0.039	= inches
	meters	X	3.281	= feet
	meters	X	1.094	= yards
	kilometers	X	0.621	= miles
Area	square meters	X	1.196	= square yards
	hectares	X	2.471	= acres
Volume	liters	X	1.057	= quarts (lq)
	cubic meters	X	1.308	= cubic yards
Mass	grams	X	0.035	= ounces (avdp)
	kilograms	X	2.205	= pounds (avdp)
Temperature	degrees Celsius	X	9/5 (then add 32)	= degrees Fahrenheit

For Units of	When You Know the Number of		Multiply by	To Find the Number of
Length	inches	X	25.4	= millimeters
	feet	X	0.305	= meters
	yards	X	0.914	= meters
	miles	X	1.609	= kilometers
Area	square yards	X	0.836	= square meters
	acres	X	0.405	= hectares
Volume	quarts (lq)	X	0.946	= liters
	cubic yards	X	0.765	= cubic meters
Mass	ounces (avdp)	X	28.35	= grams
	pounds (avdp)	X	0.454	= kilograms
Temperature	degrees Fahrenheit	X	5/9 (after subtracting 32)	= degrees Celsius

Appendix B

The Elements and Their Symbols

Element	Symbol	Element	Symbol	Element	Symbol
Actinium	Ac	Gold	Au	Radium	Ra
Aluminum	Al	Hafnium	Hf	Radon	Rn
Americium	Am	Helium	He	Rhenium	Re
Antimony	Sb	Holmium	Ho	Rhodium	Rh
Argon	Ar	Hydrogen	H	Rubidium	Rb
Arsenic	As	Indium	In	Ruthenium	Ru
Astatine	At	Iodine	I	Samarium	Sm
Barium	Ba	Iridium	Ir	Scandium	Sc
Berkelium	Bk	Iron	Fe	Selenium	Se
Beryllium	Be	Krypton	Kr	Silicon	Si
Bismuth	Bi	Lanthanum	La	Silver	Ag
Boron	B	Lawrencium	Lr	Sodium	Na
Bromine	Br	Lead	Pb	Strontium	Sr
Cadmium	Cd	Lithium	Li	Sulfur	S
Calcium	Ca	Lutetium	Lu	Tantalum	Ta
Californium	Cf	Magnesium	Mg	Technetium	Tc
Carbon	C	Manganese	Mn	Tellurium	Te
Cerium	Ce	Mendelevium	Md	Terbium	Tb
Cesium	Cs	Mercury	Hg	Thallium	Tl
Chlorine	Cl	Molybdenum	Mo	Thorium	Th
Chromium	Cr	Neodymium	Nd	Thulium	Tm
Cobalt	Co	Neon	Ne	Tin	Sn
Copper	Cu	Neptunium	Np	Titanium	Ti
Curium	Cm	Nickel	Ni	Tungsten	W
Dysprosium	Dy	Niobium	Nb	Unilquadium	Unq
Einsteinium	Es	Nitrogen	N	Unilpentium	Unp
Erbium	Er	Nobelium	No	Unilhexium	Unh
Europium	Eu	Osmium	Os	Uranium	U
Fermium	Fm	Oxygen	O	Vanadium	V
Fluorine	F	Palladium	Pd	Xenon	Xe
Francium	Fr	Phosphorus	P	Ytterbium	Yb
Gadolinium	Gd	Platinum	Pt	Yttrium	Y
Gallium	Ga	Plutonium	Pu	Zinc	Zn
Germanium	Ge	Polonium	Po	Zirconium	Zr
		Potassium	K		
		Praseodymium	Pr		
		Promethium	Pm		
		Protactinium	Pa		

Appendix C

How Resistors Are Coded

The four color bands on a resistor tell you how to calculate the amount of resistance. The four bands stand for the following, in order:

> First significant digit
> Second digit
> Multiplier
> Range or tolerance*

*Tolerance is the range in which the value of the resistor may vary.

If a resistor had red, green, black, and brown bands, its resistance would be

red	green	black	brown
2	5	x 1	±1%

or 25 ohms ±1% of 25 ohms

Resistance Codes

Color	Digit	Multiplier	Tolerance
Black	0	x 1	± 20%
Brown	1	x 10	± 1%
Red	2	x 100	± 2%
Orange	3	x 1000	± 3%
Yellow	4	x 10,000	± 0%
Green	5	x 100,000	± 5%
Blue	6	x 1,000,000	± 6%
Violet	7	x 10,000,000	± 12.5%
Gray	8	x 0.01	± 30%
White	9	x 0.1	± 10%
Gold	--	x 0.1	± 5%
Silver	--	x 0.01	± 10%

Appendix D

Scientific Notation:

A Shorthand Way to Write Numbers

Scientific notation is a great time-saver because it simplifies writing very large or very small numbers. For example, the mass of the sun is 2×10^{30} kg. To write this out would require thirty zeros. The mass of an electron is 9.1×10^{-28} g, which would require twenty-seven zeros if written as an ordinary number.

Numbers which are multiples of 10 are represented this way:

$$
\begin{aligned}
1,000,000 &= 10^6 \\
100,000 &= 10^5 \\
10,000 &= 10^4 \\
1,000 &= 10^3 \\
100 &= 10^2 \\
10 &= 10^1 \\
1 &= 10^0 \\
0.1 &= 10^{-1} \\
0.01 &= 10^{-2} \\
0.001 &= 10^{-3} \\
0.0001 &= 10^{-4} \\
0.00001 &= 10^{-5} \\
0.000001 &= 10^{-6}
\end{aligned}
$$

Numbers which are *not* multiples of 10 are represented as a product of two numbers: one number (before the times sign) that falls between 1 and 10, and one number that is a power of 10. For example, the number 186,000 would be written as 1.86×10^5, which is equivalent to 1.86 times 100,000. The number 93,000,000 would be written 9.3×10^7.

Appendix E

Understanding Words in Science

Scientists are sometimes accused of speaking a language all their own. They may use words that you have never *heard* before. But if you break down these complex words into simple parts, and you know the meaning of each part, you will find that you understand many of them after all. This appendix contains lists of parts of scientific terms with a meaning for each. When you encounter a difficult scientific word, find the parts on this table and try to determine the meaning of the word. Here is an example:

magnetohydrodynamics
Magneto means magnetic force;
hydro means fluids;
dynamic means power.
Therefore magnetohydrodynamics is power from magnetic fluids.

Numbers

mono	one
di, bi	two
tri	three
tetra, quadra	four
penta, quinta	five
hexa, sexta	six
hepta	seven
octa	eight
nona	nine
cent	hundred

Conditions

a, an	without
ab	departing from
alter	change
anti	opposed to
aud	hear
auto	self-generated
co, con	together
de	loss, removal

en	inside
equa	same
exo	outside
extra	beyond
hemi	half
hetero	different
homo	same, more
hyper	excess
hypo	less than, below
inter	between
intra	within
iso	equal
mal	bad
mega	great, large
micro	small
ortho	straight, regular
oxy	oxygen
pan	all
poly	many
post	after
pre	before
sub	underneath
super	above

Scientific roots

bio	life
chrom	color
dyna	power
geo	earth
graph	record
gyro	turn
helio	sun
hydra	water
hydro	fluid
kine	moving
logy	study of
luna	moon
magneto	magnetic force
meter	measurer
phon	sound
photo	light
scope	see (instrument used for seeing)
son	sound
stella	star
tele	far
therm	heat

Can you use this appendix to find the meaning of these words?

telescope	microscope	hydrology	dynamics
monochromatic	polygraph	isothermal	autograph
geochronology	phonograph	telephone	gyromagnetic

GLOSSARY

Glossary

A

absolute zero The temperature on the Kelvin scale at which an object would possess an absolute minimum of kinetic energy.

acceleration The rate at which velocity increases in a given amount of time.

acid Any substance that is capable of donating protons.

acid salt A salt in which the negative ion contains a hydrogen ion.

acoustics The effect of materials and their shapes on sound.

action-at-a-distance forces Forces that act on an object without touching it.

action-reaction principle Newton's third law of motion.

alloy A homogeneous mixture of metals.

alpha decay A nuclear reaction in which an alpha particle is emitted.

alpha particle A particle made up of 2 protons and 2 neutrons; a helium nucleus.

alternating current (AC) An electric current that regularly changes the direction of its flow.

amalgam A solution with a liquid solute and a solid solvent.

ammeter A device that measures the current flowing through a circuit.

amorphous solid A solid in which the particles are held in random placement.

ampere (A) The unit used to measure the amount of current that flows past a point in one second.

amplification The process of increasing the magnitude of a quantity such as voltage or current.

amplitude The distance that a wave rises or falls from its normal rest position.

amplitude modulation (AM) Varying the amplitude of a transmitted electromagnetic wave in accordance with the sounds impressed upon it.

analysis Breaking down materials into simpler substances for study.

angle of incidence The angle between the incident ray and the normal.

angle of reflection The angle between the reflected ray and the normal.

angstrom 10^{-10} meter; a hundred-millionth of a centimeter.

anion An ion with a negative charge.

applied science Scientific activities directed toward solving specific problems.

arcade A series of arches.

arch A curved structure built to support weight above an open space.

Archimedes' principle The buoyant force exerted on a body in a fluid is equal to the weight of the fluid displaced.

armature The rotating electromagnet in an electric motor.

atmosphere A unit of gas pressure equivalent to 760 mm of mercury on a barometer.

atom The fundamental particle of an element.

atomic mass The total of the masses of the particles in an atom.

atomic mass unit (amu) A unit used to measure the mass of an atom; 1/12 of the mass of a carbon-12 atom.

atomic number The number of protons in the nucleus of an atom.

B

balance An instrument for measuring mass.

base Any substance that is capable of accepting a proton.

basic salt A salt that contains a hydroxide ion.

battery A device that chemically pumps electrons through a circuit.

beam A very large number of individual light waves.

bearing A rolling device (usually a ball) that reduces the friction between two sliding surfaces.

beat The destructive interference of two sound waves with slightly different frequencies and similar amplitudes.

beta decay A nuclear reaction in which a beta particle is emitted.

beta particle A free electron emitted from a nucleus in nuclear decay.

bias A mental leaning or inclination.

binary compound A compound that is composed of two different elements.

block and tackle An arrangement of fixed and movable pulleys connected by ropes, which has a high mechanical advantage.

boiling The rapid phase change from liquid to gas.

boiling point The temperature at which a material changes rapidly from liquid to gas.

boiling point elevation The effect whereby a solute raises the boiling point of the solvent in which it is dissolved.

Boyle's law The volume of a dry gas is inversely proportional to the pressure it exerts, if the temperature remains constant.

Brönsted-Lowery theory of acids The theory that defines an acid as a proton donor; developed by J.N. Brönsted and T.M. Lowery.

Brownian movement The constant random motion of particles in a liquid or a gas.

buoyant force An upward push on matter exerted by a fluid.

buttress A support on the side of an arch.

C

caloric theory A theory that defined thermal energy as a substance that flowed from hot bodies into cold bodies.

calorie (cal) The amount of thermal energy required to increase the temperature of 1 g of water 1° C.

Calorie (Cal) 1000 calories.

cam An oddly shaped wheel that changes rotational motion into oscillatory (back-and-forth) motion.

candela The metric unit of light intensity.

capacitor An object or device that stores an electric charge.

cation An ion with a positive charge.

Celsius scale A temperature scale based on the properties of water. The Celsius scale has 100 degrees between the freezing point and the boiling point of pure water.

central processing unit (CPU) The portion of a computer that actually performs the arithmetic and logical operations.

chain reaction A nuclear change that occurs when one unstable nucleus emits neutrons which cause other nuclei to split and release neutrons, which hit other nuclei and continue the reaction, releasing a tremendous amount of energy.

Charles's law The volume of a gas at constant pressure is directly proportional to its Kelvin temperature.

chart A table of information arranged for convenient analysis.

chemical bond The attraction that holds atoms together.

chemical change A change in a material that alters its identity.

chemical composition The elemental makeup of a material.

chemical energy Energy that is stored in the position of electrons in an atom.

chemical formula A shorthand method of expressing the makeup of a compound (pure substance).

chemical property A property that describes how matter will react and change in the presence of other kinds of matter.

circuit A circular conducting path.

circuit breaker A safety device that switches to break a circuit if current becomes too high.

circuit load The resistance of an electrical device.

coefficient A number placed before a formula to balance an equation.

coherent light Light in which all waves have the same length and oscillate together.

color Our perceptions of the different frequencies of visible light as red, orange, yellow, green, blue, indigo, and violet.

commutator A split metal ring that rotates with the wire coil in a DC electric motor to change the direction of the magnetic field.

compound A substance formed when two or more atoms of different elements chemically join together.

compression A region where air molecules are pushed closer together than normal by the energy of a sound wave.

computer A general-purpose device that manipulates both numbers and words.

concave mirror A mirror that curves like the inner surface of a sphere.

condensation The phase change from gas to liquid.

condensation point The temperature at which a material changes from gas to liquid.

conduction The flow of thermal energy from an object to another object through contact.

conductor Any substance that will allow the flow of thermal energy; in electricity, a substance that holds its valence electrons loosely, allowing the flow of electricity.

conservation principles The principles that govern the way matter and energy are interchanged.

constructive interference The inphase reinforcement of waves as they pass through each other.

convection The flow of thermal energy from one place to another by the movement of particles.

convection current A mass of moving particles that carry thermal energy

coulomb (C) The unit of electrical charge.

covalent bond A chemical bond formed by atoms sharing electrons.

creationism The view that the universe was spoken into existence by the miraculous acts described in Genesis 1 and 2.

creationist One who believes the biblical account of the Creation.

crest The highest point on a wave.

crystal lattice A solid structure formed by a regular alternating pattern of positive and negative ions.

crystalline solid A solid in which the particles are held in a fixed repeating pattern.

crystal set A simple radio receiver that detects signals by means of a crystal or semiconductor diode.

Curie temperature The temperature at which a permanent magnet loses its magnetic field.

current The flow of charges.

current electricity The effects produced by moving charges.

cycle One complete wave motion.

D

data (singular, datum) Scientific information.

deceleration The rate at which velocity decreases in a given period of time.

decibel (db) The smallest difference in intensity between two sounds that the human ear is capable of detecting.

declination The correction of values between true north and magnetic north for any given location.

degree (°) A unit of temperature.

density The mass in a unit of volume.

destructive interference The out-of-phase cancellation of waves as they pass through each other.

diamagnetic Not attracted to magnets.

diatomic molecule A molecule formed of two identical atoms bonded together.

diffusion The process of mixing by particle motion.

diode A two-element vacuum tube or semiconductor.

dipole A molecule that has both negatively and positively charged poles caused by the unequal distribution of electrons.

direct current (DC) An electric current that flows in only one direction.

direct proportion A relationship in which one value increases as the other value increases.

dispersion The separation of white light into different-colored light waves.

dissociation The process whereby a solvent breaks up an ionic solid.

Glossary

domains Microscopic regions of materials that may be lined up to produce a magnetic field of force.

dome An extended arch that forms a bowl-shaped ceiling.

Doppler effect The effect of motion on sound; named in honor of the Austrian physicist, Christian Doppler.

ductile Capable of being drawn into wire.

dynamics The branch of mechanics that describes why things move.

E

effort The force that must be applied to a simple machine to make it produce work.

effort arm The distance from the fulcrum to the effort.

elastic Able to return to original shape and size after being subjected to stress.

electrical energy Energy that is associated with the flow of charged particles through a conductor.

electrical potential A measure of the electrical charge on an object.

electric field of force The sum of the strengths and directions of the electric forces at all the points around an electrical source.

electricity, current See **current electricity**.

electricity, static See **static electricity**.

electric motor A device that uses the force between magnets to produce mechanical energy from electrical energy.

electrolysis A decomposition reaction that decomposes the reactants by an electric current in solution.

electrolyte A solute that ionizes in solution and conducts electricity.

electrolyte, weak See **weak electrolyte**.

electromagnet A solenoid with a core of magnetic material.

electromagnetic waves Rhythmic disturbances that are capable of traveling through a vacuum: radio waves, microwaves, etc.

electron A negatively charged particle with an extremely small mass.

electron configuration The number and position of electrons in the energy levels of an atom.

electron dot notation A method of representing atoms and ions that uses an element's symbol for the nucleus and inner electrons and a series of dots for the valence electrons.

electronegativity The measure of how strongly an atom holds its electrons.

electron orbital The probable location of a specific electron in an energy level.

electroscope A device that detects charges.

element Any substance which cannot be broken down into simpler substances by ordinary chemical means.

endothermic reaction A reaction that requires thermal energy.

energy The ability to do work.

energy level A region in an atom which contains electrons of a certain energy.

engineering The process of using scientific knowledge in practical ways.

entropy A measure of randomness or disorder.

equilibrium In the context of heat flow, the state at which thermal energy is no longer being transferred; achievement of an even temperature throughout a system.

evaporation The phase change from liquid to gas that occurs at the surface of a liquid.

evolution The view that the physical universe somehow structured itself out of self-existing matter, and that its parts continue to organize themselves into more complex structures as time progresses.

evolutionist One who attempts to explain the origin of things by theories of gradual development.

exothermic reaction A reaction that gives off thermal energy.

experiment A carefully designed arrangement for testing a specific hypothesis.

F

family A vertical column on the periodic table; also called a group.

fatigue A weakness in a material that develops after repeated or prolonged stress.

feedback The return of a portion of an electronic device's output energy to its input.

ferromagnetic Strongly attracted to magnets.

filling order The order in which electrons add to the energy levels of an atom.

first-class lever A lever in which the fulcrum is located between the effort and the resistance.

first law of thermodynamics Energy may be converted from one form to another but cannot be created or destroyed.

fission The splitting of a nucleus.

flexible Able to bend under pressure.

flying buttress An anchored, slanted brace used to support arches in Gothic architecture.

focal length The distance from a lens to its principal focus.

force A push or a pull that acts on an object.

formula equation An equation that uses symbols to represent a reaction.

formula unit The basic repeating unit of an ionic solid.

frame of reference A system of reference points from which the position and motion of an object can be determined.

free electron theory A description of metallic bonding that uses randomly shared electrons to explain the properties of metals.

freezing The phase change from liquid to solid.

freezing point depression The effect whereby a solute lowers the freezing point of the solvent in which it is dissolved.

frequency The number of waves that pass a given point in one second.

frequency modulation (FM) Varying the frequency of a transmitted electromagnetic wave in accordance with the sounds impressed upon it.

friction A force that opposes the motion of an object.

fulcrum The fixed point about which a lever turns.

fundamental The lowest tone that a vibrating object produces.

fuse A safety device that melts to break a circuit if current becomes too high.

fusion The joining together of smaller nuclei into a larger one.

G

galvanization A process by which a metal is coated with a thin layer of zinc.

galvanometer A device that measures very slight changes in electric current.

gamma rays A form of radiation consisting of high-energy electromagnetic waves; electromagnetic waves that originate in the nucleus of an atom; the type of electromagnetic waves with the highest frequencies.

gas The state of matter in which the disruptive forces completely overcome the attractive forces, allowing particles unlimited movement.

gas pressure Force exerted on a unit of area by gas particles colliding with a surface.

gear A toothed wheel that transfers turning motion from one object to another.

generator A device that uses magnetic fields to convert mechanical energy into electrical energy.

graph A visual way to show relationships among data.

gravity The attraction that any object in the universe has for other objects in the universe.

group Another name for a family on the periodic table.

H

heat The flow of energy from one object to another.

heat of fusion The amount of thermal energy needed to change a substance from its solid phase to its liquid phase.

heat of vaporization The amount of thermal energy needed to change a substance from its liquid phase to its gaseous phase.

Henry's law The greater the pressure on a liquid, the greater the amount of gas that will remain dissolved in that liquid at any given temperature.

hertz (Hz) The unit of frequency; one cycle per second.

heterogeneous mixture A mixture with different appearances in different parts.

homogeneous mixture A mixture that appears the same throughout.

Hooke's law The stretch of a spring is directly proportional to the force on the spring.

humanism The philosophy that considers man the center of all things and the ultimate authority in the universe.

hydration The process of surrounding solute particles with solvent molecules.

hydronium ion The ion formed by the donation of a hydrogen ion to a water molecule; H_3O^+.

hydroponics A type of gardening in which plants are grown in special liquid solutions.

hydroxide ion A polyatomic ion with a negative charge, consisting of an oxygen atom and a hydrogen ion; OH^-.

hypothesis (plural, hypotheses) An educated guess at the solution of a problem.

I

image orthicon tube A vacuum tube used in a modern television camera.

incandescent Heated to glowing.

incident ray An incoming ray (toward the reflecting surface).

inclined plane A slanted surface used to raise objects.

indicator An organic compound that shows a definite color change when it reacts with an acid or a base.

induction Charging an object by shifting the paths of its electrons.

inertia The property of matter that causes objects to resist change in the state of motion.

infrared waves Electromagnetic waves with frequencies lower than visible light but greater than radio waves.

input Incoming signal(s) presented to a computer or other electronic device.

insulator Any substance that resists the flow of thermal energy; in electricity, a substance that holds its valence electrons tightly, strongly resisting the flow of electricity.

integrated circuit (IC) A device that contains many transistors and other components formed into a single unit; chip.

intensity The measure of how bright the light from a light source is.

interference The interaction of waves as they pass through each other.

inverse proportion A relationship in which one value increases as the other value decreases.

inverse square law Illumination is inversely proportional to the square of the distance from the light source.

ion A charged atom or group of atoms formed by the loss or gain of electrons.

ionic bond A chemical bond in which electrons are transferred from one atom to another.

ionization The process of splitting a molecule into charged particles.

isotopes Different forms of the same element that have different numbers of neutrons.

J

joule (J) The SI unit of energy; equal to 1 newton · meter of work.

K

kelvin (K) The basic unit of temperature in the metric system.

Kelvin scale A temperature scale that begins at absolute zero.

keystone The center stone at the top of an arch.

kilogram (kg) The mass of a liter of water.

kinematics The branch of mechanics that describes how things move.

kinescope See **picture tube**.

kinetic energy The energy of motion.

kinetic theory The theory of matter that describes the states of matter in terms of attractive forces and kinetic energy.

L

laser A device that produces a narrow beam of coherent light; light amplification by the stimulated emission of radiation.

law A statement of a consistent pattern of phenomena in nature.

law of charges Like charges repel; unlike charges attract.

law of conservation of energy Energy can be changed from one form to another but can never be created nor destroyed.

law of definite composition Every compound has its own unique molecule with its own unique combination of elements.

law of definite proportions A chemical compound is always made up of the same elements in the same proportions.

law of magnetic poles Unlike magnetic poles attract and like magnetic poles repel.

law of mass conservation In all chemical and physical changes, matter is neither created nor destroyed.

law of moments The method for computing the amount of force exerted by levers with unequal arms; $w_1 d_1 = w_2 d_2$.

law of reflection The angle of incidence must be equal to the angle of reflection.

law of the conservation of momentum Without outside influence the total momentum of objects before a change must equal the total momentum of the objects after a change.

lens A transparent object that uses the property of refraction to magnify or reduce images.

lever A rigid bar capable of turning about a fulcrum.

light, coherent See **coherent light**.

light, infrared See **infrared light**.

light, ultraviolet See **ultraviolet light**.

light, visible See **visible light**.

light-emitting diode (LED) A solid-state device that changes electricity to light.

light energy The energy due to various wavelengths of the electromagnetic spectrum.

light year The distance light travels in a year.

line spectrum A display of the various frequencies of light emitted by a source.

liquid The state of matter in which the attractive forces and the disruptive forces are balanced, allowing particles limited movement.

liter (ℓ) The volume of a cubic decimeter.

longitudinal wave A wave whose vibration is in the same direction in which it is traveling.

loudness Related to intensity; how strong or weak a sound is to an observer.

lubricant A substance used to reduce the friction between surfaces.

M

magnetic energy Energy that is stored in a magnet and its surrounding field.

magnetic field of force The sum of the strengths and directions of the magnetic forces at all the points around a magnetic source.

magnets, superconducting See **superconducting magnets**.

main memory The primary data-holding section of a computer; receives data as needed from disk drives and tapes.

malleable Capable of being hammered or rolled.

mass The quantity of matter in an object.

mass, atomic See **atomic mass**.

mass number The sum of the protons and neutrons in the nucleus of an atom.

matter Anything that has mass and volume.

mechanical advantage (M.A.) The amount by which a machine magnifies effort.

mechanical energy The energy that an object possesses because of its motion or its potential to move.

mechanical waves Rhythmic disturbances of a medium: sound waves, water waves, etc.

mechanics The study of motion.

melting The phase change from solid to liquid.

melting point The temperature at which a material changes from solid to liquid.

metal An element that tends to give up electrons in a chemical reaction.

metallic bond A chemical bond in which metal atoms are thought to randomly share their valence electrons.

metallic luster The shiny appearance of freshly cut or polished metal.

metalloid A substance that has properties of both metals and nonmetals.

meter (m) The basic unit of length of the metric system; 39.37 inches.

metric system A decimal system of measurements based on the meter; SI.

microwaves Electromagnetic waves with wavelengths from .3 cm to 30 cm, and with frequencies that range from 10^9 Hz to 10^{11} Hz.

miscibility The property that allows two liquids to be soluble in each other.

mixture A physical combination of two or more pure substances.

modulation The impressing of sound or patterns of light on a transmitted wave.

molecule A particle made up of two or more atoms chemically joined together; a particle formed by a limited number of atoms bonded covalently; the basic unit of a covalent compound.

momentum Mass multiplied by velocity; a quantity of motion.

moral judgment A decision made on the basis of right and wrong.

N

neutralization The reaction between an acid and a base that produces a salt and water.

neutron A neutral particle in the nucleus of an atom, with approximately the same mass as a proton.

newton (n) The metric unit of weight.

Newton's first law of motion Objects at rest tend to remain at rest, and objects in motion tend to remain in motion (in the same direction and at the same speed) until acted on by some outside, unbalanced force.

Newton's second law of motion The value of an unbalanced force (F) is equal to its mass (m) multiplied by its acceleration (a).

Newton's third law of motion For every action there is an equal and opposite reaction.

nonelectrolyte A solute that does not ionize in solution and will not conduct electricity.

nonmagnetic See **diamagnetic**.

nonmetal An element that tends to gain electrons in a chemical reaction.

nonpolar molecule A molecule that does not have electrical poles.

normal An imaginary line drawn perpendicular to the surface of a mirror.

normal salt A salt that is chemically neutral.

nuclear change A change that occurs in the makeup and energy of the nucleus of an atom.

nuclear energy The energy that is stored in the nucleus of an atom.

nucleus The center of an atom, which contains protons and neutrons.

number, atomic See **atomic number**.

O

observation The collection of data through the use of the senses.

ohm (Ω) The unit used to measure resistance.

ohmmeter A device that measures resistance.

oscillation A regular back-and-forth motion of electrons in a circuit.

output Outgoing signal(s) produced by a computer or other electronic device.

overtone A multiple of a fundamental tone.

oxidation numbers Symbols that indicate the number of electrons that an element gains or loses as it bonds.

P

parallel circuit A circuit with two or more paths for the electrons in it to follow.

paramagnetic Slightly attracted to magnets.

particle model A model of matter in which all matter is made up of tiny particles in constant motion.

pentode A five-element vacuum tube.

percentage by mass A method of expressing the concentration of a solute as a percentage of the total mass of the solution.

period A horizontal row in the periodic table, also called a series; the time it takes for one complete cycle.

periodic law The chemical properties of the elements are periodic functions of their atomic numbers.

periodic table A table of the elements arranged by atomic number into vertical columns called families, or groups, and horizontal rows called periods.

phase change A physical change in the state of a material caused by a change in temperature.

phenomenon (plural, phenomena) Any fact, circumstance, or experience that is apparent to the senses.

pH scale A scale that is used to indicate the relative concentrations of hydronium ions in a solution.

physical change A change in a material that does not alter its identity.

physical property A property that can be observed and measured without changing the kind of matter being studied.

physical universe The totality of matter and energy created by God.

picture tube A large vacuum tube that changes electrical impulses to light patterns in a television set.

piston A solid cylinder that slides within another cylinder.

pitch The distance between two adjacent threads on a screw; how high or low a tone sounds to an observer (related to frequency).

plasma The state of matter in which particles travel at such tremendous speeds that they become electrically charged.

polar molecule A molecule that has partially charged electrical poles.

polyatomic ion A group of several atoms that act as a single charged particle.

potential difference The difference of the electrical potential between two places.

potential drop See **potential difference**.

potential energy The energy of position; stored energy.

power The amount of work done in a given period of time; $P = w/t$.

precipitate A solid formed during a reaction that is insoluble in water.

principal focus A point through which the rays reflected or refracted from a surface will pass.

product A substance (usually on the righthand side of the equation) that is produced by a chemical change.

proton A positively charged particle in the nucleus of an atom, 1836 times heavier than an electron.

pulley A modified lever consisting of a rope that moves around a grooved wheel, which can be movable or fixed.

pulse A wave of very short duration.

pure science Scientific activities motivated by interest or curiosity and performed to gain knowledge for its own sake.

pure substance A substance that is made up of only one kind of particle and is the same throughout.

Q

qualitative data Descriptive information not involving numbers.

quality A subjective value dependent on the mixture of tones and overtones in a particular sound.

quantitative data Measurable or numerical information.

R

radar Radio detection and ranging devices that use microwaves.

radiation The transportation of thermal energy without the use of matter.

radioactivity The emission of rays and particles from an unstable nucleus.

radio astronomy The study of radio waves emitted by astronomical objects.

radiocarbon dating A method for finding the approximate age of once-living material by measuring its carbon-14 content.

radio waves Electromagnetic waves with wavelengths about 1-10 m long, and with frequencies below those of visible light waves.

random-access memory (RAM) A computer memory that temporarily holds the data on which the CPU operates.

rarefaction A region where the air molecules are spread apart by the energy of a sound wave.

rays Representations of the directions of light waves.

reactant A substance (usually on the lefthand side of an equation) that undergoes a chemical change.

reaction mechanism A theoretical explanation of how individual atoms behave during a chemical reaction.

read-only memory (ROM) A computer memory that retains data after the power is turned off.

real image An image that is produced in front of the plane of a mirror.

rectification Changing alternating current to direct current.

reflected ray An outgoing ray (away from the reflecting surface).

reflection The return of waves after striking a surface.

refraction The bending of waves as they pass from one medium into another.

resistance The force against which a simple machine works; opposition to the flow of electrons.

resistance arm The distance from the fulcrum to the resistance.

resistor Any object that resists the flow of electricity.

resonance The transfer of energy from one object to another object with the same natural frequency.

reverberations Multiple echoes of sound.

S

salt A substance that is formed from the negative ion of an acid and the positive ion of a base.

salt, acid See **acid salt**.

salt, basic See **basic salt**.

salt, normal See **normal salt**.

saturated Containing the maximum amount of a solute that can be dissolved in a given amount of solvent under normal conditions.

science The systematic use of observations to describe the physical universe.

scientific method A systematic way of solving a problem by making observations.

screw An inclined plane wound around a cylinder or cone.

second (s) The basic unit of time; 9,192,631,770 vibrations of a cesium atom.

second-class lever A lever in which the resistance is located between the fulcrum and the effort.

second law of thermodynamics Although the total energy in the universe is conserved, it is becoming less and less available for work.

semiconductor A substance that holds its electrons in a way that allows a partial flow of electricity.

series Another name for a period in the periodic table.

series circuit A circuit with a single path for all the electrons in it to follow.

short circuit A situation in which an electrical current passes through a path shorter than the entire circuit.

SI The abbreviation for the expanded metric system called *Système International d'Unités* (French for *International System of Units*).

significant figures All of the certain digits plus one doubtful digit in a measurement.

solenoid Coiled wires used to form a magnet.

solid The state of matter in which the attractive forces limit the particles to vibrating in place.

solid-state electronic components Circuit components built out of semiconducting materials.

solubility The maximum amount of a solute that can dissolve in a given amount of solvent under normal conditions.

soluble Dissolvable.

solute The substance that is dissolved in a solution.

solution A homogeneous mixture of two or more substances.

solvent The substance that does the dissolving in a solution.

sonar A type of listening device that uses sound to locate objects; sound navigation and ranging.

sound Mechanical waves that can be detected by our ears.

sound energy Energy that is produced by vibrating matter and transmitted through a medium.

specific gravity A method of determining the concentration of a solution by comparing the density of the solution to the density of water.

specific heat The amount of thermal energy needed to raise the temperature of 1 g of a substance 1° C.

spectator ion An ion that is present in a solution where a reaction is taking place but which does not participate in the reaction.

speed The rate at which an object changes position.

speed of light 300,000,000 m/s.

spring scale An instrument for measuring weight.

static electricity The effects produced by stationary charges.

stationary electric charges Electric charges that are at rest.

step-down transformer A series of coils that uses induction to produce a lower voltage.

step-up transformer A series of coils that uses induction to produce a higher voltage.

strain The distortion of a material due to stress.

stress Any force that tends to change the size or shape of a material.

subgroup One of the families of transition elements.

sublimation The phase change directly from solid to gas or from gas to solid.

subscript A small number placed beside the symbol of an element in a formula to indicate the number of atoms of that element contained in the compound represented by that formula.

superconducting magnet A magnet made from special materials and kept at extremely low temperatures.

supersaturated Having dissolved more than the normal amount of solute in a given amount of solvent.

survey The process of gathering data about an existing situation or object.

suspension A heterogeneous mixture consisting of small particles spread througout a liquid or gaseous medium, from which they will eventually settle out.

switch A device that can be used to break (open or close) a circuit.

symbol A scientific abbreviation for the name of an element, consisting of one or two letters with the first letter always capitalized.

T

technology The practical application of scientific knowledge.

teleology The study of design or purpose in nature.

temperature The measure of the average kinetic energy in a material.

tension A force caused by opposing pulls.

terminal velocity The limit of the velocity at which an object can fall through a gas or a liquid.

ternary compound A compound that is composed of three or more different elements.

tetrode A four-element vacuum tube or semiconductor.

theistic evolution The attempted harmonization of evolution with belief in a god.

theory A partially verified idea that relates a number of different observations.

thermal energy The total energy of the particles in an object, related to the motion of the molecules or ions in matter.

thermal expansion An increase in the volume of a substance caused by the addition of thermal energy.

thermionic emission The release of electrons by a heated conducting material.

thermodynamics The branch of physics that deals with thermal energy.

third-class lever A lever in which the effort is applied between the fulcrum and the resistance.

threshold of hearing The very softest sound level that can be detected by an observer.

transistor A three-element semiconductor device used for amplification, switching, and detection.

transmitter An electronic device that creates radio waves by accelerating electrons through an antenna.

transuranium element An element with an atomic number higher than that of uranium.

transverse wave A wave whose vibration is at right angles to the direction in which it is traveling.

triode A three-element vacuum tube or semiconductor.

trough The lowest point on a wave.

truss An architectural support made of materials arranged in triangles to give added support.

U

ultraviolet light Electromagnetic waves that are just beyond visible light in frequency.

unbalanced forces The unequal forces on an object that cause the object to move.

unit analysis A mathematical tool for converting units.

universal negative An absolute statement of denial.

unsaturated Capable of dissolving more of a solute.

V

vacuum tube A hollow electronic device having an internal vacuum that permits the passage of a stream of electrons through it.

valence electrons The electrons in the outermost energy level of an atom.

value judgment A decision based on the comparative merit of options.

vault An extended arch that forms a curved ceiling.

velocity The rate at which an object changes position in a specified direction.

velocity, terminal See **terminal velocity**.

verification The process of testing the correctness of a solution.

visible light Electromagnetic waves with wavelengths ranging from 4×10^{-5} cm to 7×10^{-5} cm, and with frequencies ranging from 4.5×10^{14} Hz to 7.5×10^{14} Hz; the portion of radiant energy that can be sensed by our eyes.

virtual image The images that appear to exist beyond a mirror.

voltage The amount of push needed to cause electrons to move between two points.

voltmeter A device that measures the potential difference between two points in a circuit.

volume Any space defined by length, width, and height.

W

watt (W) The SI unit of power; 1 joule of energy per second.

wavelength The distance between adjacent troughs or peaks.

Glossary

waves Rhythmic disturbances that transfer energy through space or matter.

weak electrolyte A solute that can ionize only partially and conducts electricity weakly.

wedge Two inclined planes placed "back-to-back."

weight The measure of the force of gravity on an object.

wheel and axle Modified lever in which the effort arm and the resistance arm revolve around a central fulcrum.

white sound A blend of a wide range of audible frequencies that produces the effect of quiet.

word equation An equation that uses words to represent a reaction.

work The product of the force applied on an object multiplied by the distance the object moved; $w = F \cdot d$.

X

x-ray astronomy The study of astronomical objects using x-rays instead of visible light.

x-rays Electromagnetic waves with frequencies higher than ultraviolet light, strong enough to penetrate body tissues.

INDEX

Index

A

absolute zero, 88, 347
AC See **current, electrical.**
acceleration, 300-01
  definition, 300
  equation, 300-01
  units, 301
acetate ion, 192
acetic acid, 240
  electrolyte, 233
  formula, 241
  strength, 241
acids, 237-245
  conductivity, 242
  definition, 240
  flavor, 236, 242
  in common substances, 240
  indicators, 245, 252-53
  ion, 237, 239-42
  metal corrosion, 242-43
  neutralization, 245
  properties, 242-43, 245
  rain, 254
  solution, 252
  strength, 241-42
  See also individual acids.
acoustics, 470-71
air
  as solution, 216
  composition, 103
  homogeneous mixture, 104
  in capacitors, 382-83
  pollution, 6, 389
  pressure, 80
  resistance, 313-15, 318
  thermal conductivity, 354
airplane propulsion, 307
alcohol, ethyl See **ethyl alcohol.**
alkali metals, 145, 249
alkaline-earth metals, 147
  in bases, 249
  oxidation number, 187
alloy
  definition, 104
  common examples, 215
  formation, 215
  transition metals, 147
alnico, 415
alpha particle, 120, 121-22
aluminum, 202-03
  boiling point, 363
  density, 59
  electrical conductivity, 376
  heat of fusion, 363
  heat of vaporization, 363
  melting point, 363
  purification, 202-03

specific heat, 360-61
  thermal conductivity, 354
  thermal expansion, 369
  uses, 147, 151, 165
aluminum hydroxide, 250
amalgam, 215
americium
  formation, 160
  name source, 97
ammeter, 398
ammonia, 74
  as base, 250-51
  formula, 102
  molecular representation, 102
  uses, 102
ammonium hydroxide, 250
ammonium ion, 192
Ampère, André Marie, 421
ampere (unit), 396
amplification, 540-41, 547-48
amplitude, 439
amu, 116
angstrom, 68
anion, 166
antenna, 448
  VLA, 450-51
antifreeze, 234
arch, 524-25
archaeology, 128
  confirms Bible, 17
Archimedes, 264-65, 268, 277
Archimedes' principle, 268
argon
  in air, 33
  properties, 152
Aristotle, 296, 312-13
armature, 431
Arrhenius, 237
arthritis, 271
ascorbic acid, 240
astrology, 15-16
astronomy
  measurement methods, 47
  radio, 449
  X-ray, 458-59
atom, 35, 132
  definition, 97
  light emission, 113-14
  mass of, 63
  term origin, 109-10
  See also **atomic mass; atomic model.**
atomic bomb, 124
atomic energy, 18, 424
atomic mass, 116

atomic model, 109-34
  core-envelope, 110-11
  development, 109-16
  electron levels, 130-31, 133-34
  electrons, 111-15
  energy levels, 113-14
  Greek, 109-10
  historical summary, 115
  neutrons, 112
  nucleus, 111-12
  planetary, 113-14
  plum-pudding, 111
  protons, 112
  quantum, 114-15
atomic number, 116-17, 145
atmosphere, 14
atmosphere (unit), 80
axle See **wheel and axle.**

B

Bacon, Francis, 143
baking soda
  as acid salt, 257, 259
  formula, 102, 223
  molecular representation, 102
  solubility, 23
  uses, 102
balance
  analytical, 53-54
  definition, 53
  double-pan, 53
  multiple-beam, 53-54
Bardeen, John, 547
barium
  flame color, 113
  in minerals, 146
  properties, 147
  uses, 147
barometer, 78-79
bases, 245-51
  definition, 250-51
  flavor, 236, 247
  indicators, 248, 252-53
  ion, 246-47
  neutralization, 248
  properties, 247-49
  solution, 252
  strength, 249-50
battery, 391, 393-94, 425
bauxite, 202
beaker, 57
beam, structural, 522-23
bearings, 535
Becquerel, Henri, 27, 119
bel (unit), 468
Bell, Alexander Graham, 468
benzene, 74

Index

Index

O

observation
 definition, 3
observations, 26-29
 direct, 4
 indirect, 4
 spiritual, 24-25
ocean
 as solution, 212-13
 water composition, 103
 See also **desalination.**
octave
 definition, 140
Oersted, Hans Christian, 420
ohm (unit), 397, 400
Ohm, Georg Simon, 397
ohmmeter, 398-99
Ohm's law, 397
oil
 refineries, 204
 shale, 6-7
 U.S. supplies, 6-7
opal, 59
organ of Corti, 477
origins *See* **creationism; evolution.**
orthicon tube, 558
oscillation, 542, 547-48
osmium, 59, 60
osmosis
 reverse, 220-21
oxalic acid, 240
oxidation number, 186-88
 definition, 186
 electronegativity, 186-87
 multiple, 188
 of common elements, 188
 polyatomic ions, 192-93
oxygen, 74, 96
 boiling point, 88
 condensation point, 87
 diatomic, 99
 in air, 149, 162-63
 melting point, 88
 oxidation number, 188
 rocket fuel, 72
 symbol, 96
oxygen family, 149
 oxidation number, 188
ozone, 14
 in atmosphere, 149
 layer, 457

P

paper
 density of, 60
 in capacitors, 382-83
particle *See* **matter.**

particle accelerator, 429
pendulum, 43
 motion, 317
pentode, 544
pericardial fluid, 271
pericardium, 271
periodic law, 142
 modern statement, 143
periodic table, 150-51, 139-63
 conductivity of elements, 377
 development, 140-43
 families (groups), 145-47, 151-53
 periods (series), 155
 subgroups, 147, 150
 transition elements, 147, 150
 transuranium elements, 160-61
perpetual motion, 336-37
perspiration *See* **evaporation.**
pH, 252-53, 258
phase *See* **kinetic theory; matter; solid; liquid; gas; plasma.**
phenol
 melting point, 83
phenomenon
 definition, 26
philosophy, 5
phosphate ion, 192
phosphoric acid, 241-42
phosphorus
 uses, 149
photocopying
 process, 387-88
photoelectric cell, 325
photon, 491
photosynthesis, 324
pH scale, 252-53
physical changes *See* **matter.**
physical properties *See* **matter.**
picture tube, 560-61
piezoelectric effect, 60
pipet, 57
piston, 534
pitch *See* **screw; sound.**
pitchblende, 27
plane, inclined *See* **inclined plane.**
planets
 motion of, 69
 See also **astronomy.**
plasma, 72, 81-82
 characteristics of, 81
 in nuclear fusion, 127
 kinetic model, 81
 neon lights, 153
platinum
 density of, 59
 uses, 147

plutonium
 formation, 160
 name source, 97
pollution
 control devices, 389
 detection, 455
polonium
 discovery, 27
 name source, 97
 radioactivity, 27
polyatomic ion *See* **ions.**
polywater *See* **water.**
potassium
 in diet, 145
 properties, 145
potassium hydroxide, 249-50
potassium permanganate
 dissolving, 71-72
potential energy, 328-32
 calculation of, 330
 definition, 328
potential difference
 definition, 395
 measurement of, 398
 unit, 395
power, 274-76
 and electrical energy, 405
 definition, 275
 unit, 276, 405
power plant, nuclear, 124, 126
precipitate, 226
 definition, 207
prejudice
 definition, 11
 evolutionary, 11
pressure *See* **gas; air.**
product *See* **chemical equations.**
promethium
 name source, 97
proteins, 100, 164-65
protons, 116-18
 definition, 112
 discovery, 112
 mass, 116
pulleys, 288-89
 block and tackle, 289
 single fixed, 288
 single movable, 288
pulse, wave, 443

Q

quantum theory *See* **atomic model.**
quartz, 60, 65-66

R

rack and pinion, 531

590

Index

Photo Credits